ALGORITHMIC COMBINATORICS

Algorithmic

SHIMON EVEN
The Weizmann Institute of Science

Combinatorics

The Macmillan Company, New York

Collier-Macmillan Publishers, London

The Macmillan Company
866 Third Avenue, New York, New York 10022

Collier-Macmillan Canada, Ltd., Toronto, Ontario

Library of Congress catalog card number 72-80178

Printing: 1 2 3 4 5 6 7 8   Year: 3 4 5 6 7 8 9

PREFACE

This book is a by-product of my experience in teaching and research in the general field of algorithmic combinatorics during the years 1967–1971. I felt the need of a suitable textbook for teaching this subject. My first set of notes, on graph theory, was written while I visited Harvard University during 1967 to 1969. This was a one-semester course for graduate students in computer science, and it was taught twice. In 1969–1970, I taught a combinatorics course at the Feinberg Graduate School of The Weizmann Institute of Science. This was a full-year course and was again directed toward the special needs of the graduate students in computer science. I added sections on permutations, combinations, partitions, and so on. The course notes were mimeographed for the students' convenience. This book is an advanced version of the notes used in 1970–1971.

Combinatorial techniques are of prime importance in such techniques of computer science as switching theory, circuit layout techniques, logical design, automata theory, languages, organization of computer systems, data structures, and in a large variety of nonnumeric and numeric applications. It is now widely recognized that combinatorics is a vital mathematical subject for the computer scientist, much more than several other mathematical subjects which are traditionally still compulsory in some computer science programs.

In the past ten years we have seen a rising general interest in combinatorics. New journals have been started and many books have been printed. However, even the better books are not suitable for the purposes of computer science or of most other sciences in which combinatorics can be fruitfully applied. There are two difficulties. First, the choice of subjects does not fit these fields of applications. Second, these books emphasize existence theorems and asymptotic approximations rather than algorithms and their efficiency.

A nonconstructive existence proof may be mathematically very elegant, but it is also a source of frustration. You are told that what you want exists,

v

but it safely remains beyond reach. Even many constructive proofs are algorithmicly unsatisfactory, since they may be inefficient. Often the computer scientist finds that even if the number of possibilities is finite, it is so high that exhaustive enumeration will exhaust us before we are through; that is, the number might as well be considered infinite.

There is no doubt that as computer science develops, this subject will be taught to undergraduates, and this book can also be used for this purpose. The only assumed background is the first college course of modern algebra. I have tried to illustrate the ideas by examples and to make the exposition as intuitive as possible. Sometimes, instead of developing a formal structure for the sake of proving a statement, I have illustrated the idea of the proof by means of an example. This was not done if the proof lost its validity. In general, I have tried to be rigorous, for the subject does not allow any slackness.

The annoying but common habit of not completing proofs because they are "beyond the scope of this book" is unequivocally avoided. Chancing the danger that this statement may be used against me, I will state my belief that he who cannot explain does not really understand. The only unproved statements are those made in closing remarks, and these results are not used later in the book. Therefore, I believe that the book is completely self-contained.

One criticism that has already been made about the book is that the number of references given is too small, less than the customary number of cited references. My answer is twofold. First, I do cite some of the major sources of the particular subject, and there the reader will find additional references; I see no point in mentioning sources that I have not used and have reason to doubt the reader will need. Second, I have done my best to produce a lucid text rather than a complete and detailed annotated bibliography.

No use of programming languages is made. The algorithms are explained in English, with the help of the notation which I found most suitable for the purpose.

There are many important and classical areas of combinatorics that are completely missing from the book. Clearly this fact reflects my own experience in computer science. Some of the areas omitted are the linear spaces of cuts and circuits of a graph, generating functions, Polya's counting theory, and block designs. Since I have never run into their application in computer science, I doubt that the reader will. The linear spaces of cuts and circuits are useful in network theory (of electrical engineering), but there are entire books devoted to this aspect and a superficial survey is not worthwhile.

The useful and interesting subject of linear and integer programming is too extensive to be included here and is too different in approach and technique. The problem of flow in graphs is more suitable to the general approach of the book and is therefore included.

Another important omission is the subject of planar graphs, which would have required at least two chapters. It is of interest in layout techniques only and does not have many other applications. Also, and most important, current research is most likely to make most of the presently known results obsolete within a few years.

It was my experience that there is too much material in the book for one semester and too little for two semesters. When teaching a two-semester course in algorithmic combinatorics, I have included topics from linear programming, especially the transportation problem, and planar graphs.

The book can be used as the text for a one-semester course in several ways, for example:

1. Graph theory (Chapters 4–12, skipping Chapters 9 and 12 if time runs short).
2. Algorithmic combinatorics (Chapters 1, 2, 4–8, 10, and 11, skipping Sections 1.3, 2.3, 2.4, 3.6, 5.3, 6.3, and 6.4 if time runs short).

I would like to thank some of my present and past colleagues for joint work that has greatly influenced the contents of this book: M. Cohn, F. Commoner, W. L. Eastman, A. W. Holt, P. K. Hooper, A. Lempel, K. Menger, G. Ott, and A. Pnueli. The work of two of my graduate students, G. Ehrlich and F. Gavril, is used in the book, too: and I want to thank them for what they taught me. Finally I would like to thank S. L. Hakimi and D. E. Knuth for their helpful reviews and comments on the manuscript.

Rehovot, Israel   S. E.

CONTENTS

4
PATHS IN GRAPHS

5
TREES

6
DIRECTED TREES

7
ORDERED TREES

8
CLIQUES, COVERS, AND COLORATION

9
TRANSITIVE AND PERMUTATION GRAPHS

10
MAXIMUM FLOW IN A GRAPH

11
MISCELLANIES

12
MARKED DIRECTED GRAPHS

1

PERMUTATIONS

1.1 Introduction

Assume that we have n items. An *r-permutation* of these n items consists of choosing r items out of the n and arranging them in some order. Let $P(n, r)$ be the number of different ways that this can be done. The number of ways that the first item can be chosen is n. Once the first item has been chosen, the second can be chosen in $n - 1$ ways. It follows that

$$P(n, r) = n \cdot (n - 1) \cdots (n - r + 1). \tag{1.1}$$

If all the n items are arranged, that is, $n = r$, we get

$$P(n, n) = n \cdot (n - 1) \cdots 2 \cdot 1.$$

The product on the right-hand side of this equation is called *n factorial* and is denoted $n!$. It follows immediately that

$$P(n, r) = \frac{n!}{(n - r)!}. \tag{1.2}$$

It is convenient to define $0! = 1$, for upon substituting $n = r$ in (1.2) we get $P(n, n) = n!$. We refer to an *r*-permutation in the case when $n = r$ as a permutation of *n* elements. Questions concerning permutations cover a wide range; we shall consider only a small number.

1.2   Generation of all permutations by adjacent transpositions

Let us assume that the *n* items are the integers $1, 2, \ldots, n$ and that originally they are placed in this (natural) order. We want to generate all $n!$ permutations in such a way that every permutation will be generated exactly once, that the change from one permutation to the next will be simple and easy to perform even if *n* is very large, and that we shall be able to detect termination without counting separately the number of permutations.

The algorithm to be described here is essentially that of Johnson [1] and Trotter [2]. A method to speed it up will be discussed in Section 1.3.

The way one permutation is changed to the next is by an adjacent transposition. A *transposition* consists of two items changing places; a transposition is called *adjacent* if the two items are adjacent. What we need is a way of telling which two adjacent integers are to change places next.

Let us denote by an arrow above each integer its *direction*, namely, the direction in which it tends to go. We start with all the directions pointing from right to left. Thus, if $n = 4$, our initial data are as follows:

$$\overleftarrow{1} \quad \overleftarrow{2} \quad \overleftarrow{3} \quad \overleftarrow{4}.$$

An integer *k* is *mobile* if there exists an integer smaller than *k* adjacent to *k* on the side where the direction of *k* points to. For example, in our initial position described above, the integers 2, 3, and 4 are mobile. In the case

$$\overleftarrow{2} \quad \overrightarrow{3} \quad \overleftarrow{4} \quad \overleftarrow{1},$$

only 4 is mobile.

Algorithm 1.1:
(1) If there are no mobile integers, stop.
(2) Call the largest mobile integer m.
(3) Let m switch places with the adjacent integer to which mth direction points to.
(4) Switch the direction of all integers k for which $k > m$. Return to step (1).

Let us demonstrate the algorithm for $n = 4$:

$$
\begin{array}{cccc|cccc|cccc}
\overleftarrow{1} & \overleftarrow{2} & \overleftarrow{3} & \overleftarrow{4} & \overleftarrow{3} & \overleftarrow{1} & \overleftarrow{2} & \overleftarrow{4} & \overleftarrow{2} & \overrightarrow{3} & \overleftarrow{1} & \overleftarrow{4} \\
\overleftarrow{1} & \overleftarrow{2} & \overleftarrow{4} & \overleftarrow{3} & \overleftarrow{3} & \overleftarrow{1} & \overleftarrow{4} & \overleftarrow{2} & \overleftarrow{2} & \overrightarrow{3} & \overleftarrow{4} & \overleftarrow{1} \\
\overleftarrow{1} & \overleftarrow{4} & \overleftarrow{2} & \overleftarrow{3} & \overleftarrow{3} & \overleftarrow{4} & \overleftarrow{1} & \overleftarrow{2} & \overleftarrow{2} & \overleftarrow{4} & \overrightarrow{3} & \overleftarrow{1} \\
\overleftarrow{4} & \overleftarrow{1} & \overleftarrow{2} & \overleftarrow{3} & \overleftarrow{4} & \overleftarrow{3} & \overleftarrow{1} & \overleftarrow{2} & \overleftarrow{4} & \overleftarrow{2} & \overrightarrow{3} & \overleftarrow{1} \\
\overrightarrow{4} & \overleftarrow{1} & \overleftarrow{3} & \overleftarrow{2} & \overrightarrow{4} & \overrightarrow{3} & \overleftarrow{2} & \overleftarrow{1} & \overrightarrow{4} & \overleftarrow{2} & \overleftarrow{1} & \overrightarrow{3} \\
\overleftarrow{1} & \overrightarrow{4} & \overleftarrow{3} & \overleftarrow{2} & \overrightarrow{3} & \overrightarrow{4} & \overleftarrow{2} & \overleftarrow{1} & \overleftarrow{2} & \overrightarrow{4} & \overleftarrow{1} & \overrightarrow{3} \\
\overleftarrow{1} & \overleftarrow{3} & \overrightarrow{4} & \overleftarrow{2} & \overrightarrow{3} & \overleftarrow{2} & \overrightarrow{4} & \overleftarrow{1} & \overleftarrow{2} & \overleftarrow{1} & \overrightarrow{4} & \overrightarrow{3} \\
\overleftarrow{1} & \overleftarrow{3} & \overleftarrow{2} & \overrightarrow{4} & \overrightarrow{3} & \overleftarrow{2} & \overleftarrow{1} & \overrightarrow{4} & \overleftarrow{2} & \overleftarrow{1} & \overrightarrow{3} & \overrightarrow{4} \\
\end{array}
$$

Since in $\overleftarrow{2}\ \overleftarrow{1}\ \overrightarrow{3}\ \overrightarrow{4}$ no integer is mobile, the algorithm stops.

The proof of validity of the algorithm is easily achieved by induction. In case $n = 2$ we start with $\overleftarrow{1}\ \overleftarrow{2}$, and after one step we get $\overleftarrow{2}\ \overleftarrow{1}$. No integer is now mobile, and the algorithm stops. Assume now that the algorithm works for n, and we want to show that this implies its validity for $n + 1$. It is clear that, as we start, the direction of $n + 1$ is to the left, and it will move, step by step leftwise, until we get

$$ n \overset{\leftarrow}{+} 1 \ \ \overleftarrow{1} \ \ \overleftarrow{2} \cdots \overleftarrow{n}. $$

So far the integers $1, 2, \ldots, n$ kept their relative positions and their original directions. All the permutations where $n + 1$ is interwoven into this order have been generated. Now, $n + 1$ is not mobile. Thus, m is the integer which would be determined if the algorithm were applied to $1, 2, \ldots, n$ only. Also, the two integers which switch places are the same as if $n + 1$ were not there. Now the direction on $n + 1$ is switched, and it moves all the way to the right. Again a change which would have taken place among $1, 2, \ldots, n$ if $n + 1$ were missing takes place, and again $n + 1$ sweeps to the other end. It is clear that for each of the permutations of $1, 2, \ldots, n$, the integer $n + 1$ is placed in all the possible intervals. When we reach the last permutation of $1, 2, \ldots, n$ and $n + 1$ sweeps to the other end, no integer is mobile and the algorithm stops.

Usually our items are not the integers $1, 2, \ldots, n$. It may be that a natural order between them does not exist, or that comparison is inconvenient. If this is the case, we cannot use this algorithm directly, for the decision of what moves depends on comparison between items (see the definition of mobile). One way of overcoming this difficulty is to perform the generations on $1, 2, \ldots, n$ and copy the item-switching step on our list of items. For another way to overcome this difficulty see Johnson's paper [1]. Several other methods for generating all permutations are described in reference 4.

In certain applications it may be desirable to know the number of the permutation under consideration, that is, how many permutations precede a given permutation in the order they are generated. Our aim, now, is to describe an algorithm which produces the permutation from its number in the generation by Algorithm 1.1, and an algorithm which computes the number of the permutation from the permutation, again in reference to Algorithm 1.1.

As is easily observed, the number n makes $n - 1$ moves, then it rests for one step while a new permutation on $1, 2, \ldots, n - 1$ is formed; then it makes $n - 1$ moves in the reverse direction; and so on. Thus, if we start the enumeration of the permutation from zero, and the number of the present permutation is b_n, then n has made q_n complete sweeps, each consisting of n permutations, and has made r_n additional moves, where

$$b_n = n \cdot q_n + r_n, \qquad 0 \leqslant r_n < n.$$

Also, if q_n is even, then n has a left arrow, but if q_n is odd, it has a right arrow. Consider now the permutation on $1, 2, \ldots, n - 1$ which we get by deleting n from the b_nth permutation. Its number in the Johnson generation for $1, 2, \ldots, n - 1$, where the first permutation is numbered zero, is q_n; that is, $b_{n-1} = q_n$. Again,

$$b_{n-1} = (n - 1) \cdot q_{n-1} + r_{n-1}, \qquad 0 \leqslant r_{n-1} < n - 1.$$

In general

$$b_i = i \cdot q_i + r_i, \quad 0 \leqslant r_i < i \qquad \text{for } i = n, n - 1, \ldots, 3, 2. \qquad (1.3)$$

Since there is only one permutation on one element, $b_1 = 0$ always. By repeated substitution we get

$$b_n = r_n + n(r_{n-1} + (n - 1)(r_{n-2} + \cdots (r_3 + 3(r_2)) \cdots),$$

or

$$b_n = r_n + n \cdot r_{n-1} + \frac{n!}{(n-2)!} r_{n-2} + \cdots + \frac{n!}{3!} r_3 + \frac{n!}{2!} r_2.$$

In a more compact form,

$$b_n = \sum_{i=2}^{n} \frac{n!}{i!} r_i, \qquad \text{where } 0 \leqslant r_i < i. \tag{1.4}$$

Clearly, every integer $0 \leqslant b_n < n!$ has a representation of this form. Moreover, this presentation is unique. For assume that

$$b_n = \sum_{i=2}^{n} \frac{n!}{i!} r_i', \qquad \text{where } 0 \leqslant r_i' < i.$$

Thus,

$$\sum_{i=2}^{n} \frac{n!}{i!} r_i = \sum_{i=2}^{n} \frac{n!}{i!} r_i'.$$

We can divide both sides by n. Since $n | n!/i!$ (n divides $n!/i!$) for $i = 2, 3, \ldots$, $n-1$, the remainder on the left-hand side is r_n and on the right-hand side is r_n'. Thus, $r_n = r_n'$. We have

$$\sum_{i=2}^{n-1} \frac{n!}{i!} r_i = \sum_{i=2}^{n-1} \frac{n!}{i!} r_i'$$

and by division by n we get

$$\sum_{i=2}^{n-1} \frac{(n-1)!}{i!} r_i = \sum_{i=2}^{n-1} \frac{(n-1)!}{i!} r_i'.$$

By repeating the argument above we conclude that $r_i = r_i'$ for $i = 2, 3, \ldots, n$.

Now, if q_n is even, n has made r_n steps to the left; thus, there are r_n numbers less than n on its right. However, if q_n is odd, n has made r_n steps to the right and there are $n - 1 - r_n$ numbers less than n on its right. Thus, we know where to place n. Namely, if

$$a_i = \begin{cases} r_i & \text{if } q_i \text{ is even,} \\ i - 1 - r_i & \text{if } q_i \text{ is odd,} \end{cases}$$

then i is placed on the $(a_i + 1)$st place from the right, when only available places count. Clearly, $a_n, a_{n-1}, \ldots, a_3, a_2$ define the permutation.

For example, assume that we want to find permutation number 18 (the 19th) in the generation for $n \doteq 4$. Thus,

$$18 = 4 \cdot 4 + 2 \Rightarrow a_4 = 2$$

$$4 = 3 \cdot 1 + 1 \Rightarrow a_3 = 3 - 1 - 1 = 1$$

$$1 = 2 \cdot 0 + 1 \Rightarrow a_2 = 1.$$

Now, 4 is placed in the third place from the right:

$$\boxed{\ \boxed{}\ \boxed{4}\ \boxed{}\ \boxed{}\ }$$

Next, 3 is placed in the second place from the right:

$$\boxed{\ \boxed{}\ \boxed{4}\ \boxed{3}\ \boxed{}\ }$$

Next, 2 is placed in the second place from the right (among the available places):

$$\boxed{\ \boxed{2}\ \boxed{4}\ \boxed{3}\ \boxed{}\ }$$

Finally, 1 is placed in the remaining place. The permutation 2431 is indeed the one generated in the 19th step.

The reverse computation of finding b_n from $a_2, a_3, \ldots, a_n$ is carried in the following way. First, $b_2 = r_2 = a_2$. From there on we find

$$r_i = \begin{cases} a_i & \text{if } b_{i-1} \text{ is even,} \\ i - 1 - a_i & \text{if } b_{i-1} \text{ is odd,} \end{cases}$$

and $b_i = i \cdot b_{i-1} + r_i$ for $i = 3, 4, \ldots, n$.

For example, if we start with 2431, $a_4 = 2$, $a_3 = 1$, $a_2 = 1$. Thus, $b_2 = 1$. Now,

$$r_3 = 3 - 1 - 1 = 1 \qquad \text{(since } b_2 \text{ is odd),}$$

$$b_3 = 3 \cdot 1 + 1 = 4.$$

Next,

$$r_4 = a_4 = 2 \qquad \text{(since } b_3 \text{ is even),}$$

$$b_4 = 4 \cdot 4 + 2 = 18.$$

1.3 A method for speeding up Algorithm 1.1

In this section we shall discuss a recent method of Ehrlich [3] to speed up Algorithm 1.1. (His technique applies to several other combinatorial algorithms.)

The major drawback of Algorithm 1.1 is that the search for the largest mobile integer may take as many as n elementary comparisons. It is not difficult to organize the search in such a way that, on the average, the number of comparisons per permutation is small. It is harder to make sure that the number of comparisons is always bounded by a constant, independent of n.

Let an integer i be called *active* if there are integers smaller than i on its direction, but not necessarily adjacent to it. Thus, a mobile integer is always active, but the converse is not necessarily true. Let us define a vector A of n components which may be either 0 or 1, by

$$A(i) = \begin{cases} 1 & \text{if } i \text{ is active,} \\ 0 & \text{if } i \text{ is not active.} \end{cases}$$

The largest mobile integer, m, is also the largest active integer. Thus, $A(m) = 1$ and $A(m + 1) = A(m + 2) = \cdots = A(n) = 0$.

The search which causes the buildup of comparisons is that of determining the integer to be moved next. In other words, once m has made a move, what is the largest i for which $A(i) = 1$? In an effort to avoid checking one $A(i)$ after another, let us construct a vector T of n integral components with the following interpretation. The components of T are divided into two classes: *assigned* and *neutral*. If m is the integer to move now, $T(m)$ is assumed to be assigned. In general, if $T(i)$ is assigned, its value is some integer j such that $|j| < i$. If $j > 0$, it means that after i will finish its move, the next number, among the numbers which are less than i, to move is j, and $T(j)$ is assigned. If $j < 0$, it means that after i will finish its move, the next number, among the numbers which are less than i, to move is $i - 1$, next is $i - 2, i - 3, \ldots$, $-j$, and $T(-j)$ is assigned. All components of T which are not thus assigned are neutral. Clearly, if $T(i)$ is assigned $A(i) = 1$, but the converse is not necessarily true. The assignment of a negative integer allows us to describe a run of 1's in $A(i)$. The reader should realize that the knowledge of T and m is sufficient to reconstruct A. However, many T's may represent the same A, and therefore T cannot be constructed from A. Since T and m contain all the information we need, we may dispose of A, in our algorithm, and work with T and m alone.

Let us now investigate the changes that must be taken in T and m.

1. If $m = n$ and it has not reached its last step in its present direction, no changes in T are necessary and m remains unchanged.
2. If $m = n$ and it has reached its last step in its present direction, we consider $T(n)$. If $T(n)$ is positive, no changes in T are necessary and m receives the value of $T(n)$ $(m \leftarrow T(n))$. If $T(n)$ is negative, m receives the value $n - 1$ $(m \leftarrow n - 1)$ and we have to check if $-T(n) = n - 1$; if so, no changes in T are necessary; if not, $T(n - 1)$ receives the value of $T(n)$ $(T(n - 1) \leftarrow T(n))$.
3. If $m < n$ and m has not reached its last step in its direction, then $T(n)$ is assigned the value $-m$ $(T(n) \leftarrow -m)$ and m receives the value n $(m \leftarrow n)$.
4. If $m < n$ and m has reached its last step in its direction, then $T(n)$ is assigned the value $-(m + 1)$ $(T(n) \leftarrow -(m + 1))$* and we check if $T(m) > 0$. In case it is, $T(m + 1)$ is assigned the value of $T(m)$ $(T(m + 1) \leftarrow T(m))$. If not, $T(m + 1)$ is assigned the value $m - 1$ $(T(m + 1) \leftarrow m - 1)$ and if $-T(m) < m - 1$, $T(m - 1)$ is assigned the value of $T(m)$ $(T(m - 1) \leftarrow T(m))$. Finally, m receives the value n $(m \leftarrow n)$.

Let us demonstrate these constructions on the case $n = 4$. Initially the permutation with the directions is

$$\overleftarrow{1} \ \overleftarrow{2} \ \overleftarrow{3} \ \overleftarrow{4}$$

and $T = (-, -, -, -1)$† and $m = 4$. Case 1 applies; 4 moves left and we get

$$\overleftarrow{1} \ \overleftarrow{2} \ \overleftarrow{4} \ \overleftarrow{3}.$$

Case 1 applies. Next we get

$$\overleftarrow{1} \ \overleftarrow{4} \ \overleftarrow{2} \ \overleftarrow{3}.$$

Now we detect case 2. We get ‡

$$\overrightarrow{4} \ \overleftarrow{1} \ \overleftarrow{2} \ \overleftarrow{3},$$

---

*If $m = n - 1$, the new value of $T(n)$ $(-(m + 1))$ will be changed immediately.

†The dashes for $T(1)$, $T(2)$, and $T(3)$ mean that their initial values are insignificant. In general $T(1)$ is never necessary.

‡Unlike Algorithm 1.1, we change the direction of 4.

and since $T(4) = -1 < 0$, $m \leftarrow 3$ and we check if $-T(n) = n - 1$; since it is not, $T(3) \leftarrow -1$. Thus, $T = (-, -, -1, -1)$. Now case 3 applies. We get

$$\overleftarrow{4} \ \ \overleftarrow{1} \ \ \overleftarrow{3} \ \ \overleftarrow{2}.$$

The vector T becomes $(-, -, -1, -3)$ and $m = 4$. Next, case 1 applies twice:

$$\overleftarrow{1} \ \ \overleftarrow{4} \ \ \overleftarrow{3} \ \ \overleftarrow{2}$$
$$\overleftarrow{1} \ \ \overleftarrow{3} \ \ \overleftarrow{4} \ \ \overleftarrow{2}$$

and now case 2 applies. We get

$$\overleftarrow{1} \ \ \overleftarrow{3} \ \ \overleftarrow{2} \ \ \overleftarrow{4},$$

and since $T(4)$ is negative, $m \leftarrow 3$ and we check if $-T(n) = n - 1$. Since it is, no changes in T are made. Now case 4 applies. We get

$$\overrightarrow{3} \ \ \overleftarrow{1} \ \ \overleftarrow{2} \ \ \overleftarrow{4}$$

and perform the following changes: $T(4) \leftarrow -4$, and since $T(3) < 0$, $T(4) \leftarrow 2$, and since $-T(3) < 2$, $T(2) \leftarrow -1$. Thus, $T = (-, -1, -1, 2)$ and $m = 4$. Now case 1 applies twice:

$$\overrightarrow{3} \ \ \overleftarrow{1} \ \ \overleftarrow{4} \ \ \overleftarrow{2}$$
$$\overrightarrow{3} \ \ \overleftarrow{4} \ \ \overleftarrow{1} \ \ \overleftarrow{2}$$

and we are again in case 2. We get

$$\overleftarrow{4} \ \ \overrightarrow{3} \ \ \overleftarrow{1} \ \ \overleftarrow{2}$$

and T remains unchanged while $m = 2$. Now, case 4 applies. We get

$$\overleftarrow{4} \ \ \overrightarrow{3} \ \ \overrightarrow{2} \ \ \overleftarrow{1},$$

$T(4) \leftarrow -3$, $T(3) \leftarrow 1$. Thus, $T = (-, -1, 1, -3)$ and $m = 4$. The following steps are

$$\overrightarrow{3} \ \ \overleftarrow{4} \ \ \overrightarrow{2} \ \ \overleftarrow{1},$$
$$\overrightarrow{3} \ \ \overrightarrow{2} \ \ \overleftarrow{4} \ \ \overleftarrow{1},$$

and case 2 again applies. We get

$$\overrightarrow{3}\ \overrightarrow{2}\ \overleftarrow{1}\ \overleftarrow{4},$$

and $m \leftarrow 3$ and, since $-T(n) = n - 1 = 3$, T remains unchanged. Now case 3 applies. We get

$$\overrightarrow{2}\ \overrightarrow{3}\ \overleftarrow{1}\ \overleftarrow{4}$$

and $T(4) \leftarrow -3^*$ and $m \leftarrow 4$. Now, twice case 1:

$$\overrightarrow{2}\ \overrightarrow{3}\ \overrightarrow{4}\ \overleftarrow{1},$$
$$\overrightarrow{2}\ \overrightarrow{4}\ \overrightarrow{3}\ \overleftarrow{1},$$

and we have case 2. We get

$$\overrightarrow{4}\ \overrightarrow{2}\ \overrightarrow{3}\ \overleftarrow{1}$$

and $m \leftarrow 3$ and, since $-T(n) = n - 1 = 3$, no changes in T are made. Now we have case 4. We get

$$\overrightarrow{4}\ \overrightarrow{2}\ \overleftarrow{1}\ \overleftarrow{3}$$

and $T(4) \leftarrow -4$. Since $T(3) > 0$, $T(4) \leftarrow 1$ and $m \leftarrow 4$. Thus, $T = (-, -1, 1, 1)$. Now we have case 1 twice:

$$\overrightarrow{2}\ \overrightarrow{4}\ \overleftarrow{1}\ \overleftarrow{3},$$
$$\overrightarrow{2}\ \overleftarrow{1}\ \overleftarrow{4}\ \overleftarrow{3},$$

and case 2 follows. We get

$$\overrightarrow{2}\ \overleftarrow{1}\ \overleftarrow{3}\ \overleftarrow{4}$$

and $m \leftarrow 1$; $m = 1$ is the signal to halt.

Thus, we have a way to replace steps (1) and (2) of Algorithm 1.1 to avoid the possibility of a large number of comparisons in order to decide on the value of m. One problem remains. In order to perform step (3) we have to

---

*Here it has not changed T.

find the location of m. Ehrlich suggests the following solution. In addition to storing the permutation P ($P(i)$ is the integer located in the ith position), we store the inverse permutation P^{-1} ($P^{-1}(i)$ is the location of the integer i in P). Thus, when we want to locate m we look up $P^{-1}(m)$. Initially, $P(i) = P^{-1}(i) = i$ for $i = 1, 2, \ldots, n$ and we also set $P(0) = P(n + 1) = n + 1$ as boundary detectors. $D(i) = -1$ means that i's direction is to the left and $D(i) = 1$ means that it is to the right.

Algorithm 1.2:
(1) (Initiation) $m \leftarrow n$; $P(0) \leftarrow n + 1$; $P(n + 1) \leftarrow n + 1$; $P(i) \leftarrow i$ and
      $P^{-1}(i) \leftarrow i$ for $i = 1, 2, \ldots, n$; $D(i) \leftarrow -1$ for $i = 2, 3, \ldots, n$; $T(n) \leftarrow -1$.
(2) Output $P(i)$ for $i = 1, 2, \ldots, n$.
(3) $X \leftarrow P^{-1}(m)$; $Y \leftarrow X + D(m)$; $Z \leftarrow P(Y)$; $P(Y) \leftarrow m$; $P(X) \leftarrow Z$;
      $P^{-1}(Z) \leftarrow X$; $P^{-1}(m) \leftarrow Y$.
(4) If $P(Y + D(m)) > m$, go to step (7).
(5) If $m = n$, go to step (2).
(6) (Case 3) $T(n) \leftarrow -m$; $m \leftarrow n$; go to step (2).
(7) (m has reached its last step) $D(m) \leftarrow -D(m)$; if $m = n$, go to step (13).
(8) (Case 4) $T(n) \leftarrow -(m + 1)$; if $T(m) > 0$, go to step (11).
(9) $T(m + 1) \leftarrow m - 1$; if $-T(m) = m - 1$, go to step (12).
(10) $T(m - 1) \leftarrow T(m)$; go to step (12).
(11) $T(m + 1) \leftarrow T(m)$.
(12) $m \leftarrow n$; go to step (2).
(13) (Case 2) if $T(n) < 0$, go to step (15).
(14) $m \leftarrow T(n)$ and go to step (2).
(15) $m \leftarrow n - 1$; if $-T(n) = n - 1$, go to step (2).
(16) $T(n - 1) \leftarrow T(n)$.
(17) Go to step (2).

In the worst case (case 4) the algorithm goes through 4 comparisons and 11 substitutions, but in most of the cases it performs 3 comparisons and 7 substitutions. Ehrlich's version does even better than this.

1.4   Nets for performing permutations through transpositions

Assume that n items are ordered in an arbitrary order and that we wish to change the order to some other order (which in the trivial case is the same order). Let us rename the items in such a way that the ith item in the desired order will be called item number *i*. In fact, let us assume that the items are the integers $1, 2, \ldots, n$, and we wish to order them in the natural order. The methods to be described in this section are those of Kautz, Levitt, and Waksman [5]. We shall describe now a method that has several advantages, which we shall discuss later.

By *phase A switch* we mean the following action: Numbers located in odd places are compared with the numbers on their right (if *n* is odd, the last number does not take part in this phase); if a pair is in the natural order (smaller on left, larger on right), the pair does not switch; if a pair is not in natural order, they switch places. All pairs act simultaneously.

By *phase B switch* we mean the following action: Numbers located in even places are compared with the numbers on their right (if *n* is odd, the first number does not take part in this phase, and if *n* is even, both first and last numbers do not take part in this phase). If the pair is not in natural order, they switch places; if they are in natural order, they stay put.

The algorithm consists of applying phase A and phase B switches alternately. The algorithm stops when for two consecutive phase applications no pair of numbers switches places. Let us demonstrate the algorithm on the numbers $1, 2, \ldots, 7$. Let the original order be 5, 3, 1, 4, 7, 2, 6 (Fig. 1.1).

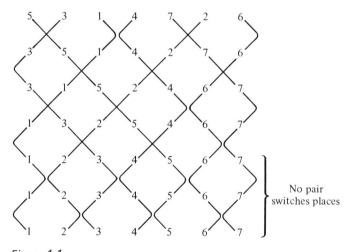

Figure 1.1

It is easy to see that once the algorithm terminates, the numbers are ordered in the natural order. In order to see that the algorithm must terminate, we observe that any pair of numbers can switch places only once. Thus, the number of phase applications is bounded by $n(n - 1) + 2$. However, a much stronger statement holds:

Theorem 1.1: In our algorithm, after applying n phase switches to the numbers $1, 2, \ldots, n$ given in any order, the natural order is obtained.

Proof : In fact, for $n = 1$, no application is necessary, and for $n = 2$, only one application is necessary. But for $n = 3$, as is shown in Fig. 1.2, three applications are necessary. It is easy to check all six permutations of three numbers to see that three applications will always suffice. Our proof continues by induction. In the proof of the inductive step we shall employ a pictorial notation.

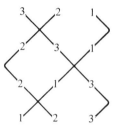

Figure 1.2

Let us use the notation for a *comparison box* as shown in Fig. 1.3. The two numbers enter the comparison box, one from the left and one from the right. The smaller one emerges from the left and the larger from the right.

Figure 1.3

Our inductive hypothesis is then that a net of n layers is sufficient to arrange n numbers in their natural order (Fig. 1.4).

Assume that we have a net of $n + 1$ layers similarly constructed. The claim is that if we follow the track that the number $n + 1$ takes, the remaining structure contains the array for n, which is assumed to be sufficient to arrange the numbers $1, 2, \ldots, n$. This is best demonstrated on an example. Assume

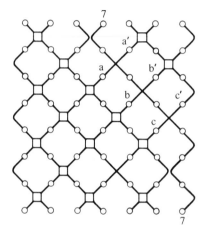

n even   *n* odd

Figure 1.4

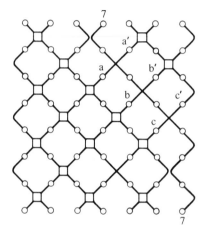

Figure 1.5

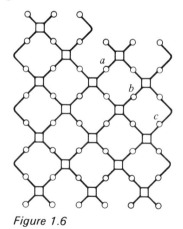

Figure 1.6

that $n = 6$. The array for 7 looks as shown in Fig. 1.5. For demonstration, assume that 7 is originally in the fourth place. The comparison boxes that are "used up" by 7 are not drawn as boxes any more, and their action is specified in the diagram. If we merge points a with a', b with b', and c with c', and if we ignore 7, which is already assured of reaching its place, and the path it takes, we get Fig. 1.6. The lower six levels consist of the array for $n = 6$, and the top "redundant" level cannot spoil a thing. The case of odd n follows similarly.

QED

It is easy to see that, in general, n is the lowest possible value for which a theorem like Theorem 1.1 can hold. For in the "worst" case each number has to switch places with all the others (as will happen if the initial order is $n, n - 1, \ldots, 2, 1$). The number of necessary switches is then $n(n - 1)/2$. The number of switches performed in each level is at most $(n - 1)/2$, for odd n, and is $n/2$ and $(n - 2)/2$ alternately for even n, that is, on the average $(n - 1)/2$ in each level. (This "computation of averages" breaks down for $n = 2$, because $(n - 2)/2 = 0$, and the second level becomes redundant.) Therefore, the necessary number of levels is at least n.

However, for many permutations the number of necessary levels is less than n, and it may be of interest to find the average number of levels necessary, if we assume that all initial permutations are equally probable.

This algorithm has several interesting features. First, the synchronism between switches of different pairs, which is implicit in the description of the phase switches, is not essential; we may simply say that any pair of adjacent numbers which are not in the correct order can switch places, and if no pair can switch places any more, the algorithm terminates. Second, the decisions on whether to switch a pair or not are local and are not dependent on the locations of the rest of the numbers. These two features make this algorithm attractive in a concurrent (parallel) mode of operation.

However, when we consider the number of switching boxes in the net, which is $n(n - 1)/2$, we may come to the conclusion that simplicity of our algorithm and its two features described above are too expensive. We shall now consider another net in which the number of switching boxes is essentially minimal, but the operation rules are much more complicated.

The description of our second net is recursive. We have nets for $n = 1$ (no switching boxes) and for $n = 2$ (a single switching box). Assuming that all nets for $m < n$ have been defined, the net for n is described as follows: Let $\lfloor x \rfloor$ denote the greatest integer which is not greater than x, and $\lceil x \rceil$

the least integer which is not less than x. Our net for n is composed of a net for $\lceil n/2 \rceil$, a net for $\lfloor n/2 \rfloor$, and $n-1$ additional switching boxes. (Clearly $\lceil n/2 \rceil + \lfloor n/2 \rfloor = n$.) The arrangements for even n and odd n are shown in Fig. 1.7.

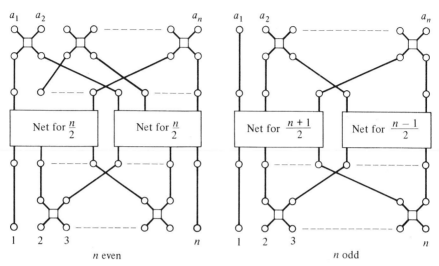

Figure 1.7

The switching boxes are not comparison boxes as before; each box has to be told whether to switch the two incoming elements or leave them in unchanged order. This decision of whether to switch is made as part of the total plan. We assume that each one of the nets can perform any permutation on its inputs. Assume that n is even. We start by searching for the number 1 among the inputs; it must reach the left-hand net and therefore the switching box which it enters on the top row has to switch it to the left-hand side if it is not there already. The number which enters the same switching box on the top row goes to the right-hand net, and this specifies which box on the bottom line it must enter, and the mode of operation of this box. Again, the number which shares the same box with it on the bottom row must come from the left-hand net. We continue in this fashion until the assignment for n is complete. If not all members have been treated yet, we can make an arbitrary switching decision on one of the undecided switching boxes on the bottom, and continue from there. The decision procedure for odd n is similar. We demonstrate the whole procedure for $n = 7$ (Fig. 1.8). Assume that the input permutation is $[2, 7, 4, 5, 6, 3, 1]$. We redraw the net and number the 14

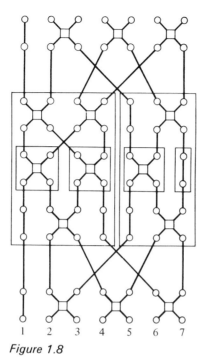

Figure 1.8

switching boxes from 1 to 14. Number 1 must enter the left-hand net. This specifies which input to it carries 1 and that box 3 must switch. This means that number 3 enters the right-hand network as indicated. Since 3 must enter box 12, this determines the output line on which 3 comes out of the right-hand net, and that box 12 does not switch. Therefore, 2 comes out of the left-hand net, and now we can make an arbitrary decision, say that box 13 does not switch. We continue in this fashion. After the inputs and outputs to each net have been determined, we repeat the same argument on each net; and so on. A final assignment is shown in Fig. 1.9.

Let us denote by $N(n)$ the number of switching boxes for the net for n elements. Clearly,

$$N(n) = N\left(\left\lceil \frac{n}{2} \right\rceil\right) + N\left(\left\lfloor \frac{n}{2} \right\rfloor\right) + n - 1.$$

Since our aim is only to get an estimate on the number of switching boxes, let us consider the easy case where $n = 2^m$. Thus,

$$N(2^m) = 2 \cdot N(2^{m-1}) + 2^m - 1.$$

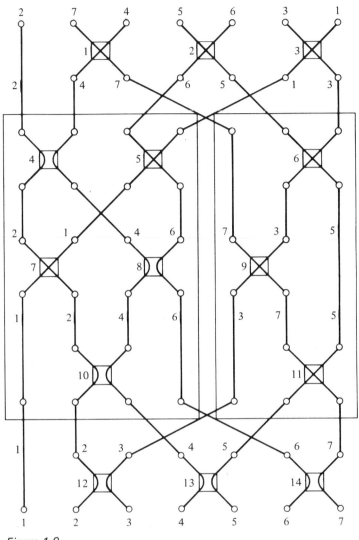

Figure 1.9

This is a linear difference equation on m. [Define $M(m) = N(2^m)$; then the equation becomes

$$M(m) = 2 \cdot M(m - 1) + 2^m - 1.]$$

Of course we have the initial condition

$$N(1) = 0.$$

It is easy to verify that the solution of this equation is

$$N(2^m) = 2^m(m - 1) + 1,$$

and as an approximation in terms of n,

$$N(n) = n(\log_2 n - 1) + 1.$$

In order to realize that this is essentially optimal, let us consider the following argument. The number of switching boxes, $N(n)$, must be large enough to ensure that the total number of modes of operations for the network is at least $n!$. For each box there are two modes, thus,

$$2^{N(n)} \geqslant n!$$

By Stirling's approximation of $n!$ we get

$$2^{N(n)} \geqslant \sqrt{2\pi n} \cdot \left(\frac{n}{\varepsilon}\right)^n,$$

and, by taking the logarithm of both sides,

$$N(n) \geqslant \log_2 \sqrt{2\pi} + (n + \tfrac{1}{2}) \log_2 n - n \cdot \log_2 \varepsilon.$$

However, the deciding term is $n \log_2 n$, which is the same as in the exact evaluation of $N(n)$. Thus, $N(n)$ is essentially minimum.

1.5   Remarks on other results

The algebraist views permutations as operators and is interested in their group-theoretic properties. Some results of this approach are of interest to the combinatorial analyst, especially in the development of Pólya's theory of counting (see, for example, references 6, 7, and 8).

Another subject of great interest to the computer scientist is sorting. This is the art of arranging data in some order by efficient algorithms. In a way Section 1.4 is about sorting. Also, we shall describe another sorting procedure in Chapter 7. An extensive study of sorting can be found in Knuth's work [9].

EXERCISES

1.1 How many permutations are there between 5173246 and 3425761 in the generation by Algorithm 1.1?

1.2 Consider the following mixed-radix representation of a positive integer m by $(a_1, a_2, \ldots, a_{n-1})$, where

$$m = a_1 \cdot 1! + a_2 \cdot 2! + \cdots + a_{n-1} \cdot (n-1)!,$$

$$0 \leqslant a_1 \leqslant i \qquad \text{for } i = 1, 2, \ldots, n-1.$$

Prove that every number m, $0 \leqslant m \leqslant n! - 1$, has a unique representation of this type. Find a correspondence between number representations of this type and permutations, and describe an algorithm for generating all $n!$ permutations by counting in this representation and constructing for each m the corresponding permutation.

1.3 Prove the following statement about the first algorithm of Section 1.4: The only way that a phase in which no switches occur can be followed by a phase in which some switches occur is that these are the first two phases of the algorithm. How can the terminating condition of the algorithm be improved in view of this fact?

1.4 Repeat the demonstration of the idea of the proof of Theorem 1.1 for $n = 7$, when 8 is originally in the second place.

1.5 Draw the complete net of the second type described in Section 1.4 for $n = 8$. Give a switching assignment to all boxes in order to arrange the input permutation [5, 3, 8, 1, 4, 7, 2, 6] in the natural order. Compute a lower bound on the number of boxes necessary (no log table is required) and compare it with the number of boxes in your net.

REFERENCES

1. Johnson, S. M., "Generation of Permutations by Adjacent Transposition," *Mathematics of Computation*, 1963, pp. 282–85.
2. Trotter, H. F., "Algorithm 115," *Comm. ACM*, Vol. 5, No. 8, August 1962, pp. 434–35.
3. Ehrlich, G., "Permutations," Research report of the Department of Applied Mathematics, The Weizmann Institute of Science, Rehovot, Israel, 1971.
4. Lehmer, D. H., "The Machine Tools of Combinatorics," in *Applied Combinatorial Mathematics*, E. F. Beckenbach (ed.), Wiley, New York, 1964, pp. 5–31.
5. Kautz, W. H., Levitt, K. N., and Waksman, A., "Cellular Interconnection Arrays," *IEEE Trans. Computers*, Vol. C-17, May 1968, pp. 443–51.
6. Riordan, J., *An Introduction to Combinatorial Analysis*, Wiley, New York, 1958.

7. De Bruijn, N. G., "Pólya's Theory of Counting," in *Applied Combinatorial Mathematics*, E. F. Beckenbach (ed.), Wiley, New York, 1964, pp. 144–84.
8. Liu, C. L., *Introduction to Combinatorial Mathematics*, McGraw-Hill, New York, 1968.
9. Knuth, D. E., *The Art of Computer Programming*, Vol. 3/Sorting and Searching, Addison-Wesley, Reading, Mass., 1972.

2
COMBINATIONS

2.1 Binomial coefficients

Assume that we have a set of n distinct elements; *a combination* (*without repetitions*) is a subset of this set. The number of combinations of r elements out of n is denoted by $\binom{n}{r}$ or C_n^r. These numbers are called *binomial coefficients*, and they are of great importance in combinatorial mathematics.

We have seen that the number of r-permutations is (see (1.2))

$$P(n, r) = \frac{n!}{(n - r)!}.$$

Here every combination of r elements has been counted $r!$ times, since this is the number of different ways to arrange r elements. Thus,

$$\binom{n}{r} = \frac{P(n, r)}{r!} = \frac{n!}{(n-r)!r!}. \tag{2.1}$$

These binomial coefficients are so named for the role they play in *Newton's binomial theorem*. This theorem states that for every x and y and for every positive integer n,*

$$(x + y)^n = \sum_{i=0}^{n} \binom{n}{i} x^i y^{n-i}. \tag{2.2}$$

One way of proving this theorem is as follows: If we write $(x + y)^n$ explicitly as a product of n factors and expand it to a parentheses-free sum of products, we get 2^n terms of the type $x^i y^{n-i}$ (before assembling similar terms). This follows from the fact that there are n factors $(x + y)$, and for each of them we can choose either the left-hand term, x, or the right-hand term, y. Altogether there are n independent choices. Thus, there are 2^n resulting products. The number of times $x^i y^{n-i}$ appears is equal to the number of combinations of i elements of a set of n elements, namely, the factors in which we choose the left-hand term, x.

The binomial theorem can also be proved by induction on n, using the following identity:

$$\binom{n}{r} + \binom{n}{r+1} = \binom{n+1}{r+1}, \tag{2.3}$$

where $0 \leqslant r < n$. This identity can be easily verified by using (2.1). However, we shall bring here another, more "combinatorial" argument.

On the right-hand side of (2.3) we have the number of $(r + 1)$-combinations in a set of $n + 1$ elements. Choose arbitrarily an element, say a. All $(r + 1)$-combinations can be divided into two classes: those which contain a and those which do not. The number of $(r + 1)$-combinations which contain a is $\binom{n}{r}$, for we only have to pick r additional elements out of the remaining n elements. The number of $(r + 1)$-combinations which do not contain a is

---

*This theorem can be generalized to hold for any n, with proper changes and restriction, but we have no interest in this here.

$\binom{n}{r+1}$, for we have to pick $r+1$ elements out of the remaining n elements.

We shall see that through such "combinatorial" arguments we can sometimes prove identities which otherwise require complicated computations.

Identity (2.3) suggests some "natural" extensions of the definition of the binomial coefficients. They are

$$\binom{n}{r} = 0 \qquad \text{if } r > n, \tag{2.4}$$

$$\binom{n}{r} = 0 \quad \text{if } r < 0, \tag{2.5}$$

$$\binom{0}{0} = 1. \tag{2.6}$$

The extension (2.6) is also suggested by (2.1), but (2.4) and (2.5) are not, since $k!$ is not defined for negative integers k.

Identity (2.3) suggests an efficient method for computing the binomial coefficient. The resulting table, which is called *Pascal's triangle*, is shown in Fig. 2.1. After assigning the value 1 for $\binom{0}{0}$, we proceed to the second line.

n \ r	0	1	2	3	4	5
0	1					
1	1	1				
2	1	2	1			
3	1	3	3	1		
4	1	4	6	4	1	
5	1	5	10	10	5	1

Figure 2.1

Each place is assigned the sum of the numbers above it and above it to its left. The places which should be assigned the value 0 by (2.4) are left blank to emphasize the triangular shape.

Assume that all we want is to evaluate $\binom{n}{r}$. If we use the Pascal's triangle approach, we have to perform $r \cdot (n - r)$ additions. If we evaluate $\binom{n}{r}$ by using (2.1) we perform $2m$ multiplications and one division, where

$$m = \text{Min}\{r - 1, n - r - 1\}.$$

Even if we want to evaluate $\binom{n}{r}$ for all $0 \leqslant r \leqslant n$, the Pascal's triangle approach is not attractive since it requires $n(n - 1)/2$ additions, while a direct evaluation requires $n - 1$ multiplications and $n - 1$ divisions. [We first evaluate $\binom{n}{0} = 1$; in order to evaluate $\binom{n}{r + 1}$ we use the relation

$$\binom{n}{r + 1} = \frac{n - r}{r + 1} \cdot \binom{n}{r},$$

and since the value of $\binom{n}{r}$ is already known, it takes one multiplication and one division.] However, if we want to find all $\binom{n}{r}$ for $0 \leqslant n \leqslant L$ and $0 \leqslant r \leqslant n$, then the Pascal's triangle approach is most attractive.

It is easy to observe and prove the identity

$$\binom{n}{r} = \binom{n}{n - r}. \tag{2.7}$$

Several other elementary identities are given in Exercises 2.1, 2.2, and 2.3. We shall now prove the following identity:

$$\sum_i \binom{m}{i} \cdot \binom{n - m}{k - i} = \binom{n}{k} \qquad \text{for } 0 \leqslant m \leqslant n. \tag{2.8}$$

The exact bounds of i are not specified, but the only nonzero terms in the summation are those for which $\text{Max}\{0, m + k - n\} \leqslant i \leqslant \text{Min}\{k, m\}$. The number of k-combinations out of n elements is $\binom{n}{k}$. Let us partition the set

of n elements into two subsets: the first containing m elements and the second the remaining $n - m$ elements. The number of ways of selecting k elements i of which are from the first subset and the remaining $k - i$ elements from the second subset is

$$\binom{m}{i} \cdot \binom{n-m}{k-i}.$$

Since i can have the values $0, 1, \ldots, k$, and no two resulting combinations are the same, the identity follows.

We shall now demonstrate some techniques of calculus and generating functions which are common in the enumerative combinatorial analysis. To begin with, let us prove the following identity:

$$\sum_{i=1}^{n} i\binom{n}{i} = n \cdot 2^{n-1}. \tag{2.9}$$

(I have chosen this example for illustration purposes; a simpler method for proving (2.9) is discussed in Exercise 2.4.) By substitution of $y = 1$ in (2.2) we get

$$(x + 1)^n = \sum_{i=0}^{n} \binom{n}{i} \cdot x^i. \tag{2.10}$$

Consider each side as an alternative expression of a function of the variable x, and differentiate both sides.

$$n(x + 1)^{n-1} = \sum_{i=1}^{n} i\binom{n}{i} \cdot x^{i-1}. \tag{2.11}$$

(The first term, for $i = 0$, which is zero, has been dropped.) Now substitution of $x = 1$ yields the desired result.

Another interesting identity is

$$\sum_{i=1}^{n} \frac{(-1)^{i-1}}{i} \binom{n}{i} = 1 + \frac{1}{2} + \cdots + \frac{1}{n}. \tag{2.12}$$

Since we have a $(-1)^{i-1}$ factor we shall use the following form of the binomial theorem:

$$(1 - x)^n = \sum_{i=0}^{n} (-1)^i \binom{n}{i} \cdot x^i. \qquad (2.13)$$

Now transfer the first term, for $i = 0$, to the left-hand side, and divide both sides by x:

$$-\frac{(1 - x)^n - 1}{(1 - x) - 1} = \sum_{i=1}^{n} (-1)^i \binom{n}{i} \cdot x^{i-1}.$$

This is equivalent to

$$-[1 + (1 - x) + (1 - x)^2 + \cdots + (1 - x)^{n-1}] = \sum_{i=1}^{n} (-1)^i \binom{n}{i} \cdot x^{i-1}.$$

By integrating both sides with respect to x we get

$$(1 - x) + \frac{(1 - x)^2}{2} + \cdots + \frac{(1 - x)^n}{n} + C = \sum_{i=1}^{n} \frac{(-1)^i}{i} \binom{n}{i} \cdot x^i.$$

By substituting $x = 0$ we find the value of the integration constant C,

$$C = -\left[1 + \frac{1}{2} + \cdots + \frac{1}{n}\right].$$

The identity (2.12) follows by substituting $x = 1$.

Many other properties of binomial coefficients and identities concerning them can be found in references 1, 2, and 3.

2.2 Combinations with repetitions

Assume that we have n types of items, with an unlimited supply of each. Assume also that the items of one type are indistinguishable, or that we do not care to distinguish among them. An *r-combination with repetitions allowed* is then a selection of a number of items, r_1, of type 1, and in general, a number of items, r_i, of type i, such that

$$r = r_1 + r_2 + \cdots + r_n. \tag{2.14}$$

Clearly, there is no ordering of the elements in the selection.

Theorem 2.1: The number of r-combinations, with repetitions allowed, out of n types, such that at least one item is selected out of each type is

$$\binom{r-1}{n-1}.$$

Proof: Consider a sequence of r 1's. We associate with each selection of $r_1, r_2, \ldots, r_n$ a distribution of $n + 1$ commas in between the 1's in the following way. One comma is placed on the left-hand side of the sequence, and one on the right-hand side. The remaining $n - 1$ commas are distributed in between the 1's, but no more than one comma is allowed to be placed in one interval between 1's. It is clear that there is a one-to-one correspondence between choices of $r_1, r_2, \ldots, r_n$ which satisfy (2.14) and $r_i > 0$ for all i, and the selections of $n - 1$ intervals, out of the $r - 1$ intervals, in which commas are placed. Thus the number of selections is

$$\binom{r-1}{n-1}.$$

QED

Theorem 2.2: The number of r-combinations, with repetitions allowed, out of n types, is $\binom{n+r-1}{r}$.

There are many proofs of this theorem and we shall describe three different proofs. The first is a consequence of Theorem 2.1. The second is a direct combinatorial algorithm. The third is an induction based on a recursion formula.

Proof 1: Let $r_1, r_2, \ldots, r_n$ be any selection satisfying (2.14). Add n to both sides:

$$n + r = (r_1 + 1) + (r_2 + 1) + \cdots + (r_n + 1).$$

This specifies an $(n + r)$-combination, out of n types, in which at least one item is selected of each type. Also, each solution to the latter problem corresponds to a solution of the former problem by reducing the number of items selected of each type by one. Thus, the number of r-combinations is

$$\binom{n + r - 1}{n - 1} = \binom{n + r - 1}{r}.$$

Proof 2:   This proof is also based on setting up a one-to-one correspondence. Let us associate with each selection of $r_1, r_2, \ldots, r_n$ a sequence of r_1 1's, r_2 2's, up to r_n n's. For example, if $n = 4$, $r = 5$ and $r_1 = 2$, $r_2 = 0$, $r_3 = 1$, $r_4 = 2$, then the sequence is 11344. Now, add $i - 1$ to the ith number in the sequence. The resulting sequence in our example is 12578. It is clear that since the original sequence is nondecreasing, the new sequence is increasing. Also, if we take any increasing sequence of r positive integers, each less than or equal to $n + r - 1$, then by subtracting $i - 1$ from the ith integer, it is now a nondecreasing sequence of positive integers each less than or equal to n. Thus, the number of sequences of the type we want to enumerate is the same as the number of sequences of the second type, which is

$$\binom{n + r - 1}{r}.$$

Proof 3:   Denote by $f(n, r)$ the number of r-combinations of n types. The number of combinations in which type 1 is represented at least once is $f(n, r - 1)$, and the number of combinations in which it is not represented at all is $f(n - 1, r)$. Thus,

$$f(n, r) = f(n, r - 1) + f(n - 1, r). \qquad (2.15)$$

It is also clear that

$$f(1, r) = 1 \qquad \text{for all } r,$$

$$f(n, 1) = n \qquad \text{for all } n.$$

It can be seen, by substitution of $r = 1$ in (2.15), that it is natural to define

$$f(n, 0) = 1.$$

As we start to fill in the table, as is done in Fig. 2.2, Pascal's triangle is immediately discovered. In fact, it is immediately discovered that, as the arrows indicate, it is the same rule of generation, and all which remains to be done is adjust the parameters. The rows of Pascal's triangle correspond to diagonals; thus, the row number in Pascal's triangle of the number in the nth row and rth column in our table is $n + r - 1$. The column numbers are the same. Thus,

$$f(n, r) = \binom{n + r - 1}{r}. \tag{2.16}$$

$n \backslash r$	0	1	2	3	4	5	6
1	1 →	1 →	1 →	1 →	1	1	1
	↓	↓	↓	↓			
2	1 →	2 →	3 →	4			
	↓	↓	↓				
3	1 →	3 →	6				
	↓	↓					
4	1 →	4					
	↓						
5	1						

Figure 2.2

This can also be verified by induction on r. We have that $f(n, 1) = n$ for all n. Assume that (2.16) holds for all $r < m$. By repeated substitution of (2.15) and $f(1, r) = 1$ we get

$$\begin{aligned} f(n, m) &= f(n, m - 1) + f(n - 1, m - 1) + f(n - 2, m - 1) + \cdots + 1 \\ &= \binom{n + m - 2}{m - 1} + \binom{n + m - 3}{m - 1} + \cdots + \binom{m - 1}{m - 1} \\ &= \binom{n + m - 1}{m}. \end{aligned}$$

Here we use the result of Exercise 2.5.

To close this section we shall consider a partition problem, which is suggested by the proof of Theorem 2.1. Different problems on partitions will be considered in Chapter 3.

Theorem 2.3:   The number of ways in which n indistinguishable items can be distributed into r distinct cells is

$$\binom{n + r - 1}{r - 1}.$$

Proof: Assume that the items are lined up. The distribution into r distinct cells can be viewed as placement of $r + 1$ dividing walls. The first wall is on the left-hand side of the line; the last wall is on the right-hand side of the line. Any number of walls can be placed in one interval. This is the same as an $(r - 1)$-combination with repetitions allowed, out of $n + 1$ types. By Theorem 2.2 this number is

$$\binom{(n + 1) + (r - 1) - 1}{(r - 1)} = \binom{n + r - 1}{r - 1}.$$

QED

2.3   An algorithm for generating all combinations in lexicographic order

In many exhaustive searches it is desirable to generate all the r-combinations of a set of n items. We shall describe here an algorithm for generating the combinations in lexicographic order.

First, assume that r-combinations without repetitions are needed. Order the set of n items in some arbitrary order. Thus, without loss of generality, we may assume that the sequence of items is $1, 2, \ldots, n$. Let us use a vector of length n of r 1's and $n - r$ zeros to represent the r-combination. Let $a_1, a_2, \ldots, a_r$ be the locations of the r 1's. We assume that

$$a_1 < a_2 < \cdots < a_r.$$

We start with $a_1 = 1, a_2 = 2, \ldots, a_r = r$, and will generate all the $\binom{n}{r}$ sequences of a's in a lexicographic order (the order used for listing words in a dictionary). The algorithm proceeds as follows: Find the largest a_i such that the place on its right contains a zero. If there is no such a_i (this will happen only when $a_i = n - r + 1$ and $a_r = n$), stop. If there is, move this one to the right (replace a_i by $a_i + 1$) and move all the 1's on its right as close to it as possible $(a_{i+1} = a_i + 1, \ldots, a_r = a_i + r - i$; here a_i is the new value). Apply the same rule again.

Let us demonstrate the algorithm for $n = 5$, $r = 3$. As we apply the rule the first time $a_i = 3$; thus, it alone moves to 4, yielding 1, 2, 4. Next we get 1, 2, 5. Now $a_i = 2$ and we move it to 3, but the one in the 5th place moves to the left as far as possible, namely, $a_3 = 4$. The complete sequence is shown in the table.

Step	The Vector	a_1	a_2	a_3	a_i
1	11100	1	2	3	3
2	11010	1	2	4	4
3	11001	1	2	5	2
4	10110	1	3	4	4
5	10101	1	3	5	3
6	10011	1	4	5	1
7	01110	2	3	4	4
8	01101	2	3	5	3
9	01011	2	4	5	2
10	00111	3	4	5	none

It is easily proved, by induction on n, that this algorithm generates all the r-combinations out of n in lexicographic order. (See Exercise 2.10.)

Assume that we do not carry the step numbers in our generation and at a given point we want to find the step number of the combination specified by $a_1, a_2, \ldots, a_r$.

Since we have 1 in place a_1, all the r-combinations in which a_1 is higher have not been considered yet; there are

$$\binom{n - a_1}{r}$$

of them. Of those in which a_1 is where it is now, all those in which a_2 is higher have not been considered yet; there are

$$\binom{n - a_2}{r - 1}$$

of them; and so on. Thus, the step number is

$$\binom{n}{r} - \left[\binom{n-a_1}{r} + \binom{n-a_2}{r-1} + \cdots + \binom{n-a_r}{1}\right]. \tag{2.17}$$

The reverse problem is to find the r-combination which we would get in the mth step, without generating all r-combinations up to this step. Clearly, $a_1, a_2, \ldots, a_r$ of the mth step must satisfy

$$\binom{n-a_1}{r} + \binom{n-a_2}{r-1} + \cdots + \binom{n-a_r}{1} = \binom{n}{r} - m.$$

Let us denote $b_i = n - a_i$; thus,

$$b_1 > b_2 > \cdots > b_r \geq 0. \tag{2.18}$$

We shall now show that for a given N

$$\binom{b_1}{r} + \binom{b_2}{r-1} + \cdots + \binom{b_r}{1} = N \tag{2.19}$$

implies unique values for $b_1, \ldots, b_r$ if condition (2.18) must hold. Assume the contrary; then we have

$$\binom{b_1}{r} + \binom{b_2}{r-1} + \cdots + \binom{b_r}{1} = \binom{b_1'}{r} + \binom{b_2'}{r-1} + \cdots + \binom{b_r'}{1}. \tag{2.20}$$

We may assume that $b_1 > b_1'$; for if $b_1 = b_1'$, these terms can be canceled and the same argument repeated for b_2 and b_2'. Since $b_1' - i \geq b_{i+1}'$ for $i = 1, 2, \ldots, r - 1$, by Exercise 2.11 we have

$$\binom{b_1'}{r} + \binom{b_2'}{r-1} + \cdots + \binom{b_r'}{1} \leq \binom{b_1'}{r} + \binom{b_1'-1}{r-1} + \cdots + \binom{b_1'-(r-1)}{1}.$$

By (2.20), the last inequality and by dropping all but the first term from the left-hand side of (2.20) we get

$$\binom{b_1}{r} \leq \binom{b_1'}{r} + \binom{b_1'-1}{r-1} + \cdots + \binom{b_1'-(r-1)}{1}. \tag{2.21}$$

Since $b_1 \geqslant b_1' + 1$, by Exercises 2.11 we have

$$\binom{b_1}{r} \geqslant \binom{b_1' + 1}{r},$$

and (2.21) implies that

$$\binom{b_1' + 1}{r} \leqslant \binom{b_1'}{r} + \binom{b_1' - 1}{r - 1} + \cdots + \binom{b_1' - (r - 1)}{1}.$$

However, by (2.3),

$$\binom{b_1' + 1}{r} = \binom{b_1'}{r} + \binom{b_1'}{r - 1}$$

$$= \binom{b_1'}{r} + \binom{b_1' - 1}{r - 1} + \binom{b_1' - 1}{r - 2}$$

$$\vdots$$

$$= \binom{b_1'}{r} + \binom{b_1' - 1}{r - 1} + \cdots + \binom{b_1' - (r - 1)}{1} + \binom{b_1' - (r - 1)}{0}.$$

This contradicts the former inequality, and therefore the values of b_1 $b_2, \ldots, b_r$ are unique.

The values of the b's are easy to obtain. Let b_1 be the greatest integer x such that

$$N \geqslant \binom{x}{r}.$$

Next, let b_2 be the greatest integer x such that

$$N - \binom{b_1}{r} \geqslant \binom{x}{r - 1}.$$

Finally, let b_r be the greatest integer x such that

$$N - \left[\binom{b_1}{r} + \binom{b_2}{r - 1} + \cdots + \binom{b_{r-1}}{2} \right] \geqslant \binom{x}{1} = x.$$

(Clearly, this last step is satisfied by equality.) This determines values for $b_1, b_2, \ldots, b_r$, but we still have to show that (2.18) holds. Let us demonstrate that $b_1 > b_2$; the rest can be proved in the same way. We have

$$\binom{b_1 + 1}{r} > N$$

and

$$N - \binom{b_1}{r} \geqslant \binom{b_2}{r - 1}.$$

Thus,

$$\binom{b_1 + 1}{r} - \binom{b_1}{r} > \binom{b_2}{r - 1}.$$

This implies, by (2.3), that

$$\binom{b_1}{r - 1} > \binom{b_2}{r - 1},$$

which, in turn, implies that $b_1 > b_2$.

A similar method for generating all r-combinations with repetitions allowed can be described, where more than a single one can be put in one place. The description of the algorithm is left as an exercise.

The results of this section are based to a large measure on Lehmer's work [4].

One of the disadvantages of the algorithm described in this section is that there may be many changes between two consecutive combinations. For example, the combination 1, 4, 5 (for $r = 3$ and $n = 5$) is followed by 2, 3, 4, in which two replacements took place. It may be desirable to have as few changes as possible between consecutive combinations. Lathroum discovered (in 1965) an algorithm in which a single change (one element is dropped and one added) takes place each time. This algorithm was implemented by Chase [5].

In the next section we shall discuss an algorithm of Ehrlich's which has an additional advantage.

2.4 A loop-free algorithm for generating all combinations

In this section we shall describe a method of Ehrlich [6] to generate combinations. First we shall describe the combinatorial structure and then will show a loop-free implementation of the algorithm.

The initial combination may be any combination in which all the r selected numbers are consecutive; in the binary representation it means that all the r 1's are in one run in the vector of length n. For example, if $r = 3$ and $n = 5$, we may start with 11100 or 01110 or 00111. The binary vector is denoted by A and its ith component is $A(i)$. The components of A may or may not be marked with a bar. Initially all the components of A, except those of the last run (either of zeros or 1's) are marked. For example, if $A = 00111000$ (for $r = 3$ and $n = 8$), then it is marked as follows:

$$\overline{001\overline{1}\overline{1}000}.$$

Algorithm 2.1:
(1) Output.
(2) If there are no marked components in A, stop.
(3) Let i be the highest index such that $A(i)$ is marked.
(4) If $A(i) = 0$, exchange it with the nearest one on its right and go to step (6).*
(5) If $A(i) = 1$, exchange it with the farthest zero on its right, without passing another one.
(6) Remove the bar from $A(i)$ and mark with a bar all the components on its right except those of the last run (which may consist of 1's or zeros, as the case may be). Go to step (1).

It is not apparent that this is an algorithm. We have to show that if $A(i) = 0$, there is a 1 on its right; and if $A(i) = 1$, then $A(i + 1) = 0$. Also, we have to show that the algorithm will generate each r-combination exactly once and will halt. Before proving these, let us consider an example.

The sequence of A's, with the marking, is shown in the accompanying list for $r = 3$ and $n = 6$, starting with 011100.

*The bars stay in the same place and do not move in the exchange.

1. $\bar{0}\bar{1}\bar{1}\bar{1}00$ 11. $10\bar{0}\bar{1}\bar{1}0$
2. $\bar{0}\bar{1}\bar{1}0\bar{0}1$ 12. $10\bar{0}\bar{1}01$
3. $\bar{0}\bar{1}\bar{1}010$ 13. $10\bar{0}011$
4. $\bar{0}\bar{1}0\bar{1}\bar{1}0$ 14. $10\bar{1}0\bar{0}1$
5. $\bar{0}\bar{1}0\bar{1}01$ 15. $10\bar{1}010$
6. $\bar{0}\bar{1}0011$ 16. $1\bar{0}1100$
7. $\bar{0}0\bar{0}111$ 17. $110\bar{1}00$
8. $\bar{0}01\bar{0}11$ 18. $110\bar{0}\bar{0}1$
9. $\bar{0}011\bar{0}1$ 19. $11\bar{0}010$
10. $\bar{0}01110$ 20. 111000

Let us introduce the following notation. If a is a symbol, a^m stands for

$$\underbrace{aa\cdots a}_{m \text{ times}} \quad \text{(a sequence of } m \text{ } a\text{'s).}$$

For example, $\bar{1}\bar{1}(\bar{0})^3 0$ stands for $1\bar{1}\bar{0}\bar{0}\bar{0}0$.

Theorem 2.4:   When Algorithm 2.1 is applied to an initial marked vector A (A is either $(\bar{0})^p(\bar{1})^r 0^{n-p-r}$, where $p \geq 0$ and $n > p + r$, or it is $(\bar{0})^{n-r}\bar{1}^r$), the algorithm will never reach a case where its operation is not well defined; it will generate each r-combination once and will halt. If $A(1) = 0$, the last vector will be $1^r 0^{n-r}$. If $A(1) = 1$ and r is even, the last vector will be $0^{n-r}1^r$; if r is odd, the last vector will be $01^r 0^{n-r-1}$. (We assume that $n > r > 0$.)

Proof: By induction on n. If $n = 2$, then initially either $A = \bar{0}1$ or $A = \bar{1}0$. In the first case the next vector is 10 and the algorithm halts; in the second case the next vector is 01 and it halts. In both cases all claims of the algorithm are held.

   Now assume that the theorem holds for $n - 1$ and let us prove that it holds for n. There are five cases:

Case 1:   Initially $A(1) = A(2) = 0$. Thus, initially $A = (\bar{0})^p(\bar{1})^r 0^{n-r-p}$, where $p \geq 2$ and $n > p + r$, or it is $(\bar{0})^{n-r}\bar{1}^r$, where $n - r \geq 2$. In either case the algorithm first acts on $A(2), A(3), \ldots, A(n)$ as if it were applied to a vector of length $n - 1$. By the inductive hypothesis this will finally yield the vector $\bar{0}1^r 0^{n-r-1}$, generating so far all the r-combinations of n elements in which

$A(1) = 0$. Now, by step (4) the next vector is $\bar{1}01^{r-1}0^{n-r-1}$. If $r = 1$, this is remarked into 10^{n-1} and the algorithm halts, as stated in the theorem. If $r > 1$, this is remarked into $1\bar{0}(\bar{1})^{r-1}0^{n-r-1}$; the algorithm now acts on the last $n - 1$ components exactly as it would have acted on $\bar{0}(\bar{1})^{r-1}0^{n-r-1}$. By the inductive hypothesis it will generate all $(r - 1)$-combinations and terminate with $1^{r-1}0^{n-r}$. Thus, it has generated all r-combinations in which $A(1) = 1$.

Case 2: Initially $A(1) = 0$, $A(2) = 1$, and r is even. If $n = r + 1$, we start with $\bar{0}1^r$. The next output is $1\bar{0}1^{r-1}$, and by the inductive hypothesis this eventually leads to halting with 1^r0. If $n > r + 1$ we start with $\bar{0}(\bar{1})^r0^{n-r-1}$. By the inductive hypothesis this leads to $\bar{0}0^{n-r-1}1^r$. The next output is $1(\bar{0})^{n-r}1^{r-1}$, and again by the inductive hypothesis this leads to halting with 1^r0^{n-r}.

Case 3: Initially $A(1) = 0$, $A(2) = 1$, and r is odd. If $n = r + 1$, we start with $\bar{0}1^r$. The next output is $1\bar{0}1^{r-1}$, and by the inductive hypothesis this eventually leads to halting with 1^r0. If $n > r + 1$ we start with $\bar{0}(\bar{1})^r0^{n-r-1}$. By the inductive hypothesis this leads to $\bar{0}01^r0^{n-r-2}$. Now, if $r = 1$, the next output is 10^{n-1} and the algorithm halts. If $r > 1$, and $n = r + 2$, the next output is $1\bar{0}01^{r-1}$, and if $n > r + 2$, it is $1\bar{0}\bar{0}(\bar{1})^{r-1}0^{n-r-2}$. In either case this leads to 1^r0^{n-r}.

Case 4: Initially $A(1) = 1$ and r is even. Thus, the initial vector is $(\bar{1})^r0^{n-r}$. If $n = r + 1$, this leads to $\bar{1}01^{r-1}$; the next output is 01^r and the algorithm halts. If $n > r + 1$, this leads to $\bar{1}01^{r-1}0^{n-r-1}$; the next output is $0(\bar{1})^r0^{n-r-1}$ and this leads to $0^{n-r}1^r$.

Case 5: Initially $A(1) = 1$ and r is odd. If $r = 1$, the initial vector is $\bar{1}0^{n-1}$; the next output is $0(\bar{0})^{n-2}1$, and this leads to 010^{n-2}. If $r > 1$, the initial vector is $(\bar{1})^r0^{n-r}$. This leads to $\bar{1}0^{n-r}1^{r-1}$. If $n = r + 1$, the next output is 01^r and the algorithm halts. If $n > r + 1$, the next output is $0(\bar{0})^{n-r-1}1^r$. This leads to 01^r0^{n-r-1}.

QED

Step (2) of the algorithm implies a linear search (checking the components one by one to see if they are marked). Similarly, each of steps (4), (5), and (6) imply a linear search. Also, (6) calls for marking a number of components which may be as large as $n - 1$. Thus, the time required to generate one more combination may be proportional to n. Our next aim is to remove this in-efficiency. For this purpose we need the following fact:

Lemma 2.1: There is always at most a single run of 1's on the right-hand side of $A(i)$ (where $A(i)$ is as defined by step (3)), and if $A(i) = 1$, then $A(i + 1) = 0$.

The proof of Theorem 2.1 easily accommodates the claims of Lemma 2.1, too.

We are now ready to understand Ehrlich's method of removing the loops, yielding an algorithm in which the largest number of elementary operations between any two combinations is bounded by a constant, independent of n.

As before, let i be the highest index such that $A(i)$ is marked. We define a vector $T(1), T(2), \ldots, T(n)$ of integers which satisfies the condition $|T(j)| < j$ for every $j = 1, 2, \ldots n$. Initially $T(1) = 0$; if the initial combination is $(\bar{0})^p(\bar{1})^r 0^{n-r-p}$, where $n > r + p$, then $T(p + r) = -1$, and all the rest are immaterial; if the initial combination is $(\bar{0})^{n-r} 1^r$, then $T(n - r) = -1$, and all the rest are immaterial. The following components of T are considered *assigned*:

1. $T(i)$ is assigned.
2. If $T(j)$ is assigned, so is $T(|T(j)|)$.

The vector T has the following interpretation:

1. If $T(j)$ is assigned, then $A(j)$ is marked (the converse is not necessarily true).
2. If $T(j)$ is assigned and $T(j) > 0$, then $A(j)$ and $A(|T(j)|)$ are marked, but no components between them are marked.
3. If $T(j)$ is assigned and $T(j) < 0$, then $A(|T(j)|)$, $A(|T(j)| + 1), \ldots, A(j)$ are all marked.

Let us now describe the changes that T must undergo in each combination generation. Two "subroutines" may be applied:
α: (i) If $T(k) = 0$, then output A and halt.
   (ii) If $T(k) > 0$, then $i \leftarrow T(k)$, output A, and go to step (1) of the procedure.
   (iii) $i \leftarrow k - 1$. If $T(k) > -(k - 1)$, then $T(k - 1) \leftarrow T(k)$.
   (iv) Output A and go to step (1) of the procedure.

β: (i) $T(i) \leftarrow -(k + 1)$. If $T(k) \geqslant 0$, then $T(k + 1) \leftarrow T(k)$, output A, and go to step (1) of the procedure.

(ii) $T(k + 1) \leftarrow k - 1$. If $T(k) > -(k - 1)$, then $T(k - 1) \leftarrow T(k)$.

(iii) Output A and go to step (1) of the procedure.

The procedure is as follows:

(1) $k \leftarrow i$. If $A(i) = 1$, go to step (8).

(2) Let $A(j)$ and $A(l)$ be the first and last 1's on $A(i)$'s right-hand side.

(3) $A(i) \leftarrow 1$, $A(j) \leftarrow 0$. If $j < l$, go to step (5).

(4) Perform α.

(5) If $l < n$, go to step (7).

(6) $i \leftarrow j$ and perform β.

(7) $i \leftarrow l$ and perform β.

(8) If there are any ones on $A(i)$'s right-hand side, go to step (12).

(9) $A(i) \leftarrow 0$, $A(n) \leftarrow 1$. If $i < n - 1$, go to step (11).

(10) Perform α.

(11) $i \leftarrow n - 1$ and perform β.

(12) Let $A(j)$ and $A(l)$ be the first and last 1's on $A(i)$'s right-hand side.

(13) $A(i) \leftarrow 0$, $A(j - 1) \leftarrow 1$. If $l < n$, go to step (17).

(14) If $i + 1 < j - 1$, go to step (16).

(15) Perform α.

(16) $i \leftarrow j - 2$ and perform β.

(17) $i \leftarrow l$ and perform β.

Let us demonstrate the procedure on our example of $r = 3$, $n = 6$ with an initial $A = 011100$. Thus, $i = 4$.

1. $T = (0, -, -, -1, -, -)$, $A = 011100$, and $i = 4$. By step (1) $k \leftarrow 4$ and we go to (8) and continue with (9). We perform $A(4) \leftarrow 0$, $A(6) \leftarrow 1$. Since $4 < 5$, we go to (11). $i \leftarrow 5$ and perform β: $T(5) \leftarrow -5$ and we move to (ii). $T(5) \leftarrow 3$ and since $T(4) > -3$, $T(3) \leftarrow -1$. Thus,

2. $T = (0, -, -1, -1, 3, -)$, $A = 011001$ and $i = 5$. Now $j = l = 6$. In step (4) $T(5) > 0$; thus, $i \leftarrow 3$ and we have

3. $T = (0, -, -1, -1, 3, -)$, $A = 011010$, and $i = 3$.

4. $T = (0, -1, -1, 2, -4, -)$, $A = 010110$, and $i = 5$.

5. $T = (0, -1, -1, 2, -4, -)$, $A = 010101$, and $i = 4$.

6. $T = (0, -1, -1, 2, -4, -)$, $A = 010011$, and $i = 2$.

7. $T = (0, -1, 1, 2, -4, -)$, $A = 000111$, and $i = 3$.

8. $T = (0, -1, 1, 1, -4, -)$, $A = 001011$, and $i = 4$.

9. $T = (0, -1, 1, 1, 1, -)$, $A = 001101$, and $i = 5$.
10. $T = (0, -1, 1, 1, 1, -)$, $A = 001110$, and $i = 1$.
11. $T = (0, 0, 1, 1, -2, -)$, $A = 100110$, and $i = 5$.
12. $T = (0, 0, 1, -2, -2, -)$, $A = 100101$, and $i = 4$.
13. $T = (0, 0, -2, -2, -2, -)$, $A = 100011$, and $i = 3$.
14. $T = (0, 0, -2, 2, -4, -)$, $A = 101001$, and $i = 5$.
15. $T = (0, 0, -2, 2, -4, -)$, $A = 101010$, and $i = 4$.
16. $T = (0, 0, -2, 2, -4, -)$, $A = 101100$, and $i = 2$.
17. $T = (0, 0, 0, -3, -4, -)$, $A = 110100$, and $i = 4$.
18. $T = (0, 0, 0, -3, 3, -)$, $A = 110001$, and $i = 5$.
19. $T = (0, 0, 0, -3, 3, -)$, $A = 110010$, and $i = 3$.
20. We get $A = 111000$, and termination is indicated.

This procedure contains no loops in correcting T (instead of the bars of Algorithm 2.1), but it still contains linear searches in steps (2), (8), and (12). In order to eliminate these we introduce another vector $F(0), F(1), \ldots, F(n)$. The meaning of F is as follows: If $A(m) = 1$ and it is the rightmost element in a run of 1's, then $F(m)$ is the index of the first 1 of this run; if not, $F(m)$ is immaterial.* Also, let l be the index of the right most 1; that is,

$$l = \max_{A(m)=1} m.$$

If F and l are known, steps (2) and (12) are easily performed by $j \leftarrow F(l)$. Step (8) becomes: If $i < l$, go to step (12). However, it becomes necessary to update F and l without linear searches. Our final procedure is as follows:

Algorithm 2.2:
(Initial conditions, α and β, are as previously discussed.)
(1) $k \leftarrow i$. If $A(i) = 1$, go to (8).
(2) $j \leftarrow F(l)$.
(3) $A(i) \leftarrow 1$, $A(j) \leftarrow 0$, $F(k) \leftarrow k$. If $A(k - 1) = 1$ and $k > 1$, then $F(k) \leftarrow F(k - 1)$. $F(l) \leftarrow j + 1$. If $j < l$, go to step (5).
(4) $l \leftarrow i$. Perform α.
(5) If $l < n$, go to step (7).
(6) $i \leftarrow j$. Perform β.
(7) $i \leftarrow l$. Perform β.
(8) $F(i - 1) \leftarrow F(i)$. If $l > i$, go to step (12).

*$F(0)$ is added in order to prevent difficulties in the forthcoming step (8).

(9) $A(i) \leftarrow 0$, $A(n) \leftarrow 1$, $F(n) \leftarrow n$, $l \leftarrow n$. If $i < n - 1$, go to step (11).
(10) Perform α.
(11) $i \leftarrow n - 1$ and perform β.
(12) $j \leftarrow F(l)$.
(13) $A(i) \leftarrow 0$, $A(j - 1) \leftarrow 1$, $F(l) \leftarrow j - 1$. If $l < n$, go to step (17).
(14) If $i + 1 < j - 1$, go to step (16).
(15) Perform α.
(16) $i \leftarrow j - 2$. Perform β.
(17) $i \leftarrow l$. Perform β.

EXERCISES

2.1 Prove that

$$\binom{2n}{i} < \binom{2n}{i+1}$$

and
$$\binom{2n+1}{i} < \binom{2n+1}{i+1} \qquad \text{for } 0 \leqslant i \leqslant n - 1.$$

2.2 Prove that

$$\sum_{i=0}^{n} \binom{n}{i} = 2^n.$$

2.3 Prove that

$$\sum_{i=0}^{n} (-1)^i \binom{n}{i} = 0.$$

2.4 Prove that

$$i\binom{n}{i} = n\binom{n-1}{i-1}$$

and use this identity to prove (2.9) as a corollary of Exercise 2.2.

2.5 Prove the identity

$$\sum_{k=0}^{n} \binom{k}{m} = \binom{n+1}{m+1}$$

(a) by induction on n,
· (b) by a "combinatorial" argument.

2.6   Prove the identity

$$\sum_{i=1}^{n} i^2 \binom{n}{i} = n(n+1)2^{n-2},$$

by differentiating (2.11) once more after multiplying both sides by x.

2.7   Prove that for every prime integer p and every $0 < i < p$, $\binom{p}{i}$ is divisible by p.

2.8   Consider the rectangular array of one-way streets which includes $a \times b$ blocks; thus, there are $a + 1$ streets from west to east and $b + 1$ streets from north to south. Prove that the number of different ways to go from A to B is $\binom{a+b}{a}$.

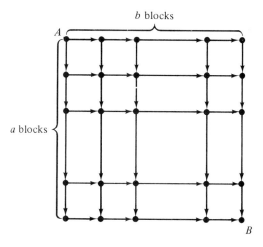

2.9   Use the result of Exercise 2.8 to provide yet another proof of Theorem 2.2.

2.10 Prove that the algorithm of Section 2.3 generates all the r-combinations out of n in lexicographic order.

2.11 (a) Prove that if $m \leqslant n$, then

$$\binom{m}{r} \leqslant \binom{n}{r}.$$

(b) Prove that if $m < n$ and $0 < r \leqslant n$, then

$$\binom{m}{r} < \binom{n}{r}.$$

2.12 Assume that we use the algorithm of Section 2.3 to generate all 4-combinations of the set $1, 2, \ldots, 7$.

(a) How many combinations are generated between 1, 3, 4, 6 and 2, 3, 5, 7? Solve this problem by generating all the steps in between. Repeat the computation by using (2.17).

(b) What is the combination generated on step (17)? Use the direct-step calculation instead of generating all steps up to (17).

2.13 Describe an algorithm for generating all r-combinations, with repetitions allowed, of n types, which is a modification of the algorithm described in Section 2.3. Develop an expression such as (2.17) for the step number of a given combination.

2.14 Describe an algorithm for generating all r-combinations, with repetitions allowed, of n-types, which is based on the algorithm of Section 2.3, without modifications, and on Proof 2 of Theorem 2.2.

2.15 Apply Algorithm 2.2 to generate all 2-combinations out of six.

REFERENCES

1. Feller, W., *An Introduction to Probability Theory and Its Applications*, Vol. 1, Wiley, New York, 1950.

2. Riordan, J., *An Introduction to Combinatorial Analysis*, Wiley, New York, 1958.

3. Knuth, D. E., *The Art of Computer Programming*, Vol. 1/Fundamental Algorithms, Addison-Wesley, Reading, Mass., 1968.

4. Lehmer, D. H., "The Machine Tools of Combinatorics," in *Applied Combinatorial Mathematics*, E. F. Beckenbach (ed.), Wiley, New York, 1964, pp. 5–31.

5. Chase, P. J., "Algorithm 382; Combinations of M Out of N Objects," *Comm. ACM*, Vol. 13, No. 6, June 1970, p. 368. See also the Remark on page 376.

6. Ehrlich, G., "Combinations of M out of N," Research report of the Department of Applied Mathematics, The Weizmann Institute of Science, Rehovot, Israel, 1971.

3

ENUMERATION
PROBLEMS

3.1   The fundamental formula of inclusion and exclusion

Assume that S is a set of n elements, and each element a has weight $w(a)$, which is a real number. Let $P_1, P_2, \ldots, P_t$ be properties which the elements of S may or may not have. For a subset of the properties, $\{P_{i_1}, P_{i_2}, \ldots, P_{i_r}\}$, denote by $W(P_{i_1}, P_{i_2}, \ldots, P_{i_r})$ the sum of the weights of all the elements of S which possess all these properties, but which may possess additional properties. In case there are no elements in S which possess these properties, $W(P_{i_1}, P_{i_2}, \ldots, P_{i_r})$ is defined to be zero. Let

$$W(r) = \sum W(P_{i_1}, P_{i_2}, \ldots, P_{i_r}) \tag{3.1}$$

where the sum is over all subsets of r properties out of the t possible properties.

Each such subset contributes one term to the sum. Thus, there are $\binom{t}{r}$ terms in the sum. We define $W(0)$ to be the sum $\sum_{i=1}^{n} w(a_i)$, where the sum is over all elements of S. This is consistent with the definition of (3.1), since there is only one term in the sum, that of the empty set of properties. However, all elements of S are thus included in the summation of their weights.

Let us denote by $E(m)$ the sum of weights of all elements of S which possess exactly m of the t properties.

Theorem 3.1:

$$E(m) = W(m) - \binom{m+1}{m} W(m+1) + \binom{m+2}{m} W(m+2)$$

$$- \cdots (-1)^{t-m} \binom{t}{m} W(t). \tag{3.2}$$

Proof: Let $a \in S$ and assume that a possesses q of the t properties. If $q < m$, then a does not contribute its weight to any of the terms on the right-hand side of (3.2). If $q = m$, then a contributes its weight exactly once in $W(m)$, in the term which corresponds to those properties which a possesses; it does not contribute its weight to any other terms. If $q > m$, then $w(a)$ is counted, on the right-hand side of (3.2), the following number of times:

$$\binom{m}{m}\cdot\binom{q}{m} - \binom{m+1}{m}\cdot\binom{q}{m+1} + \binom{m+2}{m}\cdot\binom{q}{m+2}$$

$$- \cdots (-1)^{t-m}\binom{t}{m}\cdot\binom{q}{t}.$$

Now, let us use the identity

$$\binom{b}{a}\cdot\binom{c}{b} = \binom{c}{a}\cdot\binom{c-a}{b-a},$$

which can be verified either by applying (2.1) to each one of the four co-efficients, or by realizing that on both sides we have the number of ways to choose an a-combination and a disjoint $(b - a)$-combination of a set of c

items. Thus, the number of times $w(a)$ is counted is

$$\binom{q}{m} \cdot \left[\binom{q-m}{0} - \binom{q-m}{1} + \binom{q-m}{2} - \cdots (-1)^{t-m} \binom{q-m}{t-m} \right],$$

which is equal to zero (see Exercise 2.3).   QED

A very important special case of the fundamental formula, (3.2), is called the *sieve formula*. Substitute $m = 0$ to (3.2). We get

$$E(0) = W(0) - W(1) + W(2) - \cdots (-1)^t W(t). \tag{3.3}$$

If, in addition, we assume that $w(a) = 1$ for all elements, then $W(P_{i_1}, P_{i_2}, \cdots, P_{i_r})$ is just the number of elements which possess these properties. Under this interpretation (3.3) is referred to as the sieve formula.

A very elementary application of the sieve formula is made in a solution of the following puzzle. There are 40 participants in a party: 13 of them smoke; 12 drink; 12 are married; 4 smoke and drink; 5 drink and are married; 3 smoke and are married; 2 smoke, drink, and are married. How many of the participants do not smoke, do not drink, and are not married?

Let us denote the three properties by S, D, and M. We are told that

$$W(S) = 13, \qquad W(S, D) = 4, \qquad W(S, D, M) = 2.$$
$$W(D) = 12, \qquad W(D, M) = 5,$$
$$W(M) = 12, \qquad W(S, M) = 3.$$

Thus, $W(0) = 40$, $W(1) = 13 + 12 + 12 = 37$, $W(2) = 4 + 5 + 3 = 12$, $W(3) = 2$. Therefore,

$$E(0) = 40 - 37 + 12 - 2 = 13.$$

3.2 An application of the sieve formula in number theory

Let (a, b) denote the greatest common divisor of the integers a and b. We say that a and b are relatively prime if $(a, b) = 1$. Let $a \mid b$ mean that a divides b, and $a \nmid b$ mean that a does not divide b.

Theorem 3.2: Let n be a positive integer and $a_1, a_2, \ldots, a_t$ be positive integers which are pairwise relatively prime. (That is, if $i \neq j$, then $(a_i, a_j) = 1$.) The number of integers, k, which satisfy $0 < k \leq n$ and $a_i \nmid k$ for $i = 1, 2, \ldots, t$ is

$$n - \sum_{i=1}^{t} \left\lfloor \frac{n}{a_i} \right\rfloor + \sum_{0 < i < j \leq t} \left\lfloor \frac{n}{a_i a_j} \right\rfloor - \cdots (-1)^t \left\lfloor \frac{n}{a_1 a_2 \cdots a_t} \right\rfloor.$$

Proof: Let us define the property P_i by: $P_i(k)$ if and only if $a_i \mid k$. The number of k's which have no property, $E(0)$, is exactly the number we need, when $w(k) = 1$ for all k. Also, $W(0) = n$ and

$$W(1) = \sum_{i=1}^{t} W(P_i).$$

However, the number of k's which are divisible by a_i is $\lfloor n/a_i \rfloor$. Similarly, $W(P_i, P_j) = \lfloor n/a_i a_j \rfloor$, for a positive integer $0 < k \leq n$ is divisible by both a_i and a_j only if it is a multiple of $a_i a_j$, since $(a_i, a_j) = 1$. The rest of the argument is along the same lines, and with the aid of (3.3) Theorem 3.2 is proved.
                                                                    QED

For a positive integer n, $\phi(n)$, *Euler's function* of n, is defined as the number of integers k, $0 < k < n$, which are relatively prime to n.

Let us use Theorem 3.2 to evaluate $\phi(n)$. Let $p_1, p_2, \ldots, p_t$ be all the prime divisors of n. It is clear that $(k, n) = 1$ if and only if $p_i \nmid k$ for all $i = 1, 2, \ldots, t$. Thus,

$$\phi(n) = n - \sum_{i=1}^{t} \frac{n}{p_i} + \sum_{0 < i < j \leq t} \frac{n}{p_i p_j} - \cdots (-1)^t \frac{n}{p_1 p_2 \cdots p_t}$$

$$= n \left[1 - \sum_{i=1}^{t} \frac{1}{p_i} + \sum_{0 < i < j \leq t} \frac{1}{p_i p_j} - \cdots (-1)^t \frac{1}{p_1 p_2 \cdots p_t} \right]. \quad (3.4)$$

Therefore,

$$\phi(n) = n \cdot \prod_{i=1}^{t} \left(1 - \frac{1}{p_i} \right). \quad (3.5)$$

Another important number theoretic function is $\mu(n)$, the *Möbius function*
It is defined as follows:

$$\mu(n) = \begin{cases} 1 & \text{if } n = 1; \\ 0 & \text{if there exists a prime } p \text{ such} \\ & \text{such that } p^2 \mid n; \\ (-1)^k & \text{if } n = p_1 p_2 \cdots p_k, \text{ where the } p\text{'s} \\ & \text{are all primes and distinct.} \end{cases}$$

It follows that

$$\phi(n) = n \cdot \sum_{d \mid n} \frac{\mu(d)}{d}, \tag{3.6}$$

where the sum is over all divisors, d, of n. This identity is a direct consequence
of (3.4). For all d's which are not of the form $p_{i_1} p_{i_2} \cdots p_{i_k}$, where all the p's
are distinct primes, $\mu(d) = 0$. For $d = 1$ we get the first term of (3.4). And for
all d's which are a product of distinct primes, we get the rest of the terms of
(3.4).

3.3   Möbius inversion and circular words

Let us first prove the identity

$$\sum_{d \mid n} \mu(d) = \begin{cases} 1 & \text{if } n = 1, \\ 0 & \text{if } n > 1. \end{cases} \tag{3.7}$$

If $n = 1$, it has only one positive divisor $d = 1$, and since $\mu(1) = 1$, the
statement follows. Now, assume that

$$n = p_1^{e_1} p_2^{e_2} \cdots p_k^{e_k},$$

where the p's are primes and the e's are their exponents. Let d be a divisor
of n; then

$$d = p_1^{d_1} p_2^{d_2} \cdots p_k^{d_k}.$$

If for some i, $d_i > 1$, then $\mu(d) = 0$. Thus, the only terms in (3.7) which we need consider are those for which $d_i \leqslant 1$ for every i. There are $\binom{k}{r}$ such divisors which are the product of r distinct primes and each contributes $(-1)^r$ to the sum. Thus,

$$\sum_{d|n} \mu(d) = 1 - \binom{k}{1} + \binom{k}{2} - \cdots (-1)^k \binom{k}{k}.$$

This sum is zero, as stated in Exercise 2.3. The following theorem is called the *Möbius inversion theorem*.

Theorem 3.3: Let $f(n)$ and $g(n)$ be functions defined for every positive integer n. The identity

$$g(n) = \sum_{d|n} f(d) \tag{3.8}$$

holds if and only if

$$f(n) = \sum_{d|n} \mu(d)g\left(\frac{n}{d}\right) \tag{3.9}$$

holds.

Proof: Assume that (3.8) holds for every n. Thus,

$$g\left(\frac{n}{d}\right) = \sum_{d'|(n/d)} f(d').$$

Substituting in the right-hand side of (3.9) we get

$$\sum_{d|n} \mu(d) \cdot g\left(\frac{n}{d}\right) = \sum_{d|n} \mu(d) \cdot \sum_{d'|(n/d)} f(d').$$

This double summation ranges over all d and d' such that $d \cdot d' | n$. If we choose d' first, then d ranges over all divisors of n/d'. Thus,

$$\sum_{d|n} \mu(d) \cdot g\left(\frac{n}{d}\right) = \sum_{d'|n} f(d') \cdot \sum_{d|(n/d')} \mu(d).$$

By (3.7),

$$\sum_{d\mid(n/d')} \mu(d) = 0$$

unless $n = d'$, in which case it is 1. Thus, (3.9) follows.

Now assume that (3.9) holds for every n. Thus,

$$\sum_{d\mid n} f(d) = \sum_{d\mid n} \sum_{d'\mid d} \mu(d')g\left(\frac{d}{d'}\right);$$

$d'' = d/d'$ is also a divisor of n, and this double sum can be written as

$$\sum_{d''\mid n} \sum_{d'\mid(n/d'')} \mu(d')g(d''),$$

which is equal to

$$\sum_{d''\mid n} g(d'')\cdot \sum_{d'\mid(n/d'')} \mu(d').$$

Again by (3.7) the only d'' for which the inner sum does not vanish is $d'' = n$, yielding (3.8).

QED

Assume that we have an alphabet of σ letters. Clearly there are altogether σ^n words of length n over this alphabet. In certain applications in communication theory (see references 1, 2, and 3), for synchronizability reasons, it is desirable to choose a set, S, of words of length n which satisfies the following condition: For every word $w = a_1 a_2 \cdots a_n$ in S, none of the words $a_2 a_3 \cdots a_n a_1$, $a_3 a_4 \cdots a_n a_1 a_2, \ldots, a_n a_1 a_2 \cdots a_{n-1}$ is in S. Our problem is to find what is the maximum number of words that S may contain.

The set of all σ^n words can be partitioned into classes according to the following equivalence relation: Two words are equivalent if one is a circular shift of the other. The maximum number of words in one class is n, but a class may be smaller. Let us call a class which contains less than n words a *degenerate class*, and its members, *degenerate words*. A word w is called *periodic* if there exists a shorter word u and a positive integer m such that $w = u^m$; that is, w is u repeated m times. (Here, when u and v are words, uv is the word consisting of their juxtaposition, and u^m is the juxtaposition of u m times.)

It is clear that none of the words in S can be degenerate, and that S can contain at most one word from each of the nondegenerate classes. Also, a choice of one representative from each nondegenerate class is satisfactory. Thus, the maximum number of words in S is equal to the number of nondegenerate classes. It is also clear that if a word is periodic, then it is degenerate.

Lemma 3.1: If a word w is degenerate, then it is periodic.

Proof: Assume that w is degenerate, and let p be the smallest number of places of shift to the left performed on w which yields w again. Thus, $w = ab = ba$, where the number of letters in a, $l(a)$, is p, and $l(b) = n - p$. Since p is the smallest number of shifts which leave w invariant, $l(b) \geqslant l(a)$. Thus, $ab = ba$ implies that $b = ab'$ for some word b'. Thus $w = aab' = ab'a$. If $l(b') \geqslant l(a)$, then $ab' = b'a$ implies that $b' = ab''$, for some b''. Again $w = aaab'' = aab''a$. We repeat this process until some $b^{(i)}$ satisfies $l(b^{(i)}) < l(a)$ and $w = a^{i+1}b^{(i)} = a^i b^{(i)} a$. This implies that $ab^{(i)} = b^{(i)}a$, and therefore by repeated interchanges of a with $b^{(i)}$ we have $w = b^{(i)}a^{i+1} = a^{i+1}b^{(i)}$. Since p is assumed to be the shortest shift which leaves w invariant, we conclude that $l(b^{(i)}) = 0$. Thus, $w = a^{i+1}$.

QED

Let us denote by $M(d)$ the number of classes which contain d words. Lemma 3.1 implies that $d|n$. Thus, we have

$$\sum_{d|n} dM(d) = \sigma^n,$$

since on both sides we enumerate all words of length n over an alphabet of σ letters. We apply now the Möbius inversion (Theorem 3.3), where $g(n) = \sigma^n$ and $f(d) = dM(d)$. Thus,

$$nM(n) = \sum_{d|n} \mu(d) \cdot \sigma^{n/d}$$

or

$$M(n) = \frac{1}{n} \sum_{d|n} \mu(d) \cdot \sigma^{n/d}, \tag{3.10}$$

where $M(n)$ is the number of words in a maximum S.

Clearly, $M(n)$ is an integer. Thus,

$$n \mid \sum_{d \mid n} \mu(d) \cdot \sigma^{n/d}. \tag{3.11}$$

If we choose $n = p$, a prime, then (3.11) yields

$$p \mid \sigma^p - \sigma, \tag{3.12}$$

which is the known *little Fermat theorem*, of which (3.11) is a generalization.

3.4 Derangements

A permutation of the integers $1, 2, \ldots, n$ is called a *derangement* if no integer stays in its original (natural) location. One of our purposes in this section is to compute the number of derangements, $D(n)$, of n integers. This can be achieved directly by applying the sieve formula. However, we shall compute the number of permutations, $N(n, m)$, of n integers, in which exactly m integers are in their original locations. The case of derangements will correspond to $m = 0$.

Define the properties $P_1, P_2, \ldots, P_n$ on the set of all $n!$ permutations as follows. A given permutation has property P_i if the ith integer is in its original position. The number of permutations which have the properties $P_{i_1}, P_{i_2}, \ldots, P_{i_r}$ is

$$W(P_{i_1}, P_{i_2}, \ldots, P_{i_r}) = (n - r)!.$$

(We are using the notation introduced in Section 3.1 with $W(\pi) = 1$ for every permutation π.) It follows that

$$W(r) = \binom{n}{r} \cdot (n - r)!$$

and $N(n, m)$, by Theorem 3.1, is given by

$$N(n, m) = \binom{n}{m}(n - m)! - \binom{m + 1}{m}\binom{n}{m + 1}(n - m - 1)!$$
$$+ \binom{m + 2}{m}\binom{n}{m + 2}(n - m - 2)! - \cdots (-1)^{n-m}\binom{n}{m}\binom{n}{n} \cdot 0!.$$

However, since for every $m \leqslant j \leqslant n$,

$$\binom{j}{m}\binom{n}{j}(n - j)! = \frac{n!}{m!}\cdot\frac{1}{(j - m)!},$$

we have

$$N(n, m) = \frac{n!}{m!}\left[1 - \frac{1}{1!} + \frac{1}{2!} - \cdots (-1)^{n-m}\frac{1}{(n - m)!}\right]. \qquad (3.13)$$

In particular,

$$D(n) = n!\left[1 - \frac{1}{1!} + \frac{1}{2!} - \cdots (-1)^{n}\frac{1}{n!}\right]. \qquad (3.14)$$

Since

$$\varepsilon^{-1} = 1 - \frac{1}{1!} + \frac{1}{2!} - \cdots,$$

$D(n)$ and $N(n, m)$ are well approximated for large n and $n - m$, respectively, by

$$N(n, m) \approx \frac{n!}{m!}\cdot\varepsilon^{-1},$$

and

$$D(n) \approx n!\cdot\varepsilon^{-1}.$$

3.5   Partitions

There are several related but different enumeration problems in combinatorial theory which are referred to as enumerations of partitions. The general idea is that we have n items and we want to enumerate the number of ways in which these items can be put into cells.

In some applications the items are indistinguishable; in others they are distinct. The cells may be distinguishable, or equivalently, are ordered, or they may be identical. In the case of distinct elements, the order in which the elements are put into the cell may or may not count. Some authors refer to different cases by different names—"distributions," "occupancy," and alike. We shall call all of them partitions and will state in each case the assumptions we make.

The case of indistinguishable items and distinct cells was discussed in Theorem 2.3. The case of indistinguishable items and indistinguishable cells is discussed in several texts (see, for example, references 1 and 2) and we shall not discuss this case at all. Therefore, our discussion is restricted to cases where the items are distinct, and we shall refer to them as partitions of a set.

Problem 3.5.1: What is the number of partitions of n distinct elements into r distinct cells, if the order inside the cells does not count, and the number of elements in each cell is arbitrary? (In fact, a cell may be empty.)

This problem is equivalent to the problem of the number of distinct words of length n over an alphabet of r letters (which was used in Section 3.3). A simple one-to-one correspondence can be set between partitions of this type and words of length n.

Each word of length n specifies a partition of the n elements as follows. Let the elements be $e_1, e_2, \ldots, e_n$ and the cells (also the letters of the alphabet) be $c_1, c_2, \ldots, c_r$. If the ith letter is c_j, then the ith element is in cell c_j. Thus, the number of partitions is r^n.

Problem 3.5.2: What is the number of partitions of n distinct elements into r distinct cells, if the number of elements to enter cell c_i is specified to be m_i but the elements within a cell are not ordered? Clearly, we assume that $m_1 + m_2 + \cdots + m_r = n$.

Let us first choose the m_1 elements to be in c_1. This can be done in

$$\binom{n}{m_1}$$

ways. Once this choice is made, the m_2 elements to be in c_2 can be chosen in

$$\binom{n - m_1}{m_2}$$

ways; and so on. Therefore, the number of partitions is given by

$$\binom{m_1 + m_2 + \cdots + m_r}{m_1} \cdot \binom{m_2 + m_3 + \cdots + m_r}{m_2} \cdots \binom{m_r}{m_r}.$$

and by (2.1) and elementary operations this is equal to

$$\frac{(m_1 + m_2 + \cdots + m_r)!}{m_1! m_2! \cdots m_r!} = \frac{n!}{m_1! m_2! \cdots m_r!}. \qquad (3.15)$$

These numbers are called the *multinomial coefficients* because of the following identity:

$$(x_1 + x_2 + \cdots + x_r)^n = \sum_{m_1 + m_2 + \cdots + m_r = n} \frac{n!}{m_1! m_2! \cdots m_r!} x_1^{m_1} x_2^{m_2} \cdots x_r^{m_r} \qquad (3.16)$$

where the sum ranges over all decompositions of n into nonnegative integers $m_1, m_2, \ldots, m_r$, and by Theorem 2.2 the number of such decompositions is

$$\binom{n + r - 1}{n}.$$

(The roles of n and r here and in the statement of Theorem 2.2 are reversed.) The proof of (3.16) is along the same lines as the proof of (2.2).

Problem 3.5.3:   What is the number of partitions of n distinct elements into r distinct cells if the elements within a cell are unordered and their number is arbitrary, but a cell may not be empty?

This problem is equivalent to the question of finding the number of words of length n over an alphabet of r letters, such that each letter appears in each word at least once. Denote this number by $T(n, r)$. Clearly if $n < r$, then $T(n, r) = 0$; and if $n = r$, then $T(n, r) = n!$. We shall use the sieve formula, (3.3). Let $P_i, 1 \leqslant i \leqslant r$, be the property that c_i does not appear in a word. Thus, $W(P_i) = (r - 1)^n$ and for $1 \leqslant l \leqslant r$,

$$W(P_{i_1}, P_{i_2}, \ldots, P_{i_l}) = (r - l)^n.$$

Thus,

$$W(m) = \binom{r}{m} \cdot (r - m)^n,$$

and by the sieve formula,

$$T(n, r) = r^n - \binom{r}{1}(r - 1)^n + \binom{r}{2}(r - 2)^n - \cdots (-1)^r\binom{r}{r}(r - r)^n.$$

A more compact form is

$$T(n, r) = \sum_{i=0}^{r} (-1)^i \binom{r}{i}(r - i)^n. \tag{3.17}$$

An alternative approach to the computation of $T(n, r)$ is through the following recursion formula:

$$T(n, r) = r[T(n - 1, r - 1) + T(n - 1, r)]. \tag{3.18}$$

A simple combinatorial argument is as follows. Divide all words of length n over an alphabet of r letters, in which each letter appears at least once, into two sets. The first set contains all those words in which the first letter is different from all the others. The second set contains all those in which the first letter appears at least once more. The number of words in the first set is $r \cdot T(n - 1, r - 1)$, since the first letter can be any one out of r, and after it has been chosen, we have to construct a word of length $n - 1$ out of $r - 1$ letters, each of which has to appear at least once. The number of words in the second set is $r \cdot T(n - 1, r)$, since the first letter can be any one out of r, and after it has been chosen, we have to construct a word of length $n - 1$ out of r letters, each of which has to appear at least once.

The recursion formula can be used directly to construct a table of values for $T(n, r)$. This is shown here for $n = 1, 2, 3, 4, 5$.

n \ r	1	2	3	4	5
1	1				
2	1	2			
3	1	6	6		
4	1	14	36	24	
5	1	30	150	240	120

The entries in which $T(n, r) = 0$ are left blank. Clearly $T(n, 1) = 1$ for every positive integer n. The operations required to compute one more entry in the table are one addition and one multiplication. Thus, the number of operations necessary in the computation of $T(n, r)$ is $(n - r + 1)(r - 1)$ multiplications and $(n - r)(r - 1)$ additions. Although (3.17) may be done in less operations, it requires additional effort in programming. In case a whole line or the whole table up to a given n has to be computed, the use of (3.18) is more attractive.

Problem 3.5.4:   What is the number of partitions of n distinct elements into r distinct, internally ordered cells if the number of elements in each cell is arbitrary? (In fact, a cell may be empty.)

The number of partitions of this type is

$$n!\binom{n + r - 1}{n}. \tag{3.19}$$

One way of proving this statement is as follows. First-order the n elements in any one of the $n!$ ways. We can now imagine $r + 1$ walls put in the intervals between the elements. The first wall is on the left-hand side of the sequence, and the $(r + 1)$st wall is on the right-hand side. All the elements between the ith and the $(i + 1)$st walls are in cell c_i. There are $n + 1$ intervals and $r - 1$ walls to be put into them. This is equivalent to the problem of $(r - 1)$-combinations, with repetitions allowed, out of a set of $n + 1$ elements. By Theorem 2.2 their number is

$$\binom{n + r - 1}{r - 1} = \binom{n + r - 1}{n}.$$

Since all the partitions thus described are distinct, and since every partition satisfying our assumptions is thus generated, the number of partitions is as given in (3.19).

Problem 3.5.5:   What is the number of partitions of a set of n distinct elements into r indistinguishable cells, internally unordered, if the number of elements to enter each cell is arbitrary but a cell may not be empty?

This problem is closely related to Problem 3.5.3. The number of partitions of this type is denoted by $S(n, r)$. These numbers are called *Stirling numbers of the second kind* [5].

Once a partition of the present type is specified, each cell is identified by the elements in it. However, the names of the cells can be given in $r!$ ways. Thus,

$$r!S(n, r) = T(n, r). \tag{3.20}$$

By (3.17) we have

$$S(n, r) = \frac{1}{r!} \sum_{i=0}^{r} (-1)^i \binom{r}{i} (r - i)^n. \tag{3.21}$$

Again, this is not an efficient way to compute the values of $S(n, r)$ if a whole line or table has to be calculated. The recursion formula (3.18) transforms through (3.20) into

$$S(n, r) = S(n - 1, r - 1) + rS(n - 1, r).$$

Alternatively, this can be proved directly as follows. The element e_n is either alone in a cell (there are $S(n - 1, r - 1)$ partitions of this specification) or it joins one of the r cells in the partition of $e_1, e_2, \ldots, e_{n-1}$ into r nonempty cells ($rS(n - 1, r)$ of those). A short table of $S(n, r)$ up to $n = 6$ is given here.

r \\ n	1	2	3	4	5	6
1	1					
2	1	1				
3	1	3	1			
4	1	7	6	1		
5	1	15	25	10	1	
6	1	31	90	65	15	1

Problem 3.5.6: What is the number of partitions of a set of n distinct elements into internally unordered nonempty distinct cells, if the number of cells is not specified?

A partitioning of a set in this way may be viewed as a two-phase action. First we decide on the number, r, of cells to be used. Next, we partition the set into these cells as in Problem 3.5.3. Thus, the number of partitions of this type, $Q(n)$ is given by

$$Q(n) = \sum_{r=1}^{n} T(n, r), \tag{3.22}$$

or, by (3.17),

$$Q(n) = \sum_{r=1}^{n} \sum_{i=0}^{r} (-1)^i \binom{r}{i} (r - i)^n. \tag{3.23}$$

We can use the table of $T(n, r)$ and compute $Q(n)$ by summing the entries of the nth row. Thus,

n	1	2	3	4	5
$Q(n)$	1	3	13	75	541

We shall now take a more direct approach to compute $Q(n)$. First, let us prove the following difference equation:

$$Q(n) = \sum_{i=0}^{n-1} \binom{n}{i} Q(i), \tag{3.24}$$

where we define $Q(0) = 1$.

Imagine that the selection of the partition is done in three steps. First we choose the number, i, of elements not to be in the first cell c_1. Clearly $0 \leqslant i \leqslant n - 1$. Second, we decide which i elements are not to enter c_1; this decision can be made in $\binom{n}{i}$ ways. Third, we choose a partition of these i elements; and this can be done in $Q(i)$ ways. Thus, (3.24) follows. We need now the following lemma:

Lemma 3.2:   If we start with a sequence of numbers $a(0), a(2), \ldots, a(n)$ as a first row of a table and compute the next row by adding for each entry the number above it and above it to its left (like in Pascal's triangle), the $(n + 1)$st entry in the $(n + 1)$st row is

$$A = \sum_{i=0}^{n} \binom{n}{i} a(i).$$

The table has the shape shown in Fig. 3.1. The lower left part of the table is of no significance to us and is not computed.

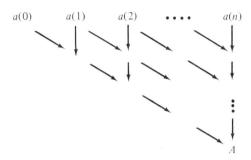

Figure 3.1

Proof: The number $a(i)$ is added into A as many times as there are paths, in the directions of the arrows, from $a(i)$ to A. This number, by Exercise 2.8, is $\binom{n}{i}$. Thus,

$$A = \sum_{i=0}^{n} \binom{n}{i} a(i).$$

QED

This suggests a method for computing $Q(n)$. We use $a(i) = Q(i)$ for $i = 0, 1,$ $\ldots, n - 1$, and $a(n) = 0$. By (3.24) A will be $Q(n)$. We reassign $a(n) = Q(n)$ and recompute the right-hand column. With $a(n + 1) = 0$ we compute one more column and get $Q(n + 1)$; and so on. This is demonstrated here for $Q(1)$ through $Q(5)$. Of course we use $Q(0) = 1$.

$$
\begin{array}{ccc}
1 & 0 & \\
& 1 = Q(1) & \\
1 & 1 & 0 \\
& 2 & 1 \\
& & 3 = Q(2)
\end{array}
$$

$$
\begin{array}{cccc}
1 & 1 & 3 & 0 \\
& 2 & 4 & 3 \\
& & 6 & 7 \\
& & & 13 = Q(3)
\end{array}
$$

$$
\begin{array}{ccccc}
1 & 1 & 3 & 13 & 0 \\
& 2 & 4 & 16 & 13 \\
& & 6 & 20 & 29 \\
& & & 26 & 49 \\
& & & & 75 = Q(4)
\end{array}
$$

$$
\begin{array}{cccccc}
1 & 1 & 3 & 13 & 75 & 0 \\
& 2 & 4 & 16 & 88 & 75 \\
& & 6 & 20 & 104 & 163 \\
& & & 26 & 124 & 267 \\
& & & & 150 & 391 \\
& & & & & 541 = Q(5)
\end{array}
$$

The number of additions for computing $Q(1)$ through $Q(n)$ is n^2.

Problem 3.5.7: What is the number of partitions of a set of n distinct elements into internally unordered and indistinguishable cells, if the number of cells is not specified?

Like Problem 3.5.6, we can get a closed form for the number of partitions, $P(n)$, by summation of $S(n, r)$ (of Problem 3.5.5). Thus,

$$
P(n) = \sum_{r=1}^{n} S(n, r). \tag{3.25}
$$

By (3.21) we get

$$
P(n) = \sum_{r=1}^{n} \frac{1}{r!} \sum_{i=0}^{r} (-1)^i \binom{r}{i} (r - i)^n. \tag{3.26}
$$

Again, we can use the table of $S(n, r)$, and by summing the entries of the nth row we get

n	1	2	3	4	5	6
$P(n)$	1	2	5	15	52	203

Again, in an effort to find a more attractive way to compute $P(n)$ we prove the following difference equation:

$$P(n) = \sum_{i=0}^{n-1} \binom{n-1}{i} P(i),\tag{3.27}$$

where we define $P(0) = 1$.

The element e_n is in some cell. We can now decide how many elements, i, will not be with e_n in one cell. Clearly, $0 \leqslant i \leqslant n - 1$. These i elements can be chosen in $\binom{n-1}{i}$ ways. They can be partitioned in $P(i)$ ways. Thus, (3.27) follows.

We can now use Lemma 4.1 to compute $P(n)$ from $P(0), P(1), \ldots, P(n-1)$. No erasures are necessary in this case. The computation of $P(1)$ through $P(6)$ is as follows:

$P(0)$	$P(1)$	$P(2)$	$P(3)$	$P(4)$	$P(5)$	$P(6)$
1	1	2	5	15	52	203
	2	3	7	20	67	⋮
		5	10	27	87	
			15	37	114	
				52	151	
					203	$= P(6)$

3.6   An algorithm for generating partitions

Ehrlich has described a few algorithms for generating partitions [11]. We shall discuss here the problem of generating all partitions of a set of n elements into internally unordered and indistinguishable cells. The number of cells is not specified. Other algorithms for various types of partitions can be constructed similarly.

We shall record each partition of $\{1, 2, \ldots, n\}$ by listing the cells one after the other with commas to mark the walls between the cells. For example, ,134, 26, 5, is a partition into three cells in case $n = 6$. We first write the cell containing 1; next, the cell containing the least element not in the previous cells; and so on.

The order in which the partitions are generated is defined recursively. The only partition for $n = 1$ is ,1,. Assume that the order for $n - 1$ is defined. We start with ,12 $\cdots$ n, . Next, n moves into a new cell on the right-hand side: ,12 $\cdots$ $(n - 1), n,$. Now we generate the next partition for $n - 1$, ignoring the n. We get ,12 $\cdots$ $(n - 2),(n - 1)n,$. Next, n moves in each step into the neighboring cell on the right-hand side, and after it is alone in a cell, it jumps into the first cell. Again a new partition for $n - 1$ is generated, and n jumps to the right into an empy cell, moves to the left until it reaches the second cell. Thus, the orbit of n is to the extreme right, moves to the left one cell at a time, stops at the second cell. After a new partition for $n - 1$ is generated (if one exists) it moves, one cell at a time, to the right until it is alone in the extreme cell on the right and jumps to the first. Again, after a new partition for $n - 1$ is generated, the orbit is restarted. For example, the sequence for $n = 4$ is as follows:

1. ,1234,
2. ,123,4
3. ,12,34,
4. ,12,3,4,
5. ,124,3,
6. ,14,23,
7. ,1,23,4,
8. ,1,234,
9. ,1,24,3
10. ,1,2,34,
11. ,1,2,3,4,
12. ,14,2,3,
13. ,134,2,
14. ,13,2,4,
15. ,13,24,.

In order to mechanize this algorithm in such a way that each new partition is generated from the previous one, we first define four vectors.

Let $A(1), A(2), \ldots, A(n)$ be the *activity vector*. An element i is called active if it is moving in its orbit and has not reached a rest state in the first or second cell. We assign $A(i) = 1$ if i is active and $A(i) = 0$ if it is not. Thus, initially $A(1) = 0$ and $A(2) = A(3) = \cdots = A(n) = 1$.

Let $D(1), D(2), \ldots, D(n)$ be the *direction vector*. We assign $D(i) = 2$ initially for all i. If i starts left-going orbit (from first to extreme right and step by step to the left, up to the second cell) we assign $D(i) = 1$. If i starts a right-going orbit (from second, step by step to the extreme right and jump into the first cell) we assign $D(i) = 0$.

Let $C(1), C(2), \ldots, C(n)$ be a cell vector; that is, $C(i)$ is the number of elements in the ith cell. Thus, initially $C(1) = n$ and $C(2) = C(3) = \cdots = C(n) = 0$.

Let $P(1), P(2), \ldots, P(n)$ be the *position vector*; that is, $P(i)$ is the number of the cell in which the element i is presently located. Thus, initially $P(i) = 1$ for all i.

Algorithm 3.1:
(1) Output.
(2) If there are no active elements, stop.
(3) $i \leftarrow \text{Max}\{j | A(j) = 1\}$.
(4) $p \leftarrow P(i), C(p) \leftarrow C(p) - 1$.
(5) If $D(i) = 2$, go to step (15).
(6) If $D(i) = 1$, go to step (10).
(7) If $C(p) = 0$, go to step (9).
(8) $C(p + 1) \leftarrow C(p + 1) + 1, P(i) \leftarrow p + 1$, and go to step (16).
(9) $C(1) \leftarrow C(1) + 1, P(i) \leftarrow 1, D(i) \leftarrow 1, A(i) \leftarrow 0$, and go to step (16).
(10) If $p = 1$, go to step (14).
(11) $C(p - 1) \leftarrow C(p - 1) + 1, P(i) \leftarrow p - 1$.
(12) If $p > 3$, go to step (16).
(13) $D(i) \leftarrow 0, A(i) \leftarrow 0$, and go to step (16).
(14) $k \leftarrow \text{Max}\{j | C(j) > 0\}, C(k + 1) \leftarrow 1, P(i) \leftarrow k + 1$, and go to step (16).
(15) $C(2) \leftarrow C(2) + 1, P(i) \leftarrow 2, D(i) \leftarrow 0, A(i) \leftarrow 0$.
(16) Assign $A(j) \leftarrow 1$ for all $i < j \leqslant n$. Go to step (1).

In the table that follows we show the state of all the vectors in each one of the steps in the generation of the partitions for $n = 4$. It should be noticed that, in general, whenever i moves all the elements, $j > i$ are in the first and second cell.

We shall now proceed to eliminate the implicit loops of steps (2), (3), (14), and (16). Instead of using the vector A we shall use a vector T and the index i; i has the same meaning as in Algorithm 3.1; namely, it is the largest active element. Thus, initially $i = n$. T will have components which are assigned, and others which are not. If $T(j)$ is assigned, then $A(j) = 1$, but the converse is not necessarily true. The assigned components are defined through the following inductive definition:

1. $T(i)$ is assigned.
2. If $T(j)$ is assigned, then $T(|T(j)|)$ is also assigned.
3. No other components are assigned.

	A	D	C	P	Partition
1	0111	2222	4000	1111	,1234,
2	0110	2220	3100	1112	,123,4,
3	0101	2200	2200	1122	,12,34,
4	0101	2200	2110	1123	,12,3,4,
5	0100	2201	3100	1121	,124,3,
6	0011	2001	2200	1221	,14,23,
7	0011	2001	1210	1223	,1,23,4,
8	0010	2000	1300	1222	,1,234,
9	0011	2000	1210	1232	,1,24,3,
10	0011	2000	1120	1233	,1,2,34,
11	0011	2000	1111	1234	,1,2,3,4,
12	0010	2001	2110	1231	,14,2,3,
13	0001	2011	3100	1211	,134,2,
14	0001	2011	2110	1213	,13,2,4,
15	0000	2010	2200	1212	,13,24,

The value of an assigned $T(j)$ will always be integral and $|T(j)| < j$ for all. If $T(j) > 0$, then $A(T(j)) = 1, A(T(j) + 1) = A(T(j) + 2) = \cdots = A(j - 1) = 0$ and $A(j) = 1$. If $T(j) < 0$, then $A(|T(j)|) = A(|T(j)| + 1) = \cdots = A(j) = 1$. Thus, if we know i and T we can reconstruct A, and indeed we shall not use A anymore. Initially $T(n) = -2$ and $T(2) = 0$.

The loop of step (14) is easily removed by keeping the integer k which is the index of the rightmost nonzero component of C; however, initially $k = 2$.

Algorithm 3.2:
(1) Output.
(2) If $i = 0$, stop.
(3) $p \leftarrow P(i), C(p) \leftarrow C(p) - 1$.
(4) If $D(i) = 2$, go to step (16).
(5) If $D(i) = 1$, go to step (10).
(6) If $C(p) = 0$, go to step (9).
(7) $C(p + 1) \leftarrow C(p + 1) + 1, P(i) \leftarrow p + 1$.
(8) If $C(p + 1) = 1$, then $k \leftarrow p + 1$. Go to step (26).
(9) $C(1) \leftarrow C(1) + 1, P(i) \leftarrow 1, D(i) \leftarrow 1, k \leftarrow p - 1$. Go to step (17).
(10) If $p = 1$, go to step (15).
(11) $C(p - 1) \leftarrow C(p - 1) + 1, P(i) \leftarrow p - 1$.
(12) If $C(p) = 0$, then $k \leftarrow p - 1$.

(13) If $p > 3$, go to step (26).
(14) $D(i) \leftarrow 0$. Go to step (17).
(15) $C(k + 1) \leftarrow 1$, $P(i) \leftarrow k + 1$, $k \leftarrow k + 1$. Go to step (26).
(16) $C(2) \leftarrow C(2) + 1$, $P(i) \leftarrow 2$, $D(i) \leftarrow 0$.
(17) If $i = n$, go to step (22).
(18) $T(n) \leftarrow -(i + 1)$. If $T(i) < 0$, go to step (20).
(19) $T(i + 1) \leftarrow T(i)$, $i \leftarrow n$. Go to step (1).
(20) $T(i + 1) \leftarrow i - 1$. If $T(i) > -(i - 1)$, then $T(i - 1) \leftarrow T(i)$.
(21) $i \leftarrow n$. Go to step (1).
(22) If $T(n) < 0$, go to step (24).
(23) $i \leftarrow T(n)$. Go to step (1).
(24) If $T(n) > -(n - 1)$, then $T(n - 1) \leftarrow T(n)$.
(25) $i \leftarrow n - 1$. Go to step (1).
(26) If $i = n$, go to step (1).
(27) $T(n) \leftarrow -i$, $i \leftarrow n$. Go to step (1).

EXERCISES

3.1 Assume that $W(m)$ and $E(m)$ have the meanings described in Section 3.1. Prove the following identity:

$$W(m) = \binom{m}{m} E(m) + \binom{m + 1}{m} E(m + 1) + \cdots + \binom{t}{m} E(t).$$

3.2 Use the Möbius inversion theorem to prove that

$$n = \sum_{d\mid n} \phi(d).$$

3.3 Show that the identity

$$\sum_{d\mid n} \Lambda(d) = \log n$$

can be used to define $\Lambda(m)$ for every positive integer m. Also prove that if $m = p^e$ for some prime p and positive integer e, then $\Lambda(m) = \log p$; and, if not, $\Lambda(m) = 0$.

3.4 Prove (3.10) by using the sieve formula instead of Theorem 3.3.

3.5 In this exercise we develop a generalization of Theorem 3.3. Let $b_1, b_2, \ldots, b_r$ be positive integers. The greatest common divisor of $b_1, b_2, \ldots, b_r$ is denoted by $(b_1, b_2, \ldots, b_r)$. Let $f(b_1, b_2, \ldots, b_r)$ and $g(b_1, b_2, \ldots, b_r)$ be functions defined for every $b_1, b_2, \ldots, b_r$. Prove the identity

$$g(b_1, b_2, \ldots, b_r) = \sum_{d|(b_1, b_2, \ldots, b_r)} f\left(\frac{b_1}{d}, \frac{b_2}{d}, \ldots, \frac{b_r}{d}\right)$$

holds if and only if

$$f(b_1, b_2, \ldots, b_r) = \sum_{d|(b_1, b_2, \ldots, b_r)} \mu(d) \cdot g\left(\frac{b_1}{d}, \frac{b_2}{d}, \ldots, \frac{b_r}{d}\right)$$

holds.

3.6 Use the result of Exercise 3.5 to prove the following statement. Let S be a set of words of length $n = b_1 + b_2 + \cdots + b_r$ with b_1 letters of type α_1, b_2 letters of type α_2, and so on. (The alphabet contains r letters.) Also, S satisfies the condition that if $w = a_1 a_2 \cdots a_n$ is in S, then none of the words $a_2 a_3 \cdots a_n a_1$, $a_3 a_4 \cdots a_n a_1 a_2$, $\ldots, a_n a_1 a_2 \cdots a_{n-1}$ is in S. The maximum number of words that S can obtain, $M(b_1, b_2, \ldots, b_r)$, is given by

$$M(b_1, b_2, \ldots, b_r) = \frac{1}{n} \sum_{d|(b_1, b_2, \ldots, b_n)} \mu(d) \cdot \frac{\left(\frac{n}{d}\right)!}{\left(\frac{b_1}{d}\right)! \left(\frac{b_2}{d}\right)! \cdots \left(\frac{b_r}{d}\right)!}.$$

In Exercises 3.7, 3.8, and 3.9 we shall develop (3.14) through a technique different from that of Section 3.4.

3.7 Prove, directly from the definition of $D(n)$, that it satisfies the following difference equation:

$$D(n) = (n-1)[D(n-1) + D(n-2)].$$

3.8 Using the result of Exercise 3.7 and the fact that $D(1) = 0$ and $D(2) = 1$, prove that

$$D(n) - nD(n-1) = (-1)^n.$$

3.9 Using the result of Exercise 3.8, prove (3.14).

3.10 What is the number of partitions of a set of n distinct elements into r distinct, internally ordered cells if the number of elements to be in cell c_i is specified to be m_i? (Clearly $m_1 + m_2 + \cdots + m_r = n$.)

3.11 Show that the number of partitions of a set of n distinct elements into r distinct, internally ordered cells is

$$n! \binom{n-1}{r-1},$$

if the number of elements in each cell is arbitrary but no cell is empty.

3.12 Show that the number of partitions of a set of n distinct elements into r indistinguishable cells, internally unordered, in such a way that there will be a cell with m_1 elements, another cell with m_2 elements, and so on, is

$$\frac{n!}{m_1! m_2! \cdots m_r! d_1! d_2! \cdots d_l!}$$

where $m_1 + m_2 + \cdots + m_r = n$, d_i is the number of m's which are equal to i and $l = \lfloor n/2 \rfloor$.

3.13 What is the number of partitions if the conditions are like those of Exercise 3.12 except that the cells are internally ordered?

3.14 Show that the number of partitions of a set of n distinct elements into r indistinguishable cells, internally ordered, if the number of elements to be in each cell is arbitrary but no cell can be empty is

$$\frac{n!}{r!} \binom{n-1}{r-1}.$$

3.15 What is the number of partitions if the conditions are like those of Exercise 3.14 except that the number of cells is not specified? (A recursion formula for these numbers is given in reference 10.)

3.16 Prove the identity

$$\sum_{i=0}^{n} (-1)^i \binom{n}{i} (n-i)^n = n!.$$

3.17 Prove that if $n < r$, then

$$\sum_{i=0}^{n} (-1)^i \binom{r}{i} (r-i)^n = 0.$$

3.18 Assume that we have n elements of t distinct types. The number of elements of the ith type is n_i, and the elements of one type are indistinguishable. Clearly,

$n_1 + n_2 + \cdots + n_t = n$. Prove that the number of partitions of these elements into r distinct and internally ordered cells is

$$\frac{n!}{n_1! n_2! \cdots n_t!} \binom{n + r - 1}{n}$$

if the number of elements to be in each cell is arbitrary and cells may be empty.

3.19 Apply Algorithm 3.2 for the case $n = 4$.

REFERENCES

1. Golomb, S. W., Gordon, B., and Welch, L. R., "Comma-free Codes," *Can. J. Math.*, Vol. 10, 1958, pp. 202–09.
2. Eastman, W. L., and Even, S., "On Synchronizable and PSK-Synchronizable Block Codes," *IEEE Trans. Information Theory*, Vol. IT-10, No. 4, October 1964, pp. 351–56.
3. Golomb, S. W., and Gordon, B., "Codes with Bounded Synchronization Delay," *Information and Control*, Vol. 8, August 1965, pp. 355–76.
4. Uspensky, J. V., and Heaslet, M. A., *Elementary Number Theory*, McGraw-Hill, New York, 1939.
5. Riordan, J., *An Introduction to Combinatorial Analysis*, Wiley, New York, 1958.
6. Ryser, H. J., *Combinatorial Mathematics*, The Mathematical Association of America, distributed by Wiley, New York, 1963.
7. Hall, M., Jr., *Combinatorial Theory*, Blaisdell, Waltham, Mass., 1967.
8. Liu, C. L., *Introduction to Combinatorial Mathematics*, McGraw-Hill, New York, 1968.
9. Eisen, M., *Elementary Combinatorial Analysis*, Gordon and Breach, New York, 1969.
10. Riordan, J., *Combinatorial Identities*, Wiley, New York, 1968, p. 194.
11. Ehrlich, G., "Algorithms for Permutations, Partitions of a Set and Gray Code," Department of Applied Mathematics, The Weizmann Institute of Science, Rehovot, Israel, 1971.

4

PATHS IN GRAPHS

4.1 Introduction to graph theory

A graph $G(V, E)$, or briefly G, is a combinatorial structure consisting of a set of *vertices* V and a set of *edges* E. Unless otherwise stated, both are assumed to be finite. Each edge is associated with two vertices called its end points. If these two end points have the same relation to the edge, the edge has no natural orientation and is considered *undirected*. If not, we may consider one of end points as the start vertex and the other as the finish vertex, and in this case the edge is considered *directed*. Usually, when we draw a representation of G, the vertices are represented by points or by circles (in order to be able to write in it the vertex's name or some other information concerning it). The edges are represented by lines, not necessarily straight. If the edge is directed, we add an arrowhead to specify its direction.

If all the graph's edges are undirected, we say that the graph is undirected; if all its edges are directed, we say that the graph is directed. If some of the graph's edges are directed while others are undirected, the graph is called *mixed*. Mixed graphs are rare in applications and will not be discussed in this book. A graph may have *parallel edges*, that is, two or more edges with the same start vertex and the same finish vertex, in the case of directed graphs, or the same two end points in the case of undirected graphs. If two directed edges have the same end points, but their directions do not agree (the start vertex of one is the finish vertex of the other), they are not considered parallel.

A directed graph with no parallel edges (sometimes referred to as linear graph or as simple graph) is nothing but a relation specified by E, a set of ordered pairs, namely, a subset of $V \times V$. This point of view is, in my judgment, not very helpful, but there are discussions in the literature concerning transitivity and closure which are in terms of relations and it is useful to be aware of them.

In case of a directed graph without parallel edges, we can specify the edges as ordered pairs of vertices, the first of which is the start vertex and the second the finish vertex. For example, $a \to b$ is shown in Fig. 4.1. If the graph

Figure 4.1

is undirected and has no parallel edges, then the edges can be specified as an unordered pair of vertices, its end points. For example, if the end points are a and b, the edge is a—b ($= a$—b), as shown in Fig. 4.2. A graph may or may not

Figure 4.2

have a self-loop (sometimes referred to as a loop), that is, an edge in which the two end points are the same. Such an edge may or may not be directed.

A *path* is a sequence of edges $e_1, e_2, \ldots$ such that e_i and e_{i+1} have a common end point; if e_i is not a self-loop, then the common end point that it has with e_{i+1} cannot be the same as that with e_{i-1}, and $e_i \neq e_{i+1}$. If the path is finite, the number of edges in it is called its *length*. If no vertex is visited more than once, the path is called *simple*. It is clear that in a simple path, no edge is used twice, but the converse is not necessarily true.

If the graph is undirected and has no parallel edges, then a path can be specified by the sequence of vertices in the order in which they are visited: $v_0, v_1, \ldots, v_l$. Clearly the length of such a path is l. If $v_0 = v_l$, the path is called a *circuit* (of length l) and it is *simple* if no other identity of vertices holds.

If the graph is directed and the direction of all the edges agrees with the direction implied by the path, the path is called *directed*, but we allow paths in which the directions of the edges are not the same as that of the path. A circuit may or may not be directed. (A directed circuit is sometimes called a cycle.) An undirected graph is said to be *connected* if for every two vertices a and b there exists a path $e_1, e_2, \ldots, e_l$ such that a is an end point of e_1 and b is an end point of e_l. Clearly, if a path between a and b exists, then a simple path exists, too. A directed graph is said to be *strongly connected* if for every two vertices a and b there exists a directed path from a to b. The *underlying undirected graph* of a directed graph is defined as the undirected graph resulting from ignoring the directions in the edges. We shall not use the term "connected" in relation to directed graphs, but we may refer to the connectivity of the underlying undirected graph of a given directed graph.

The *degree* of a vertex v, $d(v)$, is the number of times it plays the role of an end point of the edges; a self-loop $\langle v, v \rangle$ contributes two to the count. In case of a directed graph we may also speak of the *outgoing degree*, $d_0(v)$, and *incoming degree*, $d_i(v)$, of a vertex, which are defined in the natural way.

Lemma 4.1: The number of vertices of odd degree in a finite graph is even.

Proof: First, it is clear that

$$\sum_{i=1}^{|V|} d(v_i) = 2 \cdot |E|,$$

where $|V|$ and $|E|$ are the number of vertices and the number of edges, respectively. This follows from the fact that each edge is counted twice in the summation. The statement of the lemma is now immediate.

QED

4.2 Euler graphs

An *Euler path* of a finite undirected graph $G(V, E)$ is a path $e_1, e_2, \ldots, e_l$ such that every edge appears on it exactly once; thus, $l = |E|$. An undirected graph which has an Euler path is called an *Euler graph*.

Theorem 4.1:   An undirected connected finite graph is an Euler graph if and only if exactly two vertices are of odd degree or all vertices are of even degree. In the latter case, every Euler path of the graph is a circuit, and in the former case, none is.

As an immediate conclusion of Theorem 4.1 we observe that none of the graphs in Fig. 4.3 is an Euler graph, because both have four vertices of odd degree. The graph shown in Fig. 4.3(a) is the famous *Königsberg bridge problem* solved by Euler in 1736. The graph shown in Fig. 4.3(b) is a common misleading puzzle of the type "draw without lifting your pen from the paper."

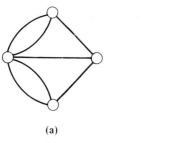
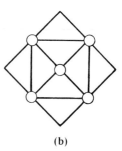

(a)   (b)

Figure 4.3

Proof: It is clear that if a graph has an Euler path which is not a circuit, then the start vertex and the finish vertex of the path are of odd degree, while all the other vertices are of even degree. Also, if a graph has a Euler circuit, then all vertices are of even degree.

Assume now that G is a finite undirected graph with exactly two vertices of odd degree, a and b. We shall describe now an agorithm for finding a Euler path from a to b. Starting from a we choose any edge adjacent to it (an edge of which a is an end point), and trace it (go to its other end point). Upon entering a vertex we search for an unused adjacent edge. If the vertex is neither a nor b, each time we pass through it we use up two of its adjacent edges. The degree of the vertex is even. Thus, the number of unused adjacent edges after leaving it is even. (Here again, a self-loop is counted twice.) Therefore, upon entering it there is at least one unused adjacent edge to leave on. Also, by a similar argument, whenever we reenter a we have an unused edge to leave on. It follows that the only place this process can stop is in b. So far we have found a path which starts in a, finishes in b, and the number of unused edges adjacent to any vertex is even. Since the graph is connected, there must be at least one unused edge which is adjacent to one of the vertices on the existing path from a to b. Starting a trail from this vertex on unused edges, the only vertex in which this process can end (because no continuation can be found) is the vertex in which it started. Thus, we have found a circuit of edges which were not used before, and in which each edge is used at most once; it starts and ends in a vertex visited in the previous path. It is easy to change our path from a to b to include this detour. We continue to add such detours to our path as long as not all edges are in it. The case of all vertices of even degrees is similar. The only difference is that we start the initial tour at any vertex, and this tour must stop at the same vertex. This initial circuit is amended as before, until all edges are included.

QED

The same techniques can be used to handle a *directed Euler path* which is a directed path in which every edge appears exactly once. Also *directed Euler graphs* are defined as graphs which have a directed Euler path. The proof of Theorem 4.2 is similar to that of Theorem 4.1.

Theorem 4.2: A directed finite graph whose underlying undirected graph is connected is an Euler graph if and only if either for one vertex a, $d_0(a) = d_i(a) + 1$, for another vertex b, $d_0(b) + 1 = d_i(b)$, and for all other vertices v, $d_0(v) = d_i(v)$, or for all vertices v, $d_0(v) = d_i(v)$. In the latter case, every directed Euler path of the graph is a directed circuit, and in the former case none is.

4.3   De Bruijn sequences

Let $\sum = \{0, 1, \ldots, \sigma - 1\}$ be an alphabet of σ letters. Clearly there are σ^n different words of length n over this alphabet. A *de Bruijn sequence* (sometimes called maximum-length shift register sequence) is a circular $a_0 a_1 \cdots a_{L-1}$ over $\sum$ such that for every word w of length n there exists a unique i such that

$$a_i a_{i+1} \cdots a_{i+n-1} = w,$$

where the computation of the indices is modulo L. Clearly if the sequence satisfies this condition, then $L = \sigma^n$. The most important case is that of $\sigma = 2$. Binary de Bruijn sequences are of great importance in coding theory and are implemented by shift registers. (See Golomb's book [1] on the subject.) The interested reader can find more information on de Bruijn sequences in references 2 and 3. The only problem we shall discuss here is the existence of de Bruijn sequences for every $\sigma \geqslant 2$ and every n.

Let us describe a directed graph $G_{\sigma,n}(V, E)$ which has the following structure:

1. V is the set of all σ^{n-1} words of length $n-1$ over $\sum$.
2. E is the set of all σ^{n} words of length n over $\sum$.
3. An edge $b_1 b_2 \cdots b_n$ emanates from the vertex $b_1 b_2 \cdots b_{n-1}$ and terminates in the vertex $b_2 b_3 \cdots b_n$.

The graphs $G_{2,3}$, $G_{2,4}$, and $G_{3,2}$ are shown in Figs. 4.4, 4.5, and 4.6, respectively.

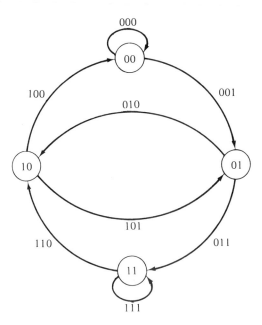

Figure 4.4

These graphs are sometimes called de Bruijn diagrams, or Good's diagrams, or shift register state diagrams. The structure of the graphs is such that the word w_2 can follow the word w_1 in a de Bruijn sequence only if w_2 emanates from the vertex which w_1 enters. Also it is clear that if we find a directed Euler circuit (a directed circuit which uses each of the graph's

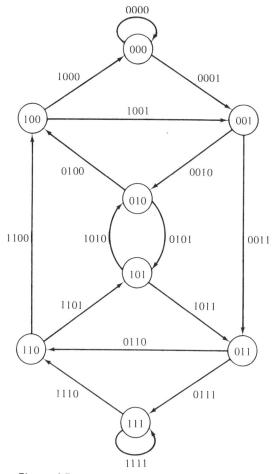

Figure 4.5

edges exactly once) of $G_{\sigma,n}$, then we also have a de Bruijn sequence. For example, consider the directed Euler circuit of $G_{2,3}$ (Fig. 4.4) consisting of the following sequence of edges:

$$000, 001, 011, 111, 110, 101, 010, 100.$$

The implied de Bruijn sequence, 00011101, follows by reading the first letter of each word in the circuit. Thus, the question of existence of de Bruijn sequences is equivalent to that of the existence of direct Euler circuits in the corresponding de Bruijn diagram.

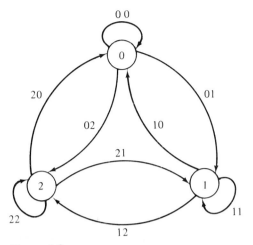

Figure 4.6

Theorem 4.3: For every positive integer σ and n, $G_{\sigma,n}$ has a directed Euler circuit.

Proof: We wish to use Theorem 4.2 to prove our theorem. First we have to show that the underlying undirected graph is connected. In fact, we shall show that $G_{\sigma,n}$ is strongly connected. Let $b_1 b_2 \cdots b_{n-1}$ and $c_1 c_2 \cdots c_{n-1}$ be any two vertices; the directed path $b_1 b_2 \cdots b_{n-1} c_1$, $b_2 b_3 \cdots b_{n-1} c_1 c_2, \ldots,$ $b_{n-1} c_1 c_2 \cdots c_{n-1}$ leads from the first to the second. Next, we have to show that $d_0(v) = d_i(v)$ for each vertex v. This follows from the fact that $d_0(v) = d_i(v)$ $= \sigma$ for all vertices v. For the vertex $b_1 b_2 \cdots b_{n-1}$ is entered by edges $c b_1 b_2$ $\cdots b_{n-1}$, where c can be chosen in σ ways, and is the start vertex of edges $b_1 b_2 \cdots b_{n-1} c$, where again c can be chosen in σ ways.

QED

Corollary 4.1: For every positive integer σ and n there exists a de Bruijn sequence.

4.4 Shortest-path algorithms

Let G be an undirected finite graph and s and t be two of its vertices. The first problem of this section is to find a shortest path (with the smallest number of edges) from s to t. We shall describe now an algorithm which finds the length of a shortest path.

Algorithm 4.1:
(1) Label vertex s with 0. Set $i = 0$.
(2) Find all unlabeled vertices which are connected by an edge to vertices labeled i. If there are no such vertices, t is not reachable from s; stop. If there are, label them $i + 1$.
(3) If t is labeled, go to step (4). If not, increment i by 1 and go to step (2).
(4) The length of a shortest path from s to t is $i + 1$; stop.

Let us demonstrate the algorithm on the graph shown in Fig. 4.7. First s is labeled 0; then a and f are labeled 1; then b, d, and e are labeled 2; then c and t are labeled 3. Since t is labeled 3, the length of a shortest path from s to t is 3.

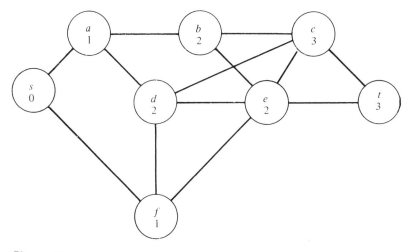

Figure 4.7

The validity of the statement of step (4) is an immediate conclusion of the following simple lemma.

Lemma 4.2:   A vertex v is labeled $\lambda(v)$ by Algorithm 4.1 if and only if the length of the shortest path from s to v is $\lambda(v)$.

Proof: The proof is by induction on i. First, it is clear that for $i = 0$, $\lambda(v) = 0$ implies that $v = s$, and indeed the length of a shortest path from s to s is zero. Next assume that the statement is true for all v for which $\lambda(c) \leqslant m$. If a vertex u is unlabeled (before step (2) is applied for $i = m$), then there is no path of length shorter than $m + 1$ from s to u; if it is connected by an edge to a vertex labeled m (it cannot be connected by an edge to a vertex with a lower label, or it would have been labeled before), then there is a path from s to u of length $m + 1$, and indeed the algorithm assigns $\lambda(u) = m + 1$; if it is not connected to any vertex labeled m by an edge, then there is no path of length $m + 1$ from s to u, for the previous vertex on such a path must be m edges away from s and would have been labeled.

QED

Algorithm 4.1 deserves several comments:

1. If the graph is finite, and there is no path from s to t, the algorithm ter-minates after all vertices which are reachable from s have been labeled.
2. If t is reachable from s, the algorithm is applicable even if G is infinite, provided the degrees of the vertices are finite; it stops once t is labeled and leaves all the vertices which are farther away from s unlabeled. (This clearly happens in the finite case, too.)
3. If the graph is directed, and the path is required to be directed, the algo-rithm is still applicable provided step (2) is changed as follows: Find all unlabeled vertices which are reachable by an edge which emanates from a vertex labeled i; and so on.

Once Algorithm 4.1 is terminated successfully (in step (4)), we can use a trace-back algorithm to find one shortest path. The algorithm uses the labels $\lambda(v)$ produced in Algorithm 4.1. It produces a path $v(0), v(1), \ldots, v(\lambda(t))$ such that $v(0) = s$ and $v(\lambda(t)) = t$.

Algorithm 4.2:
(1) Set $i = \lambda(t)$ and assign $v(i) = t$.
(2) Find a vertex u such that u is connected by an edge to $v(i)$ and $\lambda(u) = i - 1$. Assign $v(i - 1) = u$.
(3) If $i = 1$, stop. If not, decrement i by 1 and go to step (2).

It is obvious that Algorithm 4.2 terminates successfully after $\lambda(t)$ applica-tions of steps (2) and (3). In our example (Fig. 4.5), $v(3) = t, v(2) = e, v(1) = f$, and $v(0) = s$. But in general there may be many shortest paths from s to t, and Algorithm 4.2 finds just one of them. It is interesting that a simple addi-tional labeling, assigning $\mu(v)$ to vertices v which have been labeled in

Algorithm 4.1 in a trace-back manner, yields $\mu(s)$, which is the number of minimum length paths from s to t. This is done by the following algorithm:

Algorithm 4.3:
(1) Set $i = \lambda(t)$ and $\mu(t) = 1$. All other vertices v for which $\lambda(v) = \lambda(t)$ are assigned $\mu(v) = 0$.
(2) For each vertex v which satisfies $\lambda(v) = i - 1$ compute the sum

$$\sum \mu(u)$$

over all u's which satisfy the following condition: $\lambda(u) = i$ and v is connected by an edge to u; if there are parallel edges, $\mu(u)$ is repeated in the summation as many times as there are parallel edges.
(3) If $i = 1$, stop. If not, decrement i by 1 and go to step (2).

The proof of the algorithm's validity is by proving that for all vertices v for which $\lambda(v) < \lambda(t)$, $\mu(v)$ is the number of paths of length $\lambda(t) - \lambda(v)$ from v to t.

The natural generalization of the shortest-path problem is to assign to each edge e a real number $l(e)$, called the length of e, and to ask for a path $e_1, e_2,$ $\ldots, e_m$ from s to t for which the sum

$$\sum_{i=1}^{m} l(e_i) \tag{4.1}$$

is minimum. Assuming that the graph is undirected and connected, it is immediately obvious that we need the condition that $l(e) \geqslant 0$ for every edge e. Otherwise there is no shortest path from s to t, for we can take a path from s to one of the end points of a negative edge, go back and forth on it as many times as we wish (building up a large negative sum), and take a path from there to t.

One thought which comes to mind, in case all $l(e)$'s are positive integers, is to introduce artificial vertices in order to make all edge lengths equal to 1 and use the previous algorithms. This, in general, is not a good idea, for it may increase the number of vertices considerably.

We shall now describe two methods for finding a shortest path from s to t. The first is rather different from Algorithm 4.1; it applies to finite graphs only. Our description is for undirected graphs, but the changes for directed graphs are trivial. In fact, its variation for directed graphs allows negative $l(e)$'s, too, provided there is no directed circuit for which the edge-length summation is negative.

Algorithm 4.4:

(1) Assign the vertices v labels $\lambda(v)$ as follows:

$$\lambda(v) = \begin{cases} 0 & \text{if } v = s, \\ \infty & \text{if } v \neq s. \end{cases}$$

(2) Scan the whole graph to see whether there exist vertices v and u which are the end points of an edge e such that $\lambda(v) > \lambda(u) + l(e)$. If no such situation exists, go to step (3). Otherwise, replace $\lambda(v)$ by $\lambda(u) + l(e)$ and repeat step (2).

(3) For every v, $\lambda(v)$ is the length of the shortest path from s to v; stop.

First, we have to show that this process terminates. This follows from the finiteness of the number of "evaluation paths" for each vertex v. Each such evaluation path is the history of how this value has reached v; it must be a simple path from s to v and it determines $\lambda(v)$ uniquely. Since the number of vertices is finite, the set of possible assignments of $\lambda(v)$ to all vertices v is finite and the process must terminate.

In fact, if step (2) is performed by checking the edges in an orderly manner one by one, and repeating the same order again and again, we are assured of completion in $|V|$ sweeps. Thus, the number of edge checking is bounded by $|E| \cdot |V|$. Improving this algorithm is not hard once it is decided which operations are relatively cheap and in what data structure the graph is specified.

Now let us prove that upon termination, $\lambda(v)$ is the length of a shortest path from s to v. Let us record for every vertex v the edge entering it through which $\lambda(v)$ was changed last. As we backtrack from v through these edges, it is easy to see that we never return to a vertex which has already been visited on this path, and the search can stop at s only. Thus, we have found a path from s to v for which $\lambda(v)$ is equal to the sum of the $l(e)$'s of the edges on the path. Thus $\lambda(v)$ is not less than the length of a shortest path from s to v. If $\lambda(v)$ is greater than the length of a shortest path, then along each such path there must be a vertex v whose label, $\lambda(v)$, can be lowered, and the algorithm would not have stopped.

The following algorithm has some of the features of Algorithm 4.1: Each vertex is labeled, at most, once and once t is labeled the algorithm stops. Thus, it is also applicable to infinite graphs with finite degrees and with a path from s to t. However, the calculations before each labeling are more complex. Here again, the algorithm is described for undirected graphs, but works for directed graphs after minor and simple changes. However, here we must assume that $l(e) \geqslant 0$ for all e's.

Algorithm 4.5:
(1) Assign s the label 0. ($\lambda(s) = 0$.)
(2) For every edge e from a labeled vertex u to an unlabeled vertex v, compute $\lambda(u) + l(e)$. If there are no such edges, there is no path from s to t; stop. If such edges exist, continue.
(3) Find an edge $\hat{e}$ for which the quantity $\lambda(\hat{u}) + l(\hat{e})$ is minimum and assign the corresponding $\hat{v}$ the label $\lambda(\hat{v}) = \lambda(\hat{u}) + l(\hat{e})$. If $\hat{v} = t$, stop. If not, go to step (2).

The question of termination of this process is trivial. The proof that $\lambda(v)$ is the length of a shortest path from s to v is similar to the proof of Lemma 4.2. First we observe that the sequence of the $\lambda(v)$'s, in the order in which they are assigned, is a nondecreasing sequence. Next, we can prove by induction on this order, that the statement is valid. The details are left to the reader (Exercise 4.7).

The algorithm can be improved by avoiding recomputations of $\lambda(u) + l(e)$. All we have to do after $\hat{v}$ has been labeled is to add to the list the proper values $\lambda(\hat{v}) + l(e)$. However, the minimum still has to be computed. Thus, the number of comparisons is bounded here, too, by $|E|\cdot|V|$. This can be changed to $|V|^2$ if temporary labels for the unlabeled vertices are used [12].

There are many extensions of the shortest-path problem, and the interested reader can find additional information in references 4, 5, 6, and 7.

4.5 Traversal of labyrinths

If one wants to find a path between two vertices in a known undirected graph, one can use the techniques of the previous section. However, if the graph is unknown, the problem is to devise an algorithm to find a path from one vertex to another, and the more efficient the algorithm, the better.

Many different assumptions can be made on the type of memory we may use and on the signs we may leave on the graph while we traverse it, and different assumptions yield different problems.

In this section we shall describe an algorithm of Tarry [9]. Here the assumption is that we may leave marks on the entrances to the edges. (It is convenient to think of the vertices as plazas and the edges as alleys.) However, the number of marks is only two. The first entrance to a vertex is marked F upon passage. Similarly, an exit (the same place as an entrance, but a different use is made of it) is marked E upon passage. For simplicity, we shall assume that our excursion starts at vertex s and that our purpose is to visit all vertices of the graph; if all we want is to reach some vertex t, the excursion stops there upon arrival. Clearly, we make the assumption that the graph is connected, undirected, and that no working memory (in the form of pencil and paper, a counter, and so on) is available.

Algorithm 4.6 (Tarry):
(1) If there are any unmarked passages, choose one, mark it E, and walk through it to an adjacent vertex; if all passages are marked, and there is one marked F, enter it and walk along it to an adjacent vertex; if all passages are marked E, stop. The traversal is complete and the present vertex is s.
(2) Upon arrival to a vertex through a passage, check if any of the passages is marked. If so, go to step (1). If not, mark the entrance by F and go to step (1).

Let us demonstrate the algorithm on an example shown in Fig. 4.8. We start from s. We choose, say, the edge leading to vertex a and mark the exit from s by E and the entrance to a by F. Next, we choose the edge leading to b, marking the exit from a by E and the entrance to b by F. Next, we choose an edge leading back to s; the exit from b is marked E, but the entrance to s is

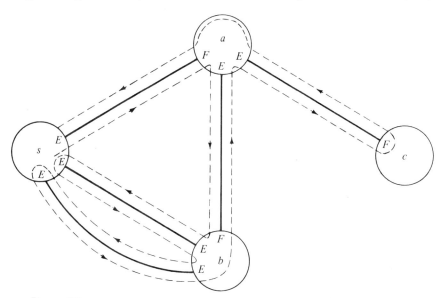

Figure 4.8

not marked, for s already has a marked passage. We choose to return on the same edge; and so on.

Lemma 4.3:   Algorithm 4.6 never allows an edge to be traversed twice in the same direction.

Proof: If a passage is used as an exit (entering an edge), then either it is being marked E in the process, and thus the edge is never traversed again in this direction, or the passage is already marked F. It remains to be shown that no passage marked F is ever reused for entering the edge.

Assume that for some vertex $v(0)$ the algorithm allows reusing a passage marked F for entering the edge. Clearly $v(0) \neq s$, for s has no passage marked F. Since the vertex $v(0)$ is left $d(v(0)) + 1$ times (once through each of the exits marked E, and twice through the passage marked F), there must be a vertex $v(1)$ and an edge from $v(1)$ to $v(0)$ which has been traversed twice in this direction. This exit from $v(1)$ (to $v(0)$) must be marked F. Thus, the first visit to $v(0)$ occurred before the first visit to $v(1)$. Repeating this argument again and again, we backtrack a path $v(0), v(1), \ldots$. No vertex in this sequence is s (for s has no passage marked F). Since the number of vertices is finite, there must be subsequence $v(i), v(i + 1), \ldots, v(j) = v(i)$. This is a contradiction, for it implies that the first visit to $v(i)$ occurred before the first visit to $v(i)$.

QED

An immediate corollary of Lemma 4.3 is that the process implied by Algorithm 4.6 terminates. Thus, the process terminates at the start vertex s (the only vertex with no passage marked F).

Lemma 4.4:   Upon termination of Algorithm 4.6 each edge of the graph has been traversed once in each direction.

Proof: For ease of proof, let us state the proposition differently: For every vertex all the adjacent edges have been traversed in both directions. Now the proof is done by an argument on the vertices.

First, consider the start vertex s. Since the algorithm has terminated, all the edges have been traversed from s outward. Thus, s has been left $d(s)$ times, and since we end up in s, it is also entered $d(s)$ times. However, by Lemma 4.3 no edge is traversed more than once in the same direction. Therefore, all edges adjacent to s have been traversed once in each direction. Assume now that the statement is true for a subset S of vertices. If $V \neq S$, then, by the connectivity of the graph there must be vertices connected to vertices of S by an edge. All these edges have been traversed in both directions. The first edge traversed from a vertex of S to a vertex of $V - S$ has also been traversed backward, thus using a passage marked F. Thus, all the exits of this vertex have been used (once). This implies that v has been entered $d(v)$ times, assuring that each of its edges have been traversed in both directions.

QED

Thus, Lemma 4.4 proves that Algorithm 4.6 is valid, and that it takes exactly $2|E|$ edge traversals to completion.

Fraenkel [10, 11] showed that the number of edge traversals can sometimes be reduced if the use of a two-way counter is allowed. The idea is that each time we enter a new vertex (no marks on the passages), of degree higher than two, the counter is incremented; and each time we realize that all the edges adjacent to a vertex of degree higher than two have been traversed we decrement the counter. If the counter reaches the start value, we return to s though F passages. (The algorithm required one more mark, F', for entrances other than the first.)

EXERCISES

4.1   Prove Theorem 4.2.

4.2   Prove that if a connected undirected finite graph has exactly $2k$ vertices of odd degree, then the set of edges can be decomposed into k paths such that every edge is used exactly once. Is the condition of connectivity necessary or can it be replaced by a weaker condition?

A *Hamiltonian path* (circuit) is a simple path (circuit) on which all the vertices of the graph appear.

4.3   Prove that the graph shown in the diagram has no Hamiltonian path or circuit.

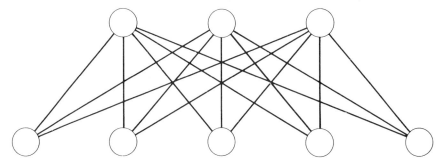

4.4 Prove that in every completely connected directed graph (a graph in which every two vertices are connected by exactly one directed edge in one of the two possible directions) there exists a directed Hamiltonian path. (*Hint:* Prove by induction on the number of vertices.)

4.5 Prove that a directed Hamiltonian circuit of $G_{\sigma,n}$ corresponds to a directed Euler circuit of $G_{\sigma,n-1}$. Is it true that $G_{\sigma,n}$ always has a directed Hamiltonian circuit?

4.6 Prove that a connected undirected graph G is orientable (by giving each edge some direction) into a directed strongly connected graph if and only if each edge of G is in some simple circuit in G.

4.7 Give a complete proof that Algorithm 4.5 assigns, $\lambda(v)$, the length of a shortest path from s to v.

4.8 Show by an example that Algorithm 4.5 may fail if $l(e) \geqslant 0$ is not true for all edges. Can the condition that $\Sigma l(e)$ on every circuit is nonnegative help?

4.9 Describe a backtracking algorithm (a generalization of Algorithm 4.2) for finding a shortest path from s to t, once Algorithm 4.4 or 4.5 has terminated successfully (assigning a finite label, $\lambda(t)$ to vertex t). Prove the validity of your algorithm.

4.10 Describe a backtracking algorithm (a generalization of Algorithm 4.3) for finding the number of shortest paths from s to t, once Algorithm 4.4 or 4.5 has terminated successfully. Prove the validity of your algorithm.

4.11 The following algorithm is a variation of an algorithm of Floyd [8] for finding, simultaneously, the minimum distances between all pairs of vertices of a finite directed graph in which no parallel edges exist. (The absence of an edge $u \xrightarrow{e} u$ is recorded by $l(e) = \infty$.) Let the vertices be $1, 2, \ldots, n$ and let $l^k(i, j)$ be the length of the shortest path from i to j among all paths that do not have as intermediate vertices any vertex of the set $\{k + 1, k + 2, \ldots, n\}$. Clearly, $l^0(i, j)$ are the original edge lengths.

(1) $k \leftarrow 1$.
(2) For every $1 \leqslant i, j \leqslant n$ compute

$$l^k(i, j) = \text{Min } \{l^{k-1}(i, j), l^{k-1}(i, k) + l^{k-1}(k, j)\}.$$

(3) If $k = n$, stop. If not, increment k and go to step (2).

Prove that if the graph contains no directed circuits for which $\Sigma l(e)$ is originally negative, then the algorithm will terminate with the stated result. Show that the number of comparisons is proportional to $|V|^3$.

4.12 Prove that one can return to s, by a simple path, at any point of Algorithm 4.6, by taking the passages marked F.

REFERENCES

1. Golomb, S. W., *Shift Register Sequences*, Holden-Day, San Francisco, 1967.
2. Berge, C., *The Theory of Graphs and Its Applications*, Wiley, New York, 1962, Chap. 17.
3. Hall, M., Jr., *Combinatorial Theory*, Blaisdell, Waltham, Mass., 1967, Chap. 9.
4. Ford, L. R., Jr., and Fulkerson, D. R., *Flows in Networks*, Princeton University Press, Princeton, N.J., 1962, Chap. III, Sec. 5.
5. Berge, C., and Ghouila-Houri, A., *Programming, Games and Transportation Networks*, Wiley, New York, 1965, Chap. 9.
6. Hu, T. C., *Integer Programming and Network Flows*, Addison-Wesley, Reading, Mass., 1969.
7. Frank, H., and Frisch, I. T., *Communication, Transmission, and Transportation Networks*, Addison-Wesley, Reading, Mass., 1971.
8. Floyd, R. W., "Algorithm 97: Shortest Path," *Comm. ACM*, Vol. 5, 1962, p. 345.
9. Tarry, G., "Le Problème des labyrinthes," *Nouvelles Ann. de Math*, Vol. 14, 1895, p. 187.
10. Fraenkel, A. S., "Economic Traversal of Labyrinths," *Math. Mag.*, Vol. 43, 1970, pp. 125–30.
11. Fraenkel, A. S., "Economic Traversal of Labyrinths (Correction)," *Math. Mag.*, Vol. 44, No. 1, January 1971.
12. Yen, J. Y., "Finding the Lengths of All Shortest Paths in N-Node Nonnegative-Distance Complete Networks Using $\frac{1}{2}N^3$ Additions and N^3 Comparisons," *J. ACM*, Vol. 19, July 1972, pp. 423–24.

5
TREES

5.1 Tree definitions

An undirected graph $G(V, E)$, finite or infinite, is called a *tree* if it is connected and is circuit-free. The following theorem provides three alternative definitions of a tree.

Theorem 5.1: Assume that $G(V, E)$ is an undirected finite or infinite graph. The following four conditions are equivalent:

(a) G is a tree.
(b) G is circuit-free, but if any edge is added to G, a circuit is formed.
(c) There is a unique path between every pair of vertices of G.
(d) G is connected, but if any edge is deleted from G, the connectivity of G is interrupted.

Proof: We shall prove that conditions (a) $\Rightarrow$ (b) $\Rightarrow$ (c) $\Rightarrow$ (d) $\Rightarrow$ (a).

(a) $\Rightarrow$ (b): We assume that G is connected and circuit-free. Let e be a new edge, that is, $e \notin E$; the two end points of e, a and b, are elements of V. If $a = b$, then e forms a self-loop and therefore a circuit exists. If $a \neq b$, there is a path in G (without e) between a and b; if we add e, this path with e form a circuit.

(b) $\Rightarrow$ (c): We assume that G is circuit-free and that no edge can be added to G without creating a circuit. Let a and b be any two vertices of G. If there is no path between them, then we can add an edge between a and b without creating a circuit. Thus, G must be connected. Moreover, if there are two paths, P and P', between a and b, then there is a circuit in G. To see this, assume that $P = e_1, e_2, \ldots, e_l$ and $P' = e'_1, e'_2, \ldots, e'_m$. Since G is circuit-free, both paths are simple, and therefore one cannot be the beginning of the other. Let i, $i \leqslant \text{Min}\{l, m\}$, be the first index for which $e_i \neq e'_i$, and let v be the first vertex on $e_i, e_{i+1}, \ldots, e_l$ which is also on $e'_i, e'_{i+1}, \ldots, e'_m$ after this branching off. The two disjoint subpaths between the branching off vertex and v form a simple circuit in G.

(c) $\Rightarrow$ (d): We assume the existence of a unique path between every pair of vertices of G; thus, this path must be simple. This implies that G is connected. Assume now that we delete an edge e from G. The uniqueness of paths in G implies that G is circuit-free in general, and in particular e is not a self-loop. Let a and b be e's end points. If there is now (after the deletion of e) a path between a and b, then G has more than one path between a and b.

(d) $\Rightarrow$ (a): We assume that G is connected and that no edge can be deleted without interrupting the connectivity. If G contains a simple circuit, any edge on this circuit can be deleted without interrupting the connectivity. Thus, G is circuit-free.

                                                                          QED

In addition to the four alternative definitions of a tree discussed so far, there are two more common definitions used for finite graphs. These are discussed in the following theorem.

Theorem 5.2:   Assume that $G(V, E)$ is a finite undirected graph whose number of vertices is $n > 0$. The following three conditions are equivalent:

(a) G is a tree.
(b) G is circuit-free and has $n - 1$ edges.
(c) G is connected and has $n - 1$ edges.

Proof: We shall prove that conditions (a) $\Rightarrow$ (b) $\Rightarrow$ (c) $\Rightarrow$ (a).

(a) $\Rightarrow$ (b): Let us prove, by induction on n, that if G is a tree, then its number of edges is $n - 1$. This statement is clearly true for $n = 1$. Assume that it is true for all $n < m$, and let G be a tree with m vertices. Let us delete from G any edge e. By condition (d) of Theorem 5.1, G is not connected any more, and clearly is broken into two connected components each of which is circuit-free, and therefore are trees. By the inductive hypothesis, each component has one edge less than the number of vertices. Thus, both have $n - 2$ edges. Add back e, and the number of edges is $n - 1$.

(b) $\Rightarrow$ (c): We assume that G is circuit-free and has $n - 1$ edges. Let us first show that G has at least two vertices of degree 1. Choose any edge, e_1. If both its end points are of degree 1, we are through. If not, there exists at least one edge e_2 which has one common end point with e_1. (If both end points are common, then G contains a circuit.) We shall continue to add edges to our collection in this manner; each one of our edge collections describes a connected part of G, and we add to it an edge which has one end point in common with the previous structure, and its second end point is a new vertex (or a circuit would have been formed). When no additional edge can be attached, the number of edges is smaller by one than the number of vertices, l. Let the set of vertices be $\{v_1, v_2, \ldots, v_l\}$; then

$$\sum_{i=1}^{l} d(v_i) = 2(l - 1).$$

Since $d(v_i) \geqslant 1$, there are at least two vertices of degree 1.

Now, the proof that G is connected proceeds by induction on the number of vertices, n. The statement is obviously true for $n = 1$. Assume that it is true for $n = m - 1$, and let G be a circuit-free graph with m vertices and $m - 1$ edges. Eliminate from G an edge, one of whose end points, v, is of degree 1; and eliminate v, too. The resulting graph is still circuit-free and has $m - 1$ vertices and $m - 2$ edges; thus, by the inductive hypothesis it is connected. Therefore, G is connected too.

(c) $\Rightarrow$ (a): Assume that G is connected and has $n - 1$ edges. If G contains circuits, we can eliminate edges (without eliminating vertices) and maintain the connectivity. When this process terminates, the resulting graph is a tree, and, by (a) $\Rightarrow$ (b), has $n - 1$ edges. Thus, no edge can be eliminated and G is circuit-free.

QED

A corollary of Theorem 5.2 and the statement proved in the (b) ⇒ (c) part of its proof is the following lemma.

Lemma 5.1:   A finite tree with more than one vertex has at least two vertices of degree 1.

A vertex whose degree is 1 is called a *terminal vertex*.

5.2   The minimum spanning tree problem

A graph $G'(V', E')$ is called a *subgraph* of a graph $G(V, E)$ if $V' \subseteq V$ and $E' \subseteq E$. Clearly, an arbitrary choice of $V' \subseteq V$ and $E' \subseteq E$ may not yield a subgraph; for some of the end points of edges in E' may not be included in V'. There are two common ways to describe a subgraph, in addition to the straightforward complete description. A subgraph $G'(V', E')$ is called a *vertex subgraph* of $G(V, E)$ if $V' \subseteq V$ and E' is the set of all edges in G both of whose end points belong to V'. (Vertex subgraphs have been called section graphs [1] and induced subgraphs [2], but I find the name "vertex subgraph" more suggestive.) A subgraph $G'(V', E')$ is called an *edge subgraph* of $G(V, E)$ if $E' \subseteq E$ and V' is the set of all end points of edges in E'. (We have used edge subgraphs in the proof of (b) ⇒ (c) of Theorem 5.2.)

Let $G(V, E)$ be a connected undirected graph, and assume that each edge is assigned a positive number, $l(e)$, called its length (as was done in Section 4.3). Our purpose is to find a connected subgraph $G'(V', E')$ of $G(V, E)$ such that $V' = V$ and the total length

$$\sum_{e \in E'} l(e)$$

is minimum. First, let us demonstrate that G' must be a tree. For if G' contains a circuit, then any edge of this circuit can be deleted, thus reducing the total length. A subgraph which includes all the vertices of the graph and which is a tree is called a *spanning tree*. Therefore, our problem is to find a spanning tree of minimum total length. Such a tree is called a *minimum spanning tree*. (Some call it a minimal connector [1]; other similar names are also common.) Prim's algorithm [3] to be described in this section is based on the following lemma.

Lemma 5.2:   Let v be any vertex of $G(V, E)$ and let e be an adjacent edge for which $l(e)$ is the minimum over the edges adjacent to v (excluding self-loops, which are of no interest here). There exist a minimum spanning tree of $G(V, E)$ which includes e.

Proof :   Let T be any minimum spanning tree of $G(V, E)$. If e is not one of T's edges, let us add e to T. By Theorem 5.1, condition (b), a circuit is formed. The edge e' on this circuit which is also adjacent to v can now be deleted. Since $l(e') \geqslant l(e)$, the resulting tree is also minimum. (In fact, if T is minimum, then $l(e') = l(e)$.)

QED

It is clear, from the proof of Lemma 5.2, that if no two edges in the graph have the same length, then the edge with the least length of all the edges adjacent to v (excluding self-loops) must be included in every minimum tree. (In fact, as we shall see later, in this case the minimum tree is unique.)

Let e be an edge, as described in Lemma 5.2. Since we may assume that e is part of the tree we seek, its two end points, v and v', are now connected through e. Let us now merge the two vertices into one vertex $\hat{v}$. For every other vertex u of the graph define an edge connecting it with $\hat{v}$, if u was connected to v or to v'. Let the length of this edge be the least length among the edges which connected u with v or v'. In fact, we may assume that $G(V, E)$ has no parallel edges by eliminating all but that of the least length; and in this case we have at most two edges to consider for each u. Therefore, this operation will require $|V| - 2$ binary (between two) comparisons. Let us call the resulting graph $\hat{G}$. We now make the following observation.

If $\hat{T}$ is a minimum spanning tree of $\hat{G}$, then the corresponding tree T of G (including all the edges of $\hat{T}$ with their restored end points and e) is a minimum spanning tree of G. This suggests our algorithm. We simply keep reducing the number of vertices until only one vertex remains, and then backtrack on our changes to restore the tree. This is demonstrated in the following example.

Example 5.1:   Let $G(V, E)$ with the corresponding edge length be given in Fig. 5.1. It is more convenient to describe the process by means of a matrix of edge lengths. Our graph is described by the following matrix:

	a	b	c	d	e	f
a	—	③	—	3	—	4
b	3	—	7	—	8	9
c	—	7	—	8	2	2
d	3	—	8	—	9	—
e	—	8	2	9	—	8
f	4	9	2	—	8	—

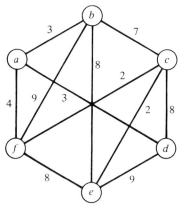

Figure 5.1

Let us, arbitrarily, start with vertex *a*. The least number appearing twice in *a*'s row is 3. Let us choose the edge (*a*, *b*). We now merge *a* and *b* into *b'*. The resulting graph is given by the following matrix:

	b'	*c*	*d*	*e*	*f*
b'	—	7	③	8	4
c	7	—	8	2	2
d	3	8	—	9	—
e	8	2	9	—	8
f	4	2	—	8	—

The least number in the first row is again 3. Thus, we merge *b'* with *d* into *d'*. The resulting matrix is

	d'	*c*	*e*	*f*
d'	—	7	8	④
c	7	—	2	2
e	8	2	—	8
f	4	2	8	—

Now we merge *d'* with *f* to form *f'*:

	f'	*c*	*e*
f'	—	②	8
c	2	—	2
e	8	2	—

Next we merge f' with c into c':

$$
\begin{array}{c|cc}
 & c' & e \\
\hline
c' & - & ② \\
e & 2 & -
\end{array}
$$

Finally, the edge (c', e) is selected. Now, going back to the previous graph we realize that (c', e) corresponds to (c, e). Here (f', c) was selected, and in the previous graph it corresponds to (f, c). Here (d', f) was selected and in the previous graph it corresponds to (b', f) and the edge selected there was (b', d). In the original matrix, (b', f) corresponds to (a, f) and (b', d) corresponds to (a, d); also, the first edge to be selected was (a, b). Thus, the resulting minimum spanning tree consists of the edges: $(c, e), (f, c), (a, f), (a, d), (a, b)$. This is shown in Fig. 5.2. Clearly, the total length of this tree is 14. In this case, as can be easily observed, the solution is unique, although not all edge lengths are distinct.

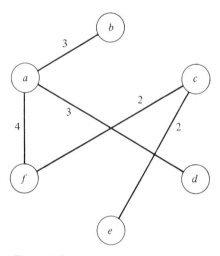

Figure 5.2

Berge and Gouila-Houri [4] describe an algorithm, which they attribute to Sollin, in which the algorithm is sped up somewhat by employing parallel computation. The algorithm works only for graphs in which all edge lengths are distinct. Instead of choosing one edge and merging, we search in each row for the minimum value and merge all the implied mergers simultaneously; the parallelism is used in the minimum searching. All the edges selected in each of these steps are compulsory (see the comments following the proof of Lemma 5.2). Thus, the minimum tree is unique. However, it is not true that the tree will always result after one iteration, for some edges may be selected in two rows.

The corresponding problem for directed graphs, namely, that of finding a minimum length strongly connected subgraph (which includes all the vertices), seems to be much harder. In fact, the author knows of no reasonable algorithm, even in the case that all edge lengths are 1.

5.3 The number of spanning trees

Our purpose in this section is to develop Kirchhoff's formula for the number of spanning trees of a given undirected graph. Prüfer's proof [5] of Cayley's formula [6] for the number of spanning trees of a completely connected graph is described too.

First, we need to develop a few preparatory results. Let $G(V, E)$ be a directed graph without self-loops, where $V = \{v_1, v_2, \ldots, v_n\}$ and $E = \{e_1, e_2, \ldots, e_m\}$. The *incidence matrix*, A, of G is an $n \times m$ matrix defined in the following way:

$$
A_{ij} = \begin{cases} +1 & \text{if } v_i \text{ is the start vertex of } e_j, \\ -1 & \text{if } v_i \text{ is the finish vertex of } e_j, \\ 0 & \text{if } v_i \text{ is not an end point of } e_j. \end{cases}
$$

A *minor*

$$
A\begin{pmatrix} i_1 i_2 \cdots i_p \\ j_1 j_2 \cdots j_p \end{pmatrix}
$$

is the determinant of the submatrix resulting from the matrix A by erasing all but the rows $i_1, i_2, \ldots, i_p$ and the columns $j_1, j_2, \ldots, j_p$.

Lemma 5.3: The minors of an incidence matrix A are all $+1$, -1, or 0.

Proof: Each of the columns of A contains one $+1$, one -1, and all the other entries are 0. If the submatrix in question contains a column of zeros, its determinant is 0. If the submatrix contains a column with a single nonzero entry (either $+1$ or -1), we can develop the determinant on this column, and our claim follows by induction on the size of the submatrix. If every column of the submatrix contains both $+1$ and -1, then the summation of all its rows yields a zero vector. Thus, the submatrix is singular, and its determinant is 0.

QED

Lemma 5.4:   A minor

$$A\begin{pmatrix} i_1 & i_2 \cdots i_{n-1} \\ j_1 & j_2 \cdots j_{n-1} \end{pmatrix}$$

is nonzero ($+1$ or -1) if and only if the underlying undirected graph $\tilde{G}$ of the edge subgraph defined by $E' = \{e_{j_1}, e_{j_2}, \ldots, e_{j_{n-1}}\}$ is a tree.

Proof: First, assume that $\tilde{G}$ is not a tree. Since the number of edges is $n - 1$, by Theorem 5.2, part (b), $\tilde{G}$ must contain circuits. If we take the sum of the columns which correspond to a simple circuit in $\tilde{G}$, with the proper signs, we get a zero vector. Thus, the submatrix is singular, and its determinant is zero. This completes the proof of the "only if" part.

Let us prove the "if" part by induction on n. If $n = 2$, then if $\tilde{G}$ is a tree, it consists of a single edge. Thus, the corresponding submatrix is a 1×1 matrix whose single entry is either $+1$ or -1, and therefore the minor is nonzero. Assume now that the fact that $\tilde{G}$ is a tree implies that the corresponding minor is nonzero for $n = k - 1$, and let G have k vertices. Let $E' = \{e_{j_1}, e_{j_2}, \ldots, e_{j_{k-1}}\}$ yield a graph $\tilde{G}$ which is a tree. Since every tree has at least two terminal vertices (Lemma 5.1), there is at least one terminal vertex among $v_{i_1}, v_{i_2}, \ldots, v_{i_{k-1}}$ in $\tilde{G}$, say v_t. Let us expand the minor by its tth row. Clearly this row consists of a single $+1$, or -1, and $k - 2$ zeros. Thus, its value, except for possibly its sign, is as that of the corresponding cofactor. However, except for possibly its sign, this cofactor is equal to the minor which corresponds to a tree $\tilde{G}'$ resulting from the following changes: Let G' be the graph resulting from G by the elimination of v_t and all the edges adjacent to it. The effect on $\tilde{G}$ is that a terminal edge is eliminated from it to yield a tree $\tilde{G}'$. Thus, by the inductive hypothesis the cofactor is nonzero.

QED

Theorem 5.3: (Binet–Cauchy) Let A be an $n \times m$ matrix and B an $m \times n$ matrix, where $n \leqslant m$. The following identity holds:

$$\det(A \cdot B) = \sum_{1 \leqslant j_1 < j_2 < \cdots < j_n \leqslant m} A\begin{pmatrix} 1 & 2 & \cdots & n \\ j_1 & j_2 & \cdots & j_n \end{pmatrix} \cdot B\begin{pmatrix} j_1 & j_2 & \cdots & j_n \\ 1 & 2 & \cdots & n \end{pmatrix}.$$

Proof: By the rule of matrix multiplication, we have

$$A \cdot B = \begin{bmatrix} \sum_{k=1}^{m} A_{1k} \cdot B_{k1} & \cdots & \sum_{k=1}^{m} A_{1k} \cdot B_{kn} \\ \vdots & & \vdots \\ \sum_{k=1}^{m} A_{nk} \cdot B_{k1} & \cdots & \sum_{k=1}^{m} A_{nk} \cdot B_{kn} \end{bmatrix}.$$

Now we use a property of determinants that they may be decomposed in a way which is expressed below:

$$\begin{vmatrix} d_{11} & \cdots & d_{1k} & \cdots & d_{1n} \\ \vdots & & \vdots & & \vdots \\ d_{n1} & \cdots & d_{nk} & \cdots & d_{nn} \end{vmatrix} = \begin{vmatrix} d_{11} & \cdots & a_{1k} & \cdots & d_{1n} \\ \vdots & & \vdots & & \vdots \\ d_{n1} & \cdots & a_{nk} & \cdots & d_{nn} \end{vmatrix} + \begin{vmatrix} d_{11} & \cdots & b_{1k} & \cdots & d_{1n} \\ \vdots & & \vdots & & \vdots \\ d_{n1} & \cdots & b_{nk} & \cdots & d_{nn} \end{vmatrix}$$

where $a_{ik} + b_{ik} = d_{ik}$ for $i = 1, 2, \ldots, n$. A repeated use of this rule yields

$$\det(A \cdot B) = \sum_{k_1=1}^{m} \sum_{k_2=1}^{m} \cdots \sum_{k_n=1}^{m} \det \begin{bmatrix} A_{1k_1} \cdot B_{k_1 1} & \cdots & A_{1k_n} \cdot B_{k_n n} \\ \vdots & & \vdots \\ A_{nk_1} \cdot B_{k_1 1} & \cdots & A_{nk_n} \cdot B_{k_n n} \end{bmatrix}.$$

Now, since a factor of all terms of a column of a determinant can be factored out, we get

$$\det(A \cdot B) = \sum_{k_1=1}^{m} \sum_{k_2=1}^{m} \cdots \sum_{k_n=1}^{m} A\begin{pmatrix} 1 & 2 & \cdots & n \\ k_1 & k_2 & \cdots & k_n \end{pmatrix} \cdot B_{k_1 1} \cdot B_{k_2 2} \cdots B_{k_n n}.$$

If any two k's are equal,

$$A\begin{pmatrix} 1 & 2 & \cdots & n \\ k_1 & k_2 & \cdots & k_n \end{pmatrix}$$

is zero, since it is a determinant of a matrix with a repeated column. Thus, the only terms, out of the m^n terms in our summation, which are of interest are those in which the k's are distinct. Furthermore,

$$A\begin{pmatrix} 1 & 2 & \cdots & n \\ k_1 & k_2 & \cdots & k_n \end{pmatrix} = (-1)^{\alpha(P)}A\begin{pmatrix} 1 & 2 & \cdots & n \\ j_1 & j_2 & \cdots & j_n \end{pmatrix},$$

where $1 \leqslant j_1 < j_2 < \cdots < j_n \leqslant m$, P is a permutation such that $P(j_i) = k_i$, and $\alpha(P)$ is its parity. Thus, we have

$$\det(A{\cdot}B) = \sum_{1 \leqslant j_1 < j_2 < \cdots < j_n \leqslant m} A\begin{pmatrix} 1 & 2 & \cdots & n \\ j_1 & j_2 & \cdots & j_n \end{pmatrix}{\cdot}\sum_P (-1)^{\alpha(P)}B_{k_1 1}B_{k_2 2} \cdots B_{k_n n}$$

and, by the determinant's definition,

$$B\begin{pmatrix} j_1 & j_2 & \cdots & j_n \\ 1 & 2 & \cdots & n \end{pmatrix} = \sum_P (-1)^{\alpha(P)}B_{k_1 1}{\cdot}B_{k_2 2} \cdots B_{k_n n}.$$

QED

Theorem 5.4: (Kirchhoff) Let M be an $(n - 1) \times m$ matrix resulting from the incidence matrix of the directed graph G by eliminating any one row. The $\det(M{\cdot}M')$ is equal to the number of spanning trees of the undirected underlying graph of G. (Here M' is the transpose of M.)

Proof: By the Binet–Cauchy formula (Theorem 5.3) we have

$$\det(M{\cdot}M') = \sum_{1 \leqslant j_1 < j_2 < \cdots < j_{n-1} \leqslant m} M\begin{pmatrix} 1 & 2 & \cdots & (n-1) \\ j_1 & j_2 & \cdots & j_{n-1} \end{pmatrix}$$
$${\cdot}M'\begin{pmatrix} j_1 & j_2 & \cdots & j_{n-1} \\ 1 & 2 & \cdots & (n-1) \end{pmatrix}.$$

Since

$$M\begin{pmatrix} 1 & 2 & \cdots & (n-1) \\ j_1 & j_2 & \cdots & j_{n-1} \end{pmatrix} = M'\begin{pmatrix} j_1 & j_2 & \cdots & j_{n-1} \\ 1 & 2 & \cdots & (n-1) \end{pmatrix},$$

$$\det(M \cdot M') = \sum_{1 \leqslant j_1 < j_2 < \cdots < j_{n-1} \leqslant m} \left[M\begin{pmatrix} 1 & 2 & \cdots & (n-1) \\ j_1 & j_2 & \cdots & j_{n-1} \end{pmatrix} \right]^2.$$

However, by Lemma 5.4 the underlying undirected graph of the edge sub-graph defined by $E' = e_{j_1}, e_{j_2}, \ldots, e_{j_{n-1}}$ is a spanning tree if and only if

$$\left[M\begin{pmatrix} 1 & 2 & \cdots & (n-1) \\ j_1 & j_2 & \cdots & j_{n-1} \end{pmatrix} \right]^2 = 1.$$

The summation is over all possible selections of E', and each E' appears exactly once. Those selections which do not correspond to a tree contribute 0, and those which correspond to a tree contribute 1.

QED

Fortunately, there is no need to go through the route of assigning directions to the edges (in an arbitrary way), writing M and multiplying it by M'. One can produce $M \cdot M'$ directly from the undirected graph $G(V, E)$, where $V = \{v_1, v_2, \ldots, v_n\}$. Assume that the row of A which is eliminated to produce M is the nth, namely, that which corresponds to v_n. The entry $(M \cdot M')_{ii}$ is the degree of v_i. The entry $(M \cdot M')_{ij}$, for $i \neq j$, is minus the number of edges which join v_i with v_j.

Example 5.2: Let G be given by Fig. 5.3:

$$M \cdot M' = \begin{bmatrix} 4 & -2 & -1 \\ -2 & 2 & 0 \\ -1 & 0 & 2 \end{bmatrix}$$

and

$$\det(M \cdot M') = 6.$$

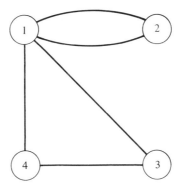

Figure 5.3

A special case which received a lot of attention from mathematicians is the number of spanning trees of a completely connected undirected graph with n vertices (one edge between every two vertices). For a detailed story on this problem, see reference 7.

Theorem 5.5: (Cayley) The number of spanning trees of an undirected completely connected graph with n vertices is n^{n-2}.

Proof 1: The matrix $M \cdot M'$ in this case has the following form:

$$\begin{bmatrix} n-1 & -1 & \cdots & -1 \\ -1 & n-1 & & -1 \\ \vdots & & & \vdots \\ -1 & -1 & \cdots & n-1 \end{bmatrix}.$$

Let us describe linear changes on the rows and columns of the matrix which do not change its determinant. First subtract the first column from every other column:

$$\begin{bmatrix} n-1 & -n & -n & \cdots & -n \\ -1 & n & 0 & & 0 \\ -1 & 0 & n & & 0 \\ \vdots & \vdots & \vdots & & \vdots \\ -1 & 0 & 0 & & n \end{bmatrix}.$$

Now add every one of the other rows to the first:

$$\begin{bmatrix} 1 & 0 & 0 & \cdots & 0 \\ -1 & n & 0 & & 0 \\ -1 & 0 & n & & 0 \\ \vdots & \vdots & \vdots & & \vdots \\ -1 & 0 & 0 & & n \end{bmatrix}$$

Clearly, the determinant of this matrix is n^{n-2}.

Proof 2: (By Prüfer) This is a very elegant and direct proof of Cayley's theorem. (Unfortunately, it does not generalize to handle arbitrary graphs.)

For brevity, let us assume the vertices are $1, 2, \ldots, n$. We shall set a one-to-one correspondence between the spanning trees to be counted and the n^{n-2} words of length $n-2$ over the alphabet $N = \{1, 2, \ldots, n\}$. The algorithm for finding the word which corresponds to a given tree is as follows:

(1) Set $i = 1$.
(2) Find among all terminal vertices in the current tree the vertex with the least name. Eliminate the implied terminal edge. The ith letter of our word is the other end point of this edge.
(3) If $i = n - 2$, stop. If not, increment i and go to step (2).

For example, assume that $n = 6$ and we are given the tree shown in Fig. 5.4. On the first application of step (2) the least terminal vertex is 2, and the other end point of this terminal edge is 4 (our first letter). The reduced tree

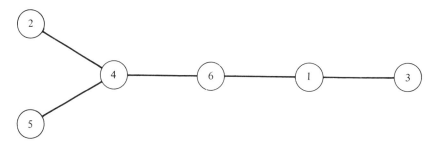

Figure 5.4

is shown in Fig. 5.5. On the second application of step (2), 3 is eliminated and 1 is the second letter. Next, 1 is eliminated and 6 is the third letter.

Figure 5.5

Finally, 5 is eliminated and 4 is our fourth letter. The resulting word is 4   1   6   4 (and upon termination the remaining tree consists of the edge connecting 4 and 6).

Clearly, each spanning tree produces through this algorithm a word of length $n - 2$ over the alphabet N. It is not difficult to prove that this mapping is one-to-one in a direct way, but instead we shall demonstrate that this mapping has a one-valued inverse which is defined for every word of length $n - 2$, thus completing our proof.

Take any word $w = a_1 a_2 \cdots a_{n-2}$ over N. Let us compute the degree $d(i)$ of vertex i in the tree which will correspond to w as follows: $d(i)$ is equal to the number of times the letter i appears in w, plus one. Thus,

$$\sum_{i=1}^{n} d(i) = 2n - 2.$$

(Clearly, this is a necessary condition which the degrees in a spanning tree must satisfy.) For example, if $w = 4164$, then $d(1) = 2$, $d(2) = 1$, $d(3) = 1$, $d(4) = 3$, $d(5) = 1$, $d(6) = 2$. Now, apply the following algorithm:

(1) Set $i = 1$.
(2) Among all vertices whose present degree is 1, find the one, v_i, with the least name. Draw an edge connecting v_i to vertex a_i. Eliminate the vertex v_i from the list and reduce $d(a_i)$ by one.
(3) If $i < n - 2$, increment i and go to step (2). If $i = n - 2$, draw an edge between the two remaining vertices (of degree 1) and stop.

Let us demonstrate the algorithm for $w = 4164$. On the first application of step (2) we join 2 with 4 and get Fig. 5.6. Vertex 2 is eliminated from the

Figure 5.6

list, and $d(4) = 2$. Next, vertex 3 is joined to 1, 3 is eliminated, and $d(1) = 1$ (Fig. 5.7). We now have $d(1) = 1$, $d(4) = 2$, $d(5) = 1$, $d(6) = 2$. Next we join 1 with 6, eliminate 1, and $d(6) = 1$ (Fig. 5.8). Next we join 5 with 4, eliminate

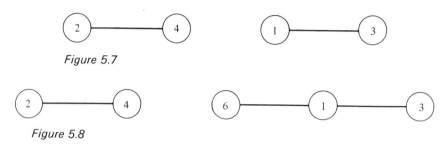

Figure 5.7

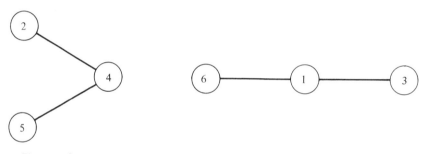

Figure 5.8

5, and remain with $d(4) = 1$ and $d(6) = 1$. The present graph is shown in Fig. 5.9. On the next application of step (3) we have $i = n - 2$; thus, we join 4 and 6 and stop. The resulting graph is the tree of Fig. 5.4.

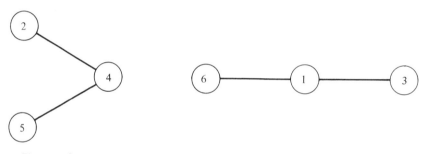

Figure 5.9

It is clear that this algorithm produces a graph for every word w. The claim that the resulting graph is a tree is easily proved by induction on n. Also, it is clear, from the construction that the resulting tree is the only one which will produce w upon the application of the previous algorithm.

QED

A similar problem, stated and solved by Lempel and Welch [8], is that of finding in how many ways m labeled (distinct) edges can be joined in their unlabeled end points to form a tree. Their proof is along the lines of Prüfer's proof of Cayley's theorem and is therefore constructive. However, a much simpler proof of the result was pointed out to me by A. Pnueli and is the subject of Exercise 5.5.

5.4   Remarks on other results

Many other problems about trees are known and we shall mention two of them here. One subject, which is popular among circuit theorists, is that of generating all the spanning trees of a given graph. Numerous papers have been written on the subject, including algorithms and other related investigations. The interested reader is advised to search for these in the *Transactions of Circuit Theory of the IEEE.*

The number of different unlabeled trees (unisomorphic trees) has been studied by a number of mathematicians. For a detailed account on the results in this area, see reference 2.

EXERCISES

5.1 Show that the number of comparisons in the algorithm of Section 5.2 is at most $(n - 1)(n - 2)$, where n is the number of vertices, and when $G(V, E)$ has no parallel edges.

5.2 Let $G(V, E)$ and $l(e)$ be as in Section 5.2. Assume that we want to find a spanning tree of $G(V, E)$ of maximum length. Show that the algorithm of Section 5.2 can be easily modified to solve this problem.

5.3 Show that if $d(v_1), d(v_2), \ldots, d(v_n)$ are positive integers which satisfy the condition

$$\sum_{i=1}^{n} d(v_i) = 2n - 2,$$

then there exists a tree with $v_1, v_2, \ldots, v_n$ as vertices and the d's specify the vertices' degree in the tree. How many such different trees are there if edges are unlabeled?

5.4 Compute the number of trees that can be built on n given labeled vertices, with unlabeled edges in such a way that one specified vertex will be of degree k.

5.5 What is the number of trees that one can build with n labeled vertices and $m = n - 1$ labeled edges? Prove that the number of trees that can be built with m labeled edges (and no labels on the vertices) is $(m + 1)^{m-2}$.

5.6 Let $T_1(V, E_1)$ and $T_2(V, E_2)$ be two spanning trees of $G(V, E)$. Prove that for every $\alpha \in E_1 \cap \bar{E}_2$ there exists a $\beta \in E_2 \cap \bar{E}_1$ such that each of the sets

$$(E_1 - \{\alpha\}) \cup \{\beta\},$$

$$(E_2 - \{\beta\}) \cup \{\alpha\}$$

defines a spanning tree.

REFERENCES

1. Ore, O., *Theory of Graphs*, American Mathematical Society, Providence, R.I., 1962.
2. Harary, F., *Graph Theory*, Addison-Wesley, Reading, Mass., 1969.
3. Prim, R. C., "Shortest Connection Networks and Some Generalizations," *Bell System Tech. J.*, Vol. 36, 1957, pp. 1389–1401.
4. Berge, C., and Ghouila-Houri, A., *Programming Games and Transportation Networks*, Wiley, New York, 1965.
5. Prüfer, H., "Neuer Beweis eines Satzes über Permutationen," *Arch. Math. Phys.*, Vol. 27, 1918, pp. 742–44.
6. Cayley, A., "A Theorem on Trees," *Quart. J. Math.*, Vol. 23, 1889, pp. 376–78; *Collected Papers*, Vol. 13, Cambridge, 1897, pp. 26–8.
7. Moon, J. W., "Various Proofs of Cayley's Formula for Counting Tress," in *A Seminar on Graph Theory*, F. Harary (ed.), Holt, Rinehart and Winston, New York, 1967, pp. 70–8.
8. Lempel, A., and Welch, L. R., "Enumeration of Arc-Labelled Trees," Department of Electrical Engineering, University of Southern California, Los Angeles, 1969.

6

DIRECTED TREES

6.1 Directed tree definitions

In this chapter all graphs are directed unless otherwise specified. A vertex v' is said to be *reachable* from vertex v if there exists a directed path from v to v'. A graph is called *arbitrated* (Berge [1] calls it quasi strongly connected) if for every two vertices v_1 and v_2 there exists a vertex v such that both v_1 and v_2 are reachable from v. A vertex v is called a *root* (center by Berge [1]) of the graph if every vertex of the graph is reachable from v.

Lemma 6.1: A finite directed graph has a root if and only if it is arbitrated.

Proof: The "only if" part is trivial. The proof of the "if" part is by finding a common arbiter for a set of vertices. First choose any subset of two vertices $S_2 = \{v_1, v_2\}$. Since the graph is arbitrated, there exists a vertex a_2 (arbiter for these two vertices) such that both v_1 and v_2 are reachable from a_2. Assume that we already have a common arbiter a_k for $S_k = \{v_1, v_2, \ldots, v_k\}$; that is, each of the vertices in S_k is reachable from a_k. A common arbiter for $S_{k+1} = \{v_1, v_2, \ldots, v_k, v_{k+1}\}$ is easily found by taking an arbiter of a_k and v_{k+1}. Thus, a_n, where n is the number of vertices of the graph, is a root.

QED

A directed graph $G(V, E)$ is called a *directed tree* if it has a root and its underlying undirected graph is a tree.

Theorem 6.1: Assume that $G(V, E)$ is a directed finite or infinite graph. The following five conditions are equivalent:

(a) G is a directed tree.
(b) G has a root with a unique directed path to each vertex.
(c) G has a root r for which $d_i(r) = 0$ and for every other vertex v, $d_i(v) = 1$.
(d) G has a root and the deletion of any edge (but no vertices) interrupts this condition.
(e) The underlying undirected graph of G is connected and G has one vertex r for which $d_i(r) = 0$, while for every other vertex v, $d_i(v) = 1$.

Proof: We shall prove that (a) $\Rightarrow$ (b) $\Rightarrow$ (c) $\Rightarrow$ (d) $\Rightarrow$ (e) $\Rightarrow$ (a).

(a) $\Rightarrow$ (b): We assume that G has a root, say r, and its underlying undirected graph is a tree. Thus, by Theorem 5.1, condition (c), in the underlying undirected graph there is a unique path between every pair of vertices. Thus, the directed path from r to each vertex in G is unique.

(b) $\Rightarrow$ (c): Here we assume that G has a root, say r, and a unique directed path to every vertex v. First, we want to show that $d_i(r) = 0$. Assume that there is an edge $v \xrightarrow{e} r$ (a directed edge, e, from a vertex v to vertex r). There exists a directed path from r to v. Returning now to r through e, we can arrive again at v, thus having more than one path from r to v.

Next we have to show that if $r \neq v$, then $d_i(v) = 1$. To begin with, $d_i(v) > 0$, for it must be reachable from r. (This shows that the root is unique.) If $d_i(v) > 1$, then there are at least two distinct edges, say

$$v_1 \xrightarrow{e_1} v \quad \text{and} \quad v_2 \xrightarrow{e_2} v,$$

entering v. Since there is a path from r to v_1, and a path from r to v_2, we get two different paths from r to v by adding to the first e_1 and e_2 to the second. (This proof works even if $v_1 = v_2$.)

(c) $\Rightarrow$ (d): This proof is trivial, for the deletion of any edge will make the vertex it enters unreachable from the root r.

(d) $\Rightarrow$ (e): We assume that G has a root, and that the deletion of any edge interrupts this condition. First, let us show that G has a unique root. Assume that both r_1 and r_2 are roots. The deletion of all edges entering r_1 (and there is at least one, for it is reachable from r_2) does not interrupt the fact that r_1 is a root. This contradicts our assumption. Thus, G has a unique root r for which $d_i(r) = 0$. Also it immediately follows that the underlying undirected graph of G is connected. Now assume that for some $v \neq r$, $d_i(v) > 1$. As before, let

$$v_1 \overset{e_1}{\to} v \qquad \text{and} \qquad v_2 \overset{e_2}{\to} v$$

be two distinct edges. Take any simple directed path, P, from r to v. If one of these two edges is not on P, then it can be deleted without disturbing r's position as a root. If both e_1 and e_2 are on P, then it is not a simple directed path.

(e) $\Rightarrow$ (a): We assume that the underlying undirected graph of G is connected. Thus, there is a simple path from r to every other vertex v. If this path is not directed, in G, from r to v, then the first edge with the wrong direction implies either $d_i(r) > 0$, if it enters r, or $d_i(v) > 1$ if it enters $v \neq r$. Thus, r is a root of G. If the underlying undirected graph is not a tree, it must contain a circuit. This circuit in G must contain at least one vertex of incoming degree greater than 1.

QED

As in the case of undirected trees, the assumption that the number of vertices, n, is finite allows a few more useful alternative definitions of a directed tree. First, the statement "G has a root" can be replaced by the seemingly weaker statement "G is arbitrated" (see Lemma 6.1). More interesting is the following:

Theorem 6.2: A finite graph $G(V, E)$ is a directed tree if and only if its underlying undirected graph is circuit-free, one of the vertices of G, r, satisfies $d_i(r) = 0$, and for all other vertices v, $d_i(v) = 1$.

Proof: The "only if" part of the theorem follows directly from the definition of a directed tree and from Theorem 6.1, condition (c).

To prove the "if" part we first observe that the number of edges is $n - 1$. Thus, by Theorem 5.2, the underlying undirected graph is a tree. Now, by Theorem 6.1, condition (e), G is a directed tree.

QED

6.2   The infinity lemma

The following theorem is known as König's infinity lemma [2].

Theorem 6.3:   If G is an infinite directed tree with root r and with finite (outgoing) degrees, then there exists an infinite directed path in G.

Before we present the proof of the theorem, we want to point out the necessity of the finiteness of the degree of vertices. For if we allow a single vertex to be of infinite (outgoing) degree, the conclusion does not follow. Consider the directed tree of Fig. 6.1. The root r is of infinite degree. It is

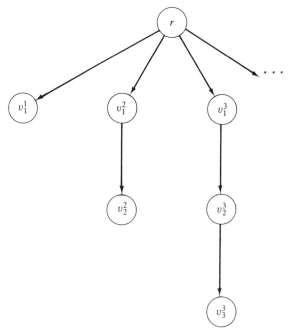

Figure 6.1

connected to vertices $v_1^1, v_1^2, v_1^3, \ldots$, where v_1^k is a beginning of a directed path containing k vertices. It is clear that the tree is infinite, and yet it has no infinite path. Furthermore, the replacement of the condition of finite degrees by the condition that for every k the tree has a path of length k, does not work either, as the same example shows.

Proof: The root r has infinitely many descendants (vertices reachable from r). Since r is of finite outgoing degree, at least one of its sons (the vertices reachable through a single edge) must have infinitely many descendants, too. Let one of these be r_1. One of r_1's sons has infinitely many descendants, too, and so we continue to construct an infinite directed path $r, r_1, r_2, \ldots$.

QED

In spite of the simplicity of the theorem, it is useful. (A slightly more general form of the infinity lemma is given in Exercise 6.2.) For example, if we conduct a search on a directed tree of finite degrees (where a bound on the degree may not be known) for which it is known that it has no infinite directed paths, then the theorem ensures us that the tree is finite and our search will terminate.

An interesting application of Theorem 6.3 was made by Wang [3]. Consider the problem of tiling the plane with square tiles, all of the same size (Wang calls the tiles "dominoes"). There is a finite number of tile families. The sides of the tiles are labeled by letters of an alphabet, and all the tiles of one family have the same labels, thus are indistinguishable. Tiles may not be rotated or reflected, and the labels are specified for their north side, south side, and so on. There is an infinite supply of tiles of each family. The tiles may be put one next to another, the sides converging only if these two sides have the same labels. For example, if the tile families are as shown in Fig. 6.2, then we can construct the torus shown in Fig. 6.3. Now, by repeating this torus infinitely many times horizontally and vertically, we can tile the whole plane.

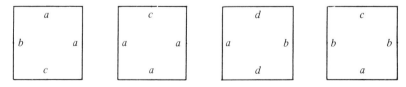

Figure 6.2

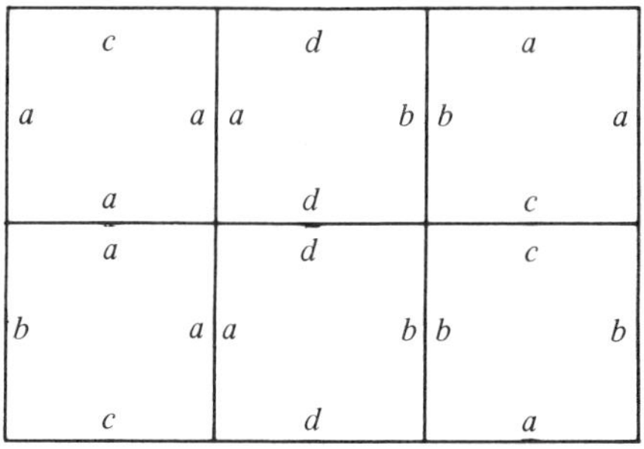

Figure 6.3

Wang proved that if it is possible to tile the upper right quadrant of the plane with a given finite set of tile families, then it is possible to tile the whole plane. The reader should realize that a southwest shift of the upper-right tiled quadrant cannot be used to cover the whole plane. In fact, if the number of tile families is not restricted to be finite, one can find sets of families for which the upper-right quadrant is tileable, while the whole plane is not (see Exercise 6.4). Consider an ordered tree defined in the following way.

The root r is the father (the relation of being connected by an edge to) of vertices representing all tiled 2×2 squares.

Every vertex representing a $2n \times 2n$ tiled square is the father of all $2(n + 1) \times 2(n + 1)$ tiled squares of which it is the center. Thus, the tree has finite degrees. The knowledge that the upper-right quadrant is tileable ensures the infiniteness of the tree. Thus, by Theorem 6.3, there is an infinite directed path in the graph, which specifies how to tile the whole plane.

6.3   The number of directed spanning trees

A subgraph H of a directed finite graph G is called a *directed spanning tree* of G if H is a directed tree which includes all the vertices of G. If r is the root of H, then it is clearly a root of G. Also, if r is a root of G, then a spanning directed tree H of G exists with a root r. This is simply observed by constructing H, edge by edge, by starting from r alone, and adding each time an edge of G from a vertex already reachable from r in H to one which is not reachable yet.

We shall now describe a method of Tutte [4] for computing the number of spanning directed trees of a given directed graph with a given specified root. (For historical details, see reference 5.)

Let us define an (incoming) *degree matrix* D of a directed finite graph G as follows:

$$D_{pq} = \begin{cases} -k & \text{if } p \neq q \text{ and there are } k \text{ parallel edges from } v_p \text{ to } v_q; \\ d_i(v_p) & \text{if } p = q. \end{cases}$$

Lemma 6.2: A directed graph $G(V, E)$, with no self-loops and with $V = \{v_1, v_2, \ldots, v_n\}$ is a directed tree with root v_r if and only if its degree matrix D has the following properties:

1.
$$D_{pp} = \begin{cases} 0 & \text{if } p = r; \\ 1 & \text{if } p \neq r; \end{cases}$$

2. The minor, resulting from erasing the rth row and column from D and computing the determinant, is 1.

Proof: Assume that $G(V, E)$ is a directed tree with root v_r. By Theorem 6.1, part 3, D satisfies property 1. Now, renumber the vertices in such a way that v_1 is the root and if $v_i \rightarrow v_j$, then $i < j$. (This can be achieved by numbering the vertices of distance 1 as $v_2, v_3, \ldots$ Next come the vertices of distance 2, then 3, and so on.) The new degree matrix is derivable from the previous one by performing some permutation on the rows, and the same permutation on the columns. Since such a permutation does not change the determinant, the two minors are the same. The new degree matrix D' satisfies the following properties:

$$D'_{11} = 0;$$

$$D'_{pp} = 1 \quad \text{for } p = 2, 3, \ldots, n;$$

$$D'_{pq} = 0 \quad \text{if } p > q.$$

Thus, the minor, resulting from the erasure of the first row and the first column from D and computing the determinant, is 1.

Now, assume that D satisfies properties 1 and 2. By property 1 and Theorem 6.2, if G is not a directed tree, then its underlying undirected graph contains a circuit. The vertex v_r cannot be one of the vertices of the circuit, for this would imply that $d_i(v_r) > 0$, or that for some other vertex $v, d_i(v) > 1$, contradicting property 1. The circuit must be of the form

$$v_{i_1} \rightarrow v_{i_2} \rightarrow v_{i_3} \cdots \rightarrow v_{i_l} \rightarrow v_{i_1},$$

where l is the length of the circuit, and no vertex appears on it twice; there may be other edges leaving $v_{i_1}, v_{i_2}, \ldots, v_{i_l}$, but none can enter. Thus, if we take the corresponding columns in D, in each row, either all entries are 0 or there is one $+1$ and -1. The sum of these columns is therefore a zero column, and thus the minor is 0. This contradicts property 2.

QED

As a side result of our proof, we have the additional property that the minor for a graph whose degree matrix satisfies property 1 is 0 if the graph is not a directed tree with root v_r.

Theorem 6.4: The number of directed spanning trees with root v_r that a directed graph with no self-loops has is given by the minor of its degree matrix which results from the erasure of the rth row and the rth column.

The proof of this theorem follows immediately from Lemma 6.2, the comment following it, and the linearity of the determinant function with respect to its columns. Let us demonstrate this in the following example. Consider the graph shown in Fig. 6.4. Its degree matrix D is as follows:

$$D = \begin{bmatrix} 2 & -1 & -1 \\ -1 & 1 & -2 \\ -1 & 0 & 3 \end{bmatrix}.$$

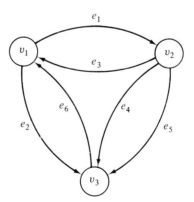

Figure 6.4

Assume that we want to compute the number of directed spanning t trees with root v_2. We erase the second row and column. The resulting determinant is

$$\begin{vmatrix} 2 & -1 \\ -1 & 3 \end{vmatrix} = 5.$$

Now let us decompose this determinant into columns which represent one edge in every column. First, the 2×2 determinant can be written as

$$\begin{vmatrix} 2 & 0 & -1 \\ -1 & 1 & -2 \\ -1 & 0 & 3 \end{vmatrix}.$$

We have returned the second row of D except its second entry, which must be made equal to 1 (in this case its value did not change). All other entries in the second column are changed into zero. Next, we decompose each column, except the second, into columns which consist of a single $+1$ and a single -1, as follows:

$$\begin{vmatrix} 2 & 0 & -1 \\ -1 & 1 & -2 \\ -1 & 0 & 3 \end{vmatrix} = \begin{vmatrix} 1 & 0 & -1 \\ -1 & 1 & -2 \\ 0 & 0 & 3 \end{vmatrix} + \begin{vmatrix} 1 & 0 & -1 \\ 0 & 1 & -2 \\ -1 & 0 & 3 \end{vmatrix}$$

$$= \begin{vmatrix} 1 & 0 & -1 \\ -1 & 1 & 0 \\ 0 & 0 & 1 \end{vmatrix} + \begin{vmatrix} 1 & 0 & 0 \\ -1 & 1 & -1 \\ 0 & 0 & 1 \end{vmatrix} + \begin{vmatrix} 1 & 0 & 0 \\ -1 & 1 & -1 \\ 0 & 0 & 1 \end{vmatrix}$$

$$+ \begin{vmatrix} 1 & 0 & -1 \\ 0 & 1 & 0 \\ -1 & 0 & 1 \end{vmatrix} + \begin{vmatrix} 1 & 0 & 0 \\ 0 & 1 & -1 \\ -1 & 0 & 1 \end{vmatrix} + \begin{vmatrix} 1 & 0 & 0 \\ 0 & 1 & -1 \\ -1 & 0 & 1 \end{vmatrix}.$$

These six determinants correspond to the following selections of sets of edges, respectively: $\{e_3, e_2\}$, $\{e_3, e_4\}$, $\{e_3, e_5\}$, $\{e_6, e_2\}$, $\{e_6, e_4\}$, $\{e_6, e_5\}$.

After erasing the second row and column, this corresponds to

$$\begin{vmatrix} 2 & -1 \\ -1 & 3 \end{vmatrix} = \begin{vmatrix} 1 & -1 \\ 0 & 1 \end{vmatrix} + \begin{vmatrix} 1 & 0 \\ 0 & 1 \end{vmatrix} + \begin{vmatrix} 1 & 0 \\ 0 & 1 \end{vmatrix}$$

$$+ \begin{vmatrix} 1 & -1 \\ -1 & 1 \end{vmatrix} + \begin{vmatrix} 1 & 0 \\ -1 & 1 \end{vmatrix} + \begin{vmatrix} 1 & 0 \\ -1 & 1 \end{vmatrix}.$$

Each of these six determinants corresponds to a selection of $n - 1$ edges of the original graph. By Lemma 6.2, the resulting edge subgraph is a directed tree with root v_2 if and only if the corresponding determinant is equal to one. Otherwise, it is zero. Thus, we get the number of directed trees with v_2 as a root. Clearly, in our case, the only set which does not yield a directed tree is $\{e_6, e_2\}$ and indeed

$$\begin{vmatrix} 1 & -1 \\ -1 & 1 \end{vmatrix} = 0.$$

6.4   Directed trees and Euler circuits

Let $G(V, E)$ be a directed Euler graph which satisfies $d_0(v) = d_i(v)$. Thus, by Theorem 4.2, every Euler path of G is a directed Euler circuit. Assume that

$$C = v_{i_1} \xrightarrow{e_1} v_{i_2} \xrightarrow{e_2} v_{i_3} \xrightarrow{e_3} \cdots \rightarrow v_{i_m} \xrightarrow{e_m} v_{i_1}$$

is one such circuit. Thus, if $i \neq j$, then $e_i \neq e_j$, and $m = |E|$; but vertices may repeat. Consider now a subgraph $H_C(V, E')$ defined in the following way: Let e_{j_1} be any one of the edges entering v_1; denote for every $p = 2, 3, \ldots, n$ by e_{j_p} the first edge on C to enter v_p after the appearance of e_{j_1}. Now $E' = \{e_{j_2}, e_{j_3}, \ldots, e_{j_n}\}$. For example, consider the graph of Fig. 6.5.

The sequence of edges $e_1, e_2, \ldots, e_6$ designates a Euler circuit C. If we choose $e_{j_1} = e_6$ (the only choice in this case), then $e_{j_2} = e_1$. $e_{j_3} = e_2$ and $e_{j_4} = e_4$. The resulting subgraph $H_C(V, E')$ is shown in Fig. 6.6, and is easily observed to be a directed spanning tree of G. The following lemma states this fact in general.

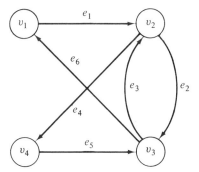

Figure 6.5

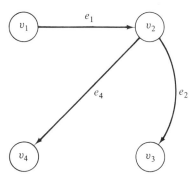

Figure 6.6

Lemma 6.3: Let C be a directed Euler circuit of a directed finite graph $G(V, E)$. The subgraph $H_C(V, E')$, constructed as described above, is a directed spanning tree of G, with root v_1.

Proof: First, it is clear from the definition of H that in H, $d_i(v_1) = 0$, while $d_i(v_p) = 1$ for $p = 2, 3, \ldots, n$. In order to be able to use Theorem 6.1, condition (c), it remains to be shown that v_1 is a root of H.

Let v_p be any vertex. In attempting to find a directed path from v_1 to v_p, we start backtracking from v_p on the unique incoming edges. If we run into v_1, then we have traced a path from v_1 to v_p. If not, sooner or later (due to the finiteness of the vertices) we must close a directed circuit C' in H, which does not include v_1. Since $d_i(v) = 1$ for every vertex on C', no other edges enter the vertices on C' but those of C' itself. However, the edge e which is the first edge of C to enter a vertex of C', after e_{j_1}, is in H and does not belong to C'.   QED

Now assume that we are given a directed spanning tree H of a finite directed Euler graph G with no self-loops and for which $d_i(v) = d_0(v)$ for every vertex v. Assume also that the root of H is v_1 and that e_{j_1} is an edge entering v_1 in G. We shall now describe a method for using this information for tracing back a Euler circuit of G, without having to add detours as in the proof of Theorem 4.1. We start from v_1 and leave it backward on any edge other than e_{j_1}, if such exists, or on e_{j_1} in case of no alternative. In general, upon arrival at v_p we leave it, backward, on an edge entering v_p which was not used before, and, if possible, other than e_{j_p} (the edge entering v_p in H, if $p = 2, 3, \ldots, n$). If no unused entering edges exist, we stop.

By the construction, we never use an edge more than once. Also, the only vertex in which the process can stop is v_1 itself; this is guaranteed by the fact that $d_i(v) = d_0(v)$ for every vertex (similar to the situation in Section 4.4). When the process stops, all the edges emanating from v_1, and among those the edges which belong to H, have been traced back. Thus, all the vertices of distance 1 from v_1 in H have been visited; furthermore, since the edges of H have been used, all other incoming edges to them have been used, too. Thus, all vertices of distance 2 from v_1 in H have been visited; and so on. By induction, all edges of G have been traced.

In the construction of a Euler circuit from H and e_{j_1}, there are places of choice. If $d_i(v_p) > 1$, there are $(d_i(v_p) - 1)!$ different orders for picking the incoming edges (with e_{j_p} in the end). Also, it is clear that different orders will yield a different Euler circuit. Thus, the number of distinct Euler circuits to be constructed from a given H and e_{j_1} is

$$\prod_{p=1}^{n} (d_i(v_p) - 1)!.$$

Furthermore, different choices of H (but with the same root v_1 and the same e_{j_1}) yield different Euler circuits; because a different e_{j_p}, for some $2 \leqslant p \leqslant n$, will yield a different first entry to v_p after e_{j_1} in the resulting Euler circuit.

Finally, Lemma 6.3 guarantees that every Euler circuit will be generated for some H and some choice of backtracking edges, because the construction of Euler circuits from a directed tree is the reversal of the procedure of deriving a directed tree from a circuit.

We have thus proved the following theorem:

Theorem 6.5: The number of Euler circuits of a given finite directed graph

G with no self-loops (and for which $d_i(v) = d_0(v)$ for every vertex) is given by

$$\Delta \cdot \prod_{p=1}^{n} (d_i(v_p) - 1)!$$

where Δ is the number of directed spanning trees of G with root v_1.

Clearly, the choice of the root is arbitrary. This proves that if $d_i(v) = d_0(v)$ for every vertex, then the number of directed spanning trees is the same for every choice of root.

For example, the degree matrix of the graph of Fig. 6.5 is

$$D = \begin{bmatrix} 1 & -1 & 0 & 0 \\ 0 & 2 & -1 & -1 \\ -1 & -1 & 2 & 0 \\ 0 & 0 & -1 & 1 \end{bmatrix}.$$

By Theorem 6.4,

$$\Delta = \begin{vmatrix} 2 & -1 & -1 \\ -1 & 2 & 0 \\ 0 & -1 & 1 \end{vmatrix} = 2,$$

which in this case is also the number of Euler circuits.

6.5   Scanning a graph by depth-first search

In this section we shall discuss a method called DFS (depth-first search) for scanning a given finite connected undirected graph $G(V, E)$. The technique was described and applied by Tarjan [6]. It is a special case of Tarry's algorithm (Algorithm 4.6) and has additional features.

As in Section 4.4, our purpose is to scan the whole graph and return to the original vertex r. Algorithm 4.6 has the property that when the search is terminated the edges which are marked on one end by F constitute a directed spanning tree of G, with r as the root and with these edges (which originally are undirected) now directed toward the end marked F. This

follows from the fact that each vertex has exactly one entrance marked *F*
and *r* has no such mark (Exercise 4.12, and Theorem 6.1, condition (c)).

The DFS algorithm has these properties, too, and an additional very
useful property.

In the process all edges will be directed. If an edge is part of the directed
tree, it is called a *branch*; otherwise, it is called a *frond*. The tail of a branch
will be labeled *D* and that of a frond will be labeled *E*. The head of a branch
will be labeled *F* and that of a frond will be labeled *G*. The algorithm starts
in some vertex *r*, to be the root.

Algorithm 6.1:

(1) $v \leftarrow r$.

(2) If all passages of v are marked, go to step (6).

(3) Choose an unmarked passage, label it *D*, and enter the edge. Go through
    the edge to its other end point. Let u be the vertex you reach.

(4) If u has no marked passages, label the passage you have just used with
    F, $v \leftarrow u$, and go to step (2).

(5) (u is not a new vertex.) Label the passage you have just used with G,
    reenter the passage and return to v. Upon arrival relabel the passage
    with E (instead of the *D*). Go to step (2).

(6) If there is no passage of v which is marked F, stop (we are now at r
    and the search is over).

(7) Enter the passage marked F and go through the edge to its other end
    point, u. $v \leftarrow u$ and go to step (2).

It is easy to see that Algorithm 6.1 is a special case of Algorithm 4.6.
Labels *D*, *E*, and *G* of 6.1 play the role of *E* of Algorithm 4.6. Label *F* plays
the same role in both. The only difference is that we restrict the liberty of
choosing which passage to take when reentering a vertex; instead of allowing
the use of any unused passage, we insist on leaving through the same passage
we have just come through. It is guaranteed that in this case this passage
was never used before for leaving the vertex because whenever an edge is
used, both its end-point passages are labeled. Thus, the algorithm is known
to halt successfully.

Let us number the vertices as follows: $v(1) = r$ and $v(i)$ is the *i*th vertex
to be entered for the first time. Tarjan does not label the passages our way
and he labels the vertices by $v(i)$. Upon entering a vertex, if it is not numbered
yet, he labels it $v(i)$ and i is incremented. This is indeed a more efficient way

to conduct the algorithm. However, in his formulation, fronds are traversed twice in each direction (see Exercise 6.7).

Clearly, the set of edges marked on one end with D and on the other F form a directed spanning tree with r as the root. For every one of these edges, $v(i) \rightarrow v(j)$, we have $i < j$, because $v(i)$ is entered for the first time before $v(j)$ is. Thus, if $v(j)$ is a descendant* of $v(i)$, then $i < j$.

Lemma 6.4:   If $v(i) \rightarrow v(j)$ is a frond, then $v(i)$ is a descendant of $v(j)$.

Proof: There are two ways by which we move to another vertex u $(v \leftarrow u)$; either u is a new vertex or there are no unmarked passages at v and we leave through the passage marked F. If the last time we have left $v(j)$, before the edge $v(i) - v(j)$ is investigated, was through F, then all the edges adjacent to $v(j)$ would have been marked on both sides and the passage into this edge at $v(i)$ would have not been taken. Thus, the last time we have left $v(j)$ must have been through moving into a new vertex. We are now at $v(i)$ and, therefore, $v(i)$ is a descendant of $v(j)$.

QED

Corollary 6.1:   Assume that $v(i) \rightarrow v(j)$ is the direction implied by the DFS algorithm. If $i < j$, then this is a branch; if $i > j$, it is a frond.

EXERCISES

6.1   Prove that if G is a directed finite graph, the following are alternative definitions of a directed tree:
(a) G is arbitrated and its underlying undirected graph is circuit-free.
(b) G is arbitrated and has $n - 1$ edges (where n is its number of vertices).

6.2   Prove the following slightly more general version of König's infinity lemma: If G is an infinite undirected connected graph whose vertices are of finite degree, then every vertex in G is the beginning of a simple infinite path.

6.3   Show that if rotation or reflection of tiles is allowed, the question of tiling the whole place becomes trivial.

6.4   Construct an infinite set of tile families which can be used to tile the upper-right quadrant but is not sufficient for tiling the whole plane.

---

*In a directed tree a vertex u is a descendant of v and v is an ancestor of u if there is a directed path from v to u.

6.5 Let us define an *outgoing degree matrix* D of a directed graph $G(V, E)$ with no self-loops as follows:

$$D_{pq} = \begin{cases} -k & \text{if } p \neq q \text{ and there are } k \text{ parallel edges from } v_p \text{ to } v_q; \\ d_0(v_p) & \text{if } p = q. \end{cases}$$

Also, an *ingoing directed tree* is a directed graph which has a vertex s reachable from every other vertex and its underlying undirected graph is a tree.

Prove that the number of ingoing directed spanning trees of a given graph G can be computed in a way analogous to Theorem 6.4. Compute this number for the graph of Fig. 6.4 with $s = v_3$.

6.6 Show that the result of Theorem 5.4 can be proved as a corollary of Theorem 6.4. (*Hint:* Replace each undirected edge by two directed edges, one in each direction and show a correspondence between trees of the undirected graph and directed trees of the resulting directed graph.)

Our purpose in Exercises 6.7, 6.8, and 6.9 is to develop de Bruijn's formula for the number of de Bruijn sequences for words of length n over an alphabet of G letters (see Section 4.2).

6.7 By subtracting rows of $D_{\sigma,n}$ (the D matrix of $G_{\sigma,n}$) and adding columns show that

$$\Delta_{\sigma,n} = \sigma^{\sigma^{n-1} - \sigma^{n-2} - 1} \cdot \Delta_{\sigma,n-1}.$$

6.8 By Exercise 6.7 show that

$$\Delta_{\sigma,n} = \sigma^{\sigma^{n-1} - n}.$$

6.9 Show that the number of de Bruijn sequences for a given σ and n is

$$\frac{(\sigma!)^{\sigma^{n-1}}}{\sigma^n}.$$

A similar development of de Bruijn's formula can be found in Knuth [7].

6.10 Construct a DFS algorithm using labels $v(i)$ for the vertices instead of the labels C, E, F, and G. In what way is this more efficient than Algorithm 6.1?

REFERENCES

1. Berge, C., and Ghouila-Houri, A., *Programming, Games and Transportation Networks*, Wiley, New York, 1965, Sec. 7.4.

2. König, D., *Theorie der endlichen und unendlichen Graphen*, Leipzig, 1936; reprinted by Chelsea, New York, 1950.
3. Wang, H., "Proving Theorems by Pattern Recognition, II," *Bell Systems Tech. J.*, Vol. 40, pp. 1–41, 1961.
4. Tutte, W. T., "The Dissection of Equilateral Triangles into Equilateral Triangles," *Proc. Cambridge Phil. Soc.*, Vol. 44, pp. 463–82, 1948.
5. Harary, F., *Graph-Theory*, Addison-Wesley, Reading, Mass., 1969, Chap. 16.
6. Tarjan, R., "Depth-First Search and Linear Graph Algorithms," Computer Science Department, Stanford University, Stanford, California.
7. Knuth, D. E., "Oriented Subtrees of an Arc Digraph," *J. Combinatorial Theory*, Vol. 3, pp. 309–14, 1967.

7

ORDERED TREES

7.1 Introduction

An *ordered tree* is a directed tree with an order defined for the sons, $\Gamma(v)$, of every vertex v. It is usually drawn in the plane with the root at the top, all edges are pointed downward, and the sons are lined up on a horizontal line in their assigned order from left to right. For example, see the ordered directed tree of Fig. 7.1. If the tree satisfies the conditions $d_0(v) \leqslant m$ for every v, then the tree is said to be *m*-ary. If for every vertex v either $d_0(v) = m$ or $d_0(v) = 0$, then we say that the tree is a *full m-ary tree*. The graph in Fig. 7.1 is a ternary ordered tree but is not full. The graph in Fig. 7.2 is a full binary ordered tree. The concept of ordered trees is useful both in the theory of coding (see, for example, reference 1) and in the theory of programming (see, for example, reference 2). In fact, in most applications there is one more condition. Each vertex has m "potential" sons; but in reality any subset of

127

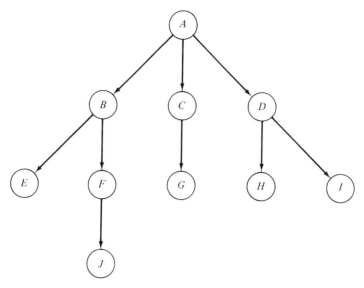

Figure 7.1

its potential sons may exist. For example, for $m = 2$, each vertex may have
a left son, or a right son, or both, or neither. The four trees shown in Fig. 7.3
are therefore distinct. When this condition is made, the tree is called *positional*. Clearly, a full directed tree can always be assumed to be positional.

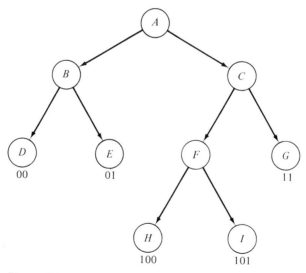

Figure 7.2

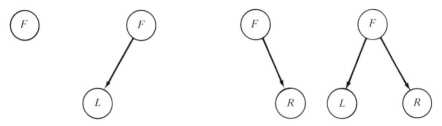

Figure 7.3

The vertices of a positional m-ary directed tree have a natural correspondence to words over an alphabet with m letters, say $\{M = 0, 1, \ldots, m - 1\}$. For example, vertex H of Fig. 7.2 corresponds to the word 100, because we take first the right son (1), then the left (0), and finally the left (0). Thus, for every vertex of the tree there exists a unique word over M. This is true whether the vertex is terminal (like H) or not (like F, which corresponds to 10). However, there may be words over M which do not correspond to vertices of the tree. Let $l(v)$ (the *level* of vertex v) be the length of the path from the root to v; it is equal to the number of letters in the word which corresponds to v.

The set of words which correspond to the terminal vertices of a positional m-ary ordered tree forms a *prefix* (sometimes called instantaneous [1]) code; that is, no word in the code is the beginning of another. Thus, if a sequence of letters is formed by concatenation of words of the code, where repetitions are allowed, the sequence can be decomposed by reading the sequence from left to right and marking off a word as soon as a word of the code is recognized. For example, the code which corresponds to the tree of Fig. 7.2 is $\{00, 01, 100, 101, 11\}$. Now, the sequence 000110110100 is easily decomposed, from left to right into 00, 01, 101, 101, 00, .

Let $C = \{w_1, w_2, \ldots, w_L\}$ be a prefix code over M. Let $l(w_i) = l_i$ be the length (number of letters) in w_i. The *characteristic sum* of C is defined as the sum

$$\sum_{i=1}^{L} m^{-l_i}.$$

As is easily observed, the sum actually characterizes the vector of word lengths $(l_1, l_2, \ldots, l_L)$.

Lemma 7.1: The characteristic sum of a vector of word lengths of a prefix code is less than or equal to 1.

Proof: Let us prove it by induction on the longest word length of the code. If the longest word length is 1, the statement follows immediately. Assume that it is true if the longest word length is less than λ, and the longest word length of C is λ. The root r of the corresponding tree has $d_0(r) \leqslant m$ sons; assume they are $v_1, v_2, \ldots, v_{d_0}$. Every v_i is the root of a subtree; let C_i be the resulting code. The words of C_i are all shorter by one than their counterparts in C. Thus, the characteristic sum of C is equal to $(1/m)(S_1 + S_2 + \cdots + S_{d_0(r)})$, where S_i is the characteristic sum of C_i. By the inductive hypothesis $S_i \leqslant 1$, and therefore

$$\frac{1}{m}(S_1 + S_2 + \cdots + S_{d_0(r)}) \leqslant 1.$$

QED

Lemma 7.2: If a vector of word lengths $(l_1, l_2, \ldots, l_L)$ satisfies the characteristic sum condition

$$\sum_{i=1}^{L} m^{-l_i} \leqslant 1, \tag{7.1}$$

then there exists a prefix code over the alphabet $M = \{0, 1, \ldots, m - 1\}$ with the given vector of code-word lengths.

Proof: Let us assume that the word lengths are arranged in nondecreasing order; that is, $l_1 \leqslant l_2 \leqslant \cdots \leqslant l_L$. Let μ be the number of word lengths equal to l_L; thus, $l_{L-\mu} < l_{L-\mu+1} = l_{L-\mu+2} = \cdots = l_L$. Now multiply (7.1) by m^{l_L}. We get

$$\sum_{i=1}^{L-\mu} m^{l_L - l_i} + \mu \leqslant m^{l_L}.$$

Clearly, $\sum_{i=1}^{L-\mu} m^{l_L - l_i}$ is a positive integer divisible by m, and so is m^{l_L}. Now divide μ by m: $\mu = \sigma \cdot m + \rho$, where σ and ρ are nonnegative integers and $0 \leqslant \rho < m$. Define

$$\pi = \begin{cases} 0 & \text{if } \rho = 0; \\ m - \rho & \text{if } \rho > 0. \end{cases}$$

Therefore, π can be added to the left-hand side of the inequality:

$$\sum_{i=1}^{L-\mu} m^{l_L-l_i} + \mu + \pi \leqslant m^{l_L}.$$

However, $\mu + \pi = \tau \cdot m$, where

$$\tau = \begin{cases} \sigma & \text{if } \rho = 0; \\ \sigma + 1 & \text{if } \rho > 0. \end{cases}$$

Thus, we have

$$\sum_{i=1}^{L-\mu} m^{l_L-l_i} + \tau \cdot m \leqslant m^{l_L}.$$

Now, divide back by m^{l_L}. We get

$$\sum_{i=1}^{L-\mu} m^{-l_i} + \tau \cdot m^{-(l_L-1)} \leqslant 1.$$

This characteristic sum corresponds to a vector of word lengths with $L - \mu + \tau$ words. This vector still satisfies the characteristic sum condition, and its largest word length is smaller by one than the largest word length of the original vector.

This suggests a proof by induction of the size of the largest word length. If $l_L = 1$, then (7.1) implies that $l_i = 1$ for all i and that $L \leqslant m$. Thus, there exists a prefix code with the given vector of code-word lengths in which each word consists of one letter of the alphabet.

Assume now that the lemma holds if the largest word length is less than λ. By the technique described above, we can find a vector whose largest word length is $\lambda - 1$, and therefore, by the inductive hypothesis, can be assigned a proper prefix code. Each of the last τ words is now split into m words by concatenating to it one of M's letters at a time. Since $\tau \cdot m \geqslant \mu$, we get a prefix code whose vector of code-word lengths coincides with the original vector of code-word lengths in the first L places.

QED

The proof of Lemma 7.2 suggests an algorithm for finding a prefix code, and therefore a tree, for a vector of word lengths which satisfies the characteristic sum condition.

7.2 The Huffman tree

In this section we shall discuss a construction of an optimal positional m-ary ordered tree (in a sense to be discussed shortly). We shall present it as a communication problem, both because it is a natural application, and because historically it was the context of its invention by Huffman [3]. Later we shall point out two more applications: in sorting and in searching.

Assume that we have L basic messages to be transmitted over a communication channel which transfers letters of $M = \{0, 1, \ldots, m - 1\}$, one at a time. (We assume that each letter of M requires the same time to transmit. The harder problem, in which this assumption is not made was treated by Karp [4].) Also assume that these messages appear one after the other with probabilities $p_1, p_2, \ldots, p_L$ and the next message to be sent is chosen with these probabilities, independent of the previous messages. Our purpose is to find a prefix code with a vector of word lengths $(l_1, l_2, \ldots, l_L)$ such that the *average word length*,

$$\sum_{i=1}^{L} p_i l_i,$$

will be minimum. By Lemmas 7.1 and 7.2 we know that all we have to do is find a vector of word lengths which has the minimum average word length among all the vectors which satisfy the characteristic sum condition.

Let us first demonstrate Huffman's construction in the case $m = 2$ (the binary case) by means of an example. We shall always assume that $p_1 \geqslant p_2 \geqslant \cdots \geqslant p_L$. Let our vector of probabilities be (0.6, 0.2, 0.05, 0.05, 0.03, 0.03, 0.03, 0.01). We shall write it as our top row (see Fig. 7.4). We add the last (and therefore least) two numbers, and put the result (0.04, in our case) in its proper place.

We repeat this operation until we get a vector with only two probabilities. Now we assign each of them a word length 1 and start working our way back up by assigning each of the probabilities in the previous step its length in the present step if it is not one of the last two, and each of the two last probabilities is assigned a length larger by one than the length assigned to their sum in the present step.

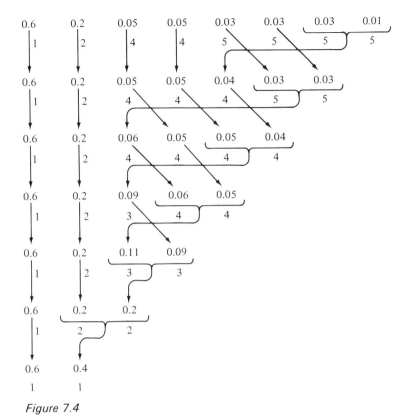

Figure 7.4

In general, we add in each step the last d out of the present L' probabilities, where $d = 2$ if $m = 2$, and in case $m > 2$, d is given by

$$d = \begin{cases} m & \text{if } L' \equiv 1 \ (\text{mod } m - 1) \\ m - 1 & \text{if } L' \equiv 0 \ (\text{mod } m - 1) \\ \rho & \text{if } L' \equiv \rho \ (\text{mod } m - 1) \text{ and } 2 \leqslant \rho \leqslant m - 2. \end{cases} \qquad (7.2)$$

(We assume the nontrivial case, $L > m$.) After the first step the length of the vector, L', satisfies $L' \equiv 1 \ (\text{mod } m - 1)$ and will be equal to one modulo $m - 1$ from there on. The reason for this rule is that we should end up with exactly m probabilities, each to be assigned length 1. Now $m \equiv 1 \ (\text{mod } m - 1)$, and since in each ordinary step the number of probabilities is reduced by $m - 1$, we want $L \equiv 1 \ (\text{mod } m - 1)$. In case this condition is not satisfied by L automatically, we have to correct it in the first step, as is done by our rule. We shall now prove that this indeed leads to an assignment of an optimal vector.

Let us denote by Π_0 the original vector of probabilities (in a nonincreasing order), and by Π_i the probability vector after i steps of our process. The vector of word lengths assigned to Π_i is denoted by Λ_i.

Lemma 7.3: For every i, Λ_i satisfies the characteristic sum condition.

Proof: The last Π_s ($s = \lceil (L - 1)/(m - 1) \rceil - 1$) consists of m probabilities, and the characteristic sum of Λ_s is exactly 1. In every one of the backtracking steps we replace one word length λ by d word lengths $\lambda + 1$. In all transitions, $d \leqslant m$, with equality in all transitions except possibly the last. The contribution of λ to the characteristic sum is $m^{-\lambda}$, and since $d \cdot m^{-(\lambda + 1)} \leqslant m \cdot m^{-(\lambda + 1)} = m^{-\lambda}$, the contribution of the new d word lengths does not exceed that of λ.

QED

We shall now prove a few properties that an optimal word length's vector must satisfy.

Lemma 7.4: Let $\Lambda = (\lambda_1, \lambda_2, \ldots, \lambda_L)$ be an optimal-word-length vector for the probability vector $\Pi = (p_1, p_2, \ldots, p_L)$. If $p_i > p_j$, then $\lambda_i \leqslant \lambda_j$.

Proof: The average word length $\bar{\lambda}$ satisfies

$$\bar{\lambda} = \sum_{k=1}^{L} p_k \lambda_k = p_i \lambda_i + p_j \lambda_j + \sum_{k \neq i,j} p_k \lambda_k.$$

Assume that $\lambda_i > \lambda_j$. Since $p_i > p_j$ we have that

$$(p_i - p_j)(\lambda_i - \lambda_j) > 0$$

or

$$p_i \lambda_i + p_j \lambda_j > p_i \lambda_j + p_j \lambda_i.$$

Therefore, if we exchange these two word lengths, the average word length reduces. This contradicts the assumption that Λ is optimal.

QED

The lemma implies that we may assume that $p_1 \geqslant p_2 \geqslant \cdots \geqslant p_L$ and also $\lambda_1 \leqslant \lambda_2 \leqslant \cdots \leqslant \lambda_L$, for if $\lambda_i > \lambda_{i+1}$, then $p_i = p_{i+1}$ and therefore the two word lengths can be exchanged without changing the average word length.

Lemma 7.5: Let Λ and Π be as above. Λ satisfies $\lambda_{L-d+1} = \lambda_{L-d+2} = \cdots = \lambda_{L-1} = \lambda_L$, where d is as in (7.2).

Proof: First let us show that

$$m - 2 \geqslant m^{\lambda_L} - \sum_{i=1}^{L} m^{\lambda_L - \lambda_i} \geqslant 0. \tag{7.3}$$

The right-hand inequality follows directly from the characteristic sum condition (Lemma 7.1). The left-hand inequality can be proved indirectly. Assume that

$$m - 1 \leqslant m^{\lambda_L} - \sum_{i=1}^{L} m^{\lambda_L - \lambda_i}.$$

Thus,

$$\sum_{i=1}^{L-1} m^{\lambda_L - \lambda_i} + m \leqslant m^{\lambda_L}.$$

Dividing by m^{λ_L} we get

$$\sum_{i=1}^{L-1} m^{-\lambda_i} + m^{-(\lambda_L - 1)} \leqslant 1,$$

which contradicts the optimality of Λ.

Now, let $L \equiv \rho \pmod{m - 1}$, where $0 \leqslant \rho \leqslant m - 2$. Since $m \equiv 1 \pmod{m - 1}$, for every nonnegative integer $k, m^k \equiv 1 \pmod{m - 1}$. Therefore,

$$m^{\lambda_L} - \sum_{i=1}^{L} m^{\lambda_L - \lambda_i} \equiv 1 - L \equiv 1 - \rho \pmod{m - 1}.$$

By (7.3) we conclude that if $m = 2$ then

$$m^{\lambda_L} - \sum_{i=1}^{L} m^{\lambda_L - \lambda_i} = 0.$$

and if $m > 2$

$$m^{\lambda_L} - \sum_{i=1}^{L} m^{\lambda_L - \lambda_i} = \begin{cases} 0 & \text{if } \rho = 1, \\ 1 & \text{if } \rho = 0, \\ m - \rho & \text{if } 2 \leqslant \rho \leqslant m - 2. \end{cases} \tag{7.4}$$

Now, let j be the last index which satisfies $\lambda_j < \lambda_L$. By the remark preceding the lemma

$$\lambda_{j+1} = \lambda_{j+2} = \cdots = \lambda_L. \tag{7.5}$$

In case $m = 2$ it is easy to see that $L - j \geqslant 2 = d$. In case $m > 2$ we can rewrite (7.4)

$$m^{\lambda_L} - \sum_{i=1}^{j} m^{\lambda_L - \lambda_i} = \begin{cases} L - j & \text{if } \rho = 1, \\ L - j + 1 & \text{if } \rho = 0, \\ L - j + m - \rho & \text{if } 2 \leqslant \rho \leqslant m - 2. \end{cases}$$

Here the left-hand side is divisible by m (since all powers of m are positive). Thus, the right-hand side, in addition to being positive, must be divisible by m, too. Thus,

if $\rho = 1$,   then $L - j = k \cdot m$ for some positive integer k,

if $\rho = 0$,   then $L - j + 1 = k \cdot m$ for some positive integer k,

if $2 \leqslant \rho \leqslant m - 2$,   then $L - j + m - \rho = k \cdot m$ for some positive integer k.

By (7.2) this implies that

if $\rho = 1$,   then $L - j \geqslant m = d$,

if $\rho = 0$,   then $L - j \geqslant m - 1 = d$,

if $2 \leqslant \rho \leqslant m - 2$,   then $L - j \geqslant \rho = d$.

QED

Theorem 7.1:   Let $\Pi_0, \Pi_1, \ldots, \Pi_s$ and $\Lambda_0, \Lambda_1, \ldots, \Lambda_s$ be the probability vectors and the word-length vectors, as constructed in Huffman's process. For every $0 \leqslant i \leqslant s$ Λ_i is optimal for Π_i.

Proof: The construction assures that L_i, the number of probabilities in Π_i, satisfies $L_i \equiv 1 \pmod{m-1}$ for $i \geqslant 1$. Also, $L_s = m$ and obviously Λ_s is optimal for Π_s. We shall now show that if Λ_{i+1} is optimal for Π_{i+1}, then Λ_i is optimal for Π_i.

Assume the contrary; namely, Λ_{i+1} is optimal for Π_{i+1}, but Λ_i is not optimal for Π_i. Thus, there exists an optimal word-length vector $\tilde{\Lambda}_i$ for Π_i with a smaller average word length. We have

$$\Pi_i = (p_1, p_2, \ldots, p_{L_i}) \qquad \text{with } p_1 \geqslant p_2 \geqslant \cdots \geqslant p_{L_i},$$

$$\Lambda_i = (l_1, l_2, \ldots, l_{L_i}),$$

$$\tilde{\Lambda}_i = (\lambda_1, \lambda_2, \ldots, \lambda_{L_i}) \qquad \text{with } \lambda_1 \leqslant \lambda_2 \leqslant \cdots \leqslant \lambda_L.$$

and

$$\sum_{k=1}^{L_i} p_k l_k > \sum_{i=1}^{L_i} p_k \lambda_k. \tag{7.6}$$

Now, $\Pi_{i+1} = (q_1, q_2, \ldots, q_{L_{i+1}})$, where for some $1 \leqslant u \leqslant L_{i+1}$ we have

$$p_{L_i - d_i + 1} + p_{L_i - d_i + 2} + \cdots + p_{L_i} = q_u$$

(d_i is as in (7.2) for L_i) and the remaining q's are $p_1, p_2, \ldots, p_{L_i - d_i}$. Also, $\Lambda_{i+1} = (l'_1, l'_2, \ldots, l'_{L_{i+1}})$, where $l'_u = l_{L_i} - 1$. Thus, the average word length of Λ_{i+1} is given by

$$\sum_{k+1}^{L_{i+1}} q_k \cdot l'_k = \sum_{k=1}^{L_i} p_k \cdot l_k - q_u. \tag{7.7}$$

By Lemma 7.5, $\lambda_{L_i - d_i + 1} = \lambda_{L_i - d_i + 2} = \cdots = \lambda_{L_i}$; thus the same type of transformation as the one which relates Λ_i to Λ_{i+1} can be applied to form a new word-length vector $\tilde{\Lambda}_{i+1}$ from $\tilde{\Lambda}_i$, and it satisfies

$$\sum_{k=1}^{L_{i+1}} q_k \cdot \lambda'_k = \sum_{k=1}^{L_i} q_k \cdot \lambda_k - q_u. \tag{7.8}$$

The relations (7.6), (7.7), and (7.8) imply that Λ_{i+1} is not optimal.

QED

7.3   Application of the Huffman tree to sort-by-merge techniques

Assume we have n items, and there is an order defined between them. For ease of presentation, let us assume that the items are the integers $1, 2, \ldots, n$ and the order is "less than." Assume that we want to organize the numbers in nondecreasing order, where initially they are put in L lists $A_1, A_2, \ldots, A_L$. Each A_i is assumed to be ordered already. Our method of building larger lists from smaller ones is as follows. Let $B_1, B_2, \ldots, B_m$ be any m existing lists. We read the first, and therefore least, number in each of the lists, take the least number among them away from its list and put it as the first number of the merged list. The list from which we took the first number is now shorter by one. We repeat this operation on the same m lists until they merge into one. Clearly, some of the lists become empty before others, but since this depends on the structure of the lists, we only know that the general step of finding the least number among m numbers (or less) and transfer it to a new list is repeated $b_1 + b_2 + \cdots + b_m$ times, where b_i is the number of numbers in B_i.

The number m is dictated by our equipment or decided upon in some other way. However, we shall assume that its value is fixed and predetermined. In fact, in most cases $m = 2$.

The whole procedure can be described by a positional m-ary ordered tree. Consider the example shown in Fig. 7.5, where $m = 2$. First we merge the list $\langle 3 \rangle$ with $\langle 1, 4 \rangle$ to form $\langle 1, 3, 4 \rangle$. Next we merge $\langle 2, 5 \rangle$ with $\langle 1, 3, 4 \rangle$. The original lists, $A_1, A_2, \ldots, A_L$, correspond to the terminal vertices of the tree. The number of transfers can be computed as follows: Let a_i be the number of numbers in A_i, and l_i be the level of the list A_i in the tree. The number of elementary merge operations is then

$$\sum_{i=1}^{L} a_i \cdot l_i. \tag{7.9}$$

Burge [5] observed that the attempt to find a positional m-ary ordered tree which minimizes (7.9) is similar to that of the minimum-average-word-length problem solved by Huffman. The fact that the Huffman construction is in terms of probabilities does not matter, since the fact that $p_1 + p_2 + \cdots + p_L = 1$ is never used in the construction or its validity proof. Let us demonstrate the implied procedure by the following example.

Assume $L = 12$ and $m = 4$; the b_i's are given in nonincreasing order: $9, 8, 8, 7, 6, 6, 6, 5, 5, 4, 3, 3$. Since $L \equiv 0 \pmod 3$, according to (7.2) $d = 3$.

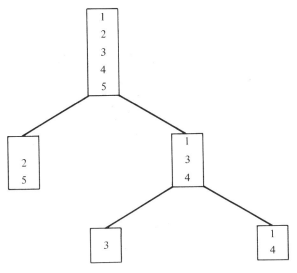

Figure 7.5

Thus, in the first step we merge the last three lists to form a list of length 10 which is now put in the first place (see Fig. 7.6). From there on, we merge each time the four lists of least length. The whole merge procedure is described in the tree shown in Fig. 7.7.

We shall briefly mention here another application of the Huffman tree. In certain cases, data are stored in the terminal vertices of a binary tree, and when we reach a vertex all we can find is whether we have to take the

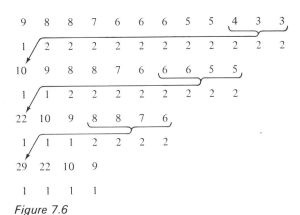

Figure 7.6

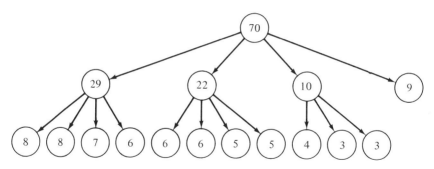

Figure 7.7

left son or the right son in order to get closer to the datum we seek. The question of how to construct this tree when the probabilities of the various data are given and when we want to minimize the average search time is identical with the problem which the Huffman construction solves.

7.4   The number of full binary ordered trees with *n* vertices

The set of *well-formed sequences of parentheses* is defined by the following recursive definition:

1. The empty sequence is well formed.
2. If *A* and *B* are well-formed sequences, so is *AB* (the concatenation of *A* and *B*).
3. If *A* is well formed, so is (*A*).
4. There are no other well-formed sequences.

For example, (()(())) is well formed; (()))(() is not.

Lemma 7.6:   A sequence of (left and right) parentheses is well formed if and only if it contains an even number of parentheses, half of which are left and the other half are right, and as we read the sequence from left to right, the number of right parentheses never exceeds the number of left parentheses.

Proof: First let us prove the "only if" part. Since the construction of every well-formed sequence starts with no parentheses (the empty sequence) and each time we add on parentheses (step 3) there is one left and one right, it is clear that there are n left parentheses and n right parentheses. Now, assume that for every well-formed sequence of m left and m right parentheses, where $m < n$, it is true that as we read it from left to right the number of right parentheses never exceeds the number of left parentheses. If the last step in the construction of our sequence was 2, then since A is a well-formed sequence, as we read from left to right, as long as we still read A the condition is satisfied. When we are between A and B, the count of left and right parentheses equalizes. From there on the balance of left and right is safe since B is well formed and contains less than n parentheses. If the last step in the construction of our sequence was 3, then since A satisfies the condition, so does (A).

Now we shall prove the "if" part, again by induction on the number of parentheses. (Here, as before, the basis of the induction is trivial.) Assume that the statement holds for all sequences of m left and m right parentheses, if $m < n$, and we are given a sequence of n left and n right parentheses which satisfies the condition. Clearly, if after reading $2m$ symbols of it from left to right the number of left and right parentheses is equal and if $m < n$, this subsequence, A, by the inductive hypothesis is well formed. Now, the remainder of our sequence, B, must satisfy the condition, too, and again by the inductive hypothesis is well formed. Thus, by step 2, AB is well formed. If there is no such nonempty subsequence A, which leaves a nonempty B, then as we read from left to right the number of right parentheses, after reading one symbol and before reading the whole sequence, is strictly less than the number of left parentheses. Thus, if we delete the first symbol, which is a "(", and the last, which is a ")", the remaining sequence, A, still satisfies the condition, and by the inductive hypothesis is well formed. By step 3 our sequence is well formed, too.

QED

We shall now show a one-to-one correspondence between the non-well-formed sequences of n left and n right parentheses, and all sequences of $n - 1$ left parentheses and $n + 1$ right parentheses.

Let $p_1 p_2 \cdots p_{2n}$ be a sequence of n left and n right parentheses which is not well formed. Thus, by Lemma 7.6, let j be the least integer such that the number of right parentheses exceeds the number of left parentheses in the subsequence $p_1 p_2 \cdots p_j$. Clearly, the number of right parentheses is then one larger than the number of left parentheses, or j is not the least index to satisfy the condition. Now, invert all p_i's where $i > j$ from left parentheses to right parentheses, and from right parentheses to left parentheses. Clearly, the number of left parentheses is now $n - 1$, and the number of right parentheses is now $n + 1$.

Conversely, given any sequence $p_1 p_2 \cdots p_{2n}$ of $n - 1$ left parentheses and $n + 1$ right parentheses, let j be the first index such that $p_1 p_2 \cdots p_j$ contains one right parenthesis more than left parentheses. If we now invert all the parentheses in the section $p_{j+1} p_{j+2} \cdots p_{2n}$ from left to right and from right to left, we get a sequence of n left and n right parentheses which is not well formed. This transformation is the inverse of the one of the previous paragraph. Thus, the one-to-one correspondence is established.

The number of sequences of $n - 1$ left and $n + 1$ right parentheses is

$$\binom{2n}{n-1},$$

for we can choose the places for the left parentheses, and the remaining places will have right parentheses. Thus, the number of well-formed sequences of length n is

$$\binom{2n}{n} - \binom{2n}{n-1} = \frac{1}{1+n}\binom{2n}{n}. \tag{7.10}$$

An *ordered forest* is a collection of ordered trees, put in some order one next to the other with all roots on one horizontal line. For example, the forest shown in Fig. 7.8 consists of three ordered directed trees whose roots are A, B, and C. There is a natural correspondence between well-formed sequences of n pairs of parentheses and ordered directed forests of n vertices.

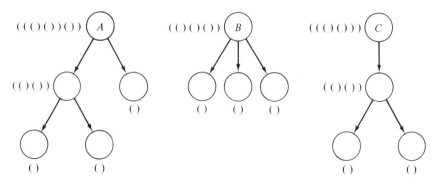

Figure 7.8

Each terminal vertex corresponds to the sequence ( ). Every other vertex corresponds to a sequence composed of a left parenthesis, the expressions of its sons in their given order, and a right parenthesis. The expression of the whole forest is the concatenation of the expressions of the roots, in the same order from left to right. For example, the expression of the forest of Fig. 7.8 is ((()())())(()()())((()())). The inverse transformation clearly exists and thus the one-to-one correspondence is established. Therefore, the number of ordered forests of n vertices is given by (7.10).

We shall now describe a one-to-one correspondence between ordered directed forests and positional binary ordered trees. The leftmost root of the forest is the root of the binary tree. The leftmost son of the vertex in the forest is the left son of the vertex in the binary tree. The next brother on the right, or, in the case of a root, the next root on the right is the right son in the binary tree. For example, see Fig. 7.9, where an ordered directed forest and its corresponding binary tree are drawn. Again, it is clear that this is a one-to-one correspondence and therefore the number of positional binary ordered trees with n vertices is given by (7.10).

There is yet another combinatorial enumeration which is directly related to these.

A *stack* is a storage device which can be described as follows. Suppose that n cars travel on a narrow one-way street where no passing is possible. This leads into a narrow two-way street on which the cars can park or back up to enter another narrow one-way street (see Fig. 7.10). Our problem is to find how many permutations of the cars can be realized from input to output if we assume that the cars enter in the natural order.

The order of operations in the stack is fully described by the sequence of drive-in and drive-out operations. There is no need to specify which car drives in, for it must be the first one on the leading-in present queue; also, the only one which can drive out is the top one in the stack. If we denote a drive-in operation by "(", and a drive-out operation by ")", the whole procedure is described by a well-formed sequence of n pairs of parentheses. Different sequences yield different sequences of operations and different sequences of operation produce different permutations. Thus, the number of permutations on n cars realizable by a stack is given by (7.10).

We shall now consider the problem of finding the number of full binary ordered trees. Let t and i denote the number of terminal and internal vertices of a given full binary ordered tree T, respectively. It is easy to prove by induction on the number of vertices of the tree (Exercise 7.7) that $t = i + 1$. Also, if all terminal vertices of T are removed, the resulting tree of i vertices

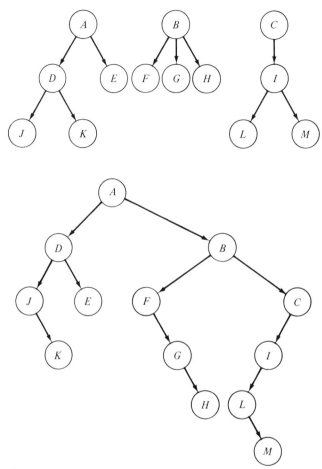

Figure 7.9

is a positional binary ordered tree τ. Clearly, different T's will yield different τ's, and one can reconstruct T from τ by hanging two terminal vertices on every terminal vertex of τ, and one terminal vertex (son) for every vertex of τ which has only one son. Thus, the number of full binary ordered trees of n vertices is equal to the number of positional binary ordered trees of $(n-1)/2$ vertices. By (7.10) this number is

$$\frac{2}{n+1}\binom{n-1}{\frac{n-1}{2}}. \tag{7.11}$$

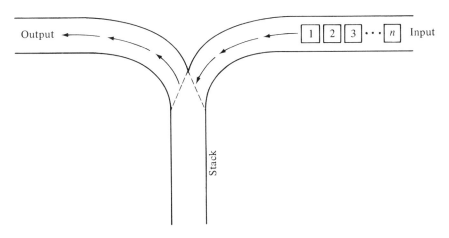

Figure 7.10

EXERCISES

7.1 Construct a prefix binary code, with a minimum average word length, which consists of 10 words whose frequencies are 0.20, 0.18, 0.12, 0.10, 0.10, 0.08, 0.06, 0.06, 0.06, and 0.04. Repeat the construction for $m = 3$ and $m = 4$.

7.2 Prove that if a prefix code corresponds to a full binary positional tree, then its characteristic sum is equal to 1.

7.3 Prove that if a word-length vector $(l_1, l_2, \ldots, l_L)$ satisfies the characteristic sum condition and if $l_1 \leqslant l_2 \leqslant \cdots \leqslant l_L$ and $l_j < l_{j+1} = l_{j+2} = \cdots = l_L$, then the vector $(l_1, l_2, \ldots, l_j, l_{j+1} - 1, l_{j+d+1}, l_{j+d+2}, \ldots, l_L)$ satisfies the characteristic sum condition, too, and the word lengths are still in a nondecreasing order. (Here d is as in (7.2).)

7.4 Show that the construction of Exercise 7.3 can be used to construct a positional m-ary ordered tree for the original word-length vector, in which the order of the terminal vertices, from left to right, is as in the vector. This proves that there exists an optimal tree with this property. (This result is attributed by Knuth [2] to E. S. Schwartz.)

7.5 Construct the ordered directed forest, the positional binary ordered tree, and the permutation through a stack which correspond to the following well-formed sequence of 10 pairs of parentheses:

$$(()((()))(()()))$$

7.6 A direct method for computing the number of positional binary ordered trees of n vertices through the use of a generating function goes as follows: Let b_n be the number of trees of n vertices. Define $b_0 = 1$ and define the function

$$B(x) = b_0 + b_1 x + b_2 x^2 + \cdots.$$

(a) Prove that $b_n = b_0 \cdot b_{n-1} + b_1 b_{n-2} + \cdots + b_{n-1} \cdot b_0$.
(b) Prove that $x B^2(x) - B(x) + 1 = 0$.
(c) Use the formula

$$(1 + a)^{1/2} = 1 + \frac{\frac{1}{2}}{1!} a + \frac{\frac{1}{2}(\frac{1}{2} - 1)}{2!} a^2 + \frac{\frac{1}{2}(\frac{1}{2} - 1)(\frac{1}{2} - 2)}{3!} a^3 + \cdots$$

to prove that

$$b_n = \frac{1}{n+1} \binom{2n}{n}.$$

7.7 Prove that the number of terminal vertices in a full binary tree is one more than the number of internal vertices.

REFERENCES

1. Abramson, N., *Information Theory and Coding*, McGraw-Hill, New York, 1963.
2. Knuth, D. E., *The Art of Computer Programming*, Addison-Wesley, Reading, Mass., Vol. 1, 1968.
3. Huffman, D. A., "A Method for the Construction of Minimum Redundancy Codes," *Proc. IRE*, Vol. 40, No. 10, pp. 1098–1101, September 1952.
4. Karp, R. M., "Minimum-Redundancy Coding for the Discrete Noiseless Channel," *IRE Trans. Information Theory*, Vol. IT-7, pp. 27–39, January 1961.
5. Burge, W. H., "Sorting, Trees, and Measures of Order," *Information and Control*, Vol. 1, pp. 181–97, 1958.

8

CLIQUES, COVERS,
AND COLORATION

8.1 Cliques and their number

In this chapter we shall discuss a few problems concerning important sets of vertices of a finite undirected graph $G(V, E)$ which has no self-loops and no parallel edges.

A set of vertices, S, is called *completely connected* if every pair of vertices of S is connected through a single edge. (These sets are sometimes called full, or completely dependent.) If S is maximal,* in the sense that no vertex can be added to it without violating the complete connectivity, then the set is called a *clique*.† Another way of defining cliques is to say that these are

---

*The word "maximal" is used here in the local maximality sense. We use the word "maximum" in reference to total maximality.

†Some authors call any completely connected set a clique, but I shall use it only for maximal completely connected sets.

147

the completely connected sets which are not subsets of larger completely connected sets. Clearly, it is not necessarily true that each clique contains the maximum number of vertices a clique of this graph can. For example, the graph shown in Fig. 8.1 has two cliques: $\{1, 2, 3, 4\}$ and $\{2, 5\}$. The completely connected set $\{1, 2, 3\}$ is not a clique, although it contains more vertices than $\{2, 5\}$.

A set of vertices, S, is called *independent* if no pair of vertices of S are connected by an edge; it is called *maximal independent* if no larger independent set contains it. Let $G(V, E)$ be a graph and $G'(V, E')$ and $G''(V, E'')$ be two subgraphs. We say that G' is the *complement* of G'' *with respect to* G if $E' \cup E'' = E$ and $E' \cap E'' = \varnothing$. If $G(V, E)$ is an undirected graph with no self-loops and no parallel edges, we say that $G'(V, E')$ is the *complement* of $G(V, E)$ if $E' \cap E = \varnothing$ and $E' \cup E$ contains one edge between every pair of vertices.

It is clear that a set of vertices S is a clique of $G(V, E)$ if and only if S is a maximal independent set of $G'(V, E')$, the complement of $G(V, E)$. Thus, if one wants to find all maximal independent sets of one graph, he can use an algorithm for finding all cliques of a graph and apply it to the given graph's complement.

We shall now investigate the problem of the greatest number, $f(n)$, of cliques a graph with n vertices can have. This problem was solved in 1960 by Miller and Muller [1], but we shall follow the independent work of Moon and Moser [2].

Let $G(V, E)$ be an undirected graph with n vertices $(n = |V|)$. Let x be one of the vertices and $G_x(V_x, E_x)$ be the vertex subgraph of G defined by $V_x = \Gamma(x)$. We say that a vertex v is *isolated* if it is not the end point of any edge.

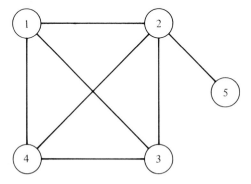

Figure 8.1

Lemma 8.1: If C is a subset of V and $x \in C$ is a nonisolated vertex, then C is a clique of $G(V, E)$ if and only if $C - \{x\}$ is a clique of G_x.

Proof: Assume that C is a clique of G. Thus, $C - \{x\}$ is a nonempty subset of $\Gamma(x)$ and the set is completely connected in G. By the definition of G_x, $C - \{x\} \subset V_x$ and the set is completely connected in G_x. If $C - \{x\}$ is not a clique in G_x, then there exists a vertex y in $\Gamma(x)$ which is connected by an edge, in G, to every vertex in $C - \{x\}$. Thus, C is not a clique of G.

Now assume that $C - \{x\}$ is a clique of G_x. Thus, C is completely connected in G. If C is not a clique of G, then there exists a vertex y, $y \notin C$, such that $C \cup \{y\}$ is completely connected. But in this case $(C \cup \{y\}) - \{x\}$ is completely connected in G_x and, therefore, $C - \{x\}$ is not a clique of G_x.

$$\text{QED}$$

Some of the cliques of G_x are not cliques of the vertex subgraph $\tilde{G}_x(V - \{x\}, \tilde{E})$ of $G(V, E)$. These cliques of G_x are proper subsets of cliques of $\tilde{G}_x$. Let $\alpha(x)$ be the number of cliques of G_x which are also cliques of $\tilde{G}_x$, and $\beta(x)$ be the number of cliques of G_x which are not cliques of $\tilde{G}_x$. Thus, the number of cliques of G_x is $\alpha(x) + \beta(x)$. Let $\chi(x)$ be the number of cliques of G which contain x. Lemma 8.1 implies that

$$\chi(x) = \alpha(x) + \beta(x). \tag{8.1}$$

Let $c(G)$ be the number of cliques in G.

Lemma 8.2: $c(G) = c(\tilde{G}_x) + \beta(x)$ for every nonisolated vertex x.

Proof: Every clique C' of $\tilde{G}_x$ yields a clique of G by the following rule:

$$C = \begin{cases} C' & \text{if } C' \not\subset \Gamma(x); \\ C' \cup \{x\} & \text{if } C' \subset \Gamma(x). \end{cases}$$

This is a one-to-one mapping of the set of cliques of $\tilde{G}_x$ into the set of cliques of G. In addition, for every clique C' of G_x which is not a clique of $\tilde{G}$, we get a clique C of G by $C = C' \cup \{x\}$. It is easy to see that these are all the cliques of G.

$$\text{QED}$$

Assume that x and y are vertices of G which are not connected by an edge. Let $G\langle x, y \rangle$ be the graph resulting from G by eliminating all edges of which x is an end point and connecting an edge between x and each of the vertices in $\Gamma(y)$.

Lemma 8.3:   For every pair of nonisolated vertices x and y in G which are not connected by an edge

$$c(G\langle x, y \rangle) = c(G) + \chi(y) - \beta(x).$$

Proof: When all the edges which have x as an end point are eliminated, the $\beta(x)$ cliques of G, which correspond to cliques of G_x that are not cliques of $\tilde{G}_x$, are not cliques anymore. The $\chi(y)$ cliques of G which contain y are also cliques of $\tilde{G}_x$, since x and y are not connected by an edge. Now, we add edges which connect x with each one of the vertices in $\Gamma(y)$. The result is that every one of the $\chi(y)$ cliques is now duplicated, with x playing the role of y.

QED

Lemma 8.4:   Assume that $G(V, E)$ is a graph with $n \geqslant 2$ vertices and that $c(G) = f(n)$. For every vertex x, $\Gamma(x) \neq V - \{x\}$.

Proof: Assume that for some vertex x, $\Gamma(x) = V - \{x\}$. Thus, $\chi(x) = \alpha(x)$. By disconnecting x from all the vertices in $\Gamma(x)$ no cliques of G are lost and we have one more, namely, $\{x\}$. Thus, $c(G)$ was not maximum.

QED

Lemma 8.5:   If G is a graph with $n \geqslant 5$ vertices and $c(G) = f(n)$, then G is connected.

It is not hard to establish, by exhaustion, that for $n < 5$, $f(n) = n$. However, the graph with no edges achieves it, too. For $n = 5$, $f(n) > n$, as in the graph shown in Fig. 8.2, which has six cliques.

Proof: Let G be a graph with $n \geqslant 5$ vertices for which $c(G) = f(n)$, and let the number of isolated vertices in G be i. (A vertex is called isolated if it is not an end point of any edge.) Clearly $i < 5$, for if $i \geqslant 5$, a construction like that of Fig. 8.2 among these vertices can increase the number of cliques. Clearly $n - i \geqslant 2$, for $n - i = 1$ implies that the number of isolated vertices

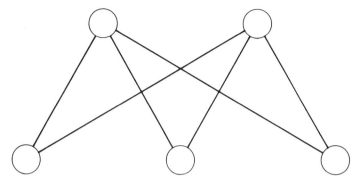

Figure 8.2

is $i + 1$. Consider the vertex subgraph $\tilde{G}(\tilde{V}, \tilde{E})$ defined by the set of vertices, $\tilde{V}$, which are not isolated in G; thus, $|\tilde{V}| = n - i$. By Lemma 8.4 there are two vertices x_1 and x_2 in $\tilde{G}$ which are not connected by an edge. If $i > 0$, connect one of the isolated vertices, y, by two edges to x_1 and to x_2. The new graph has two new cliques, $\{x_1, y\}$ and $\{x_2, y\}$, and $\{y\}$ is no more a clique. No other clique is changed by these connections. Thus, the number of cliques has increased by one. This contradicts the assumption that $c(G) = f(n)$. Thus, we conclude that $i = 0$.

If G is not connected and x and y are vertices in two different components, the connection of x to y by an edge does not eliminate any of the previous cliques but adds the clique $\{x, y\}$, again a contradiction.

QED

Lemma 8.6: If G has $n \geqslant 5$ vertices and $f(n) = c(G)$, and if x and y are two vertices of G which are not connected by an edge, then $c(G\langle x, y\rangle) = c(G)$, $\chi(x) = \chi(y)$, $\alpha(x) = \alpha(y) = 0$, and $\beta(x) = \beta(y)$.

Proof: By Lemma 8.5, $f(n) = c(G)$ implies that x and y are not isolated. By Lemma 8.3 we have

$$c(G\langle x, y\rangle) = c(G) + \chi(y) - \beta(x)$$

and

$$c(G\langle y, x\rangle) = c(G) + \chi(x) - \beta(y).$$

(8.2)

But since

$$c(G\langle x, y\rangle) \leqslant c(G) \qquad \text{and} \qquad c(G\langle y, x\rangle) \leqslant c(G),$$

we have

$$\chi(y) \leqslant \beta(x) \qquad \text{and} \qquad \chi(x) \leqslant \beta(y).$$

By (8.1) we have

$$\alpha(y) + \beta(y) \leqslant \beta(x) \qquad \text{and} \qquad \alpha(x) + \beta(x) \leqslant \beta(y). \tag{8.3}$$

Now,

$$\beta(y) \leqslant \alpha(y) + \beta(y) \leqslant \beta(x) \leqslant \alpha(x) + \beta(x) \leqslant \beta(y).$$

Thus,

$$\beta(x) = \beta(y)$$

and (8.3) implies that $\alpha(x) = \alpha(y) = 0$. Therefore, $\chi(x) = \chi(y) = \beta(x) = \beta(y)$ and (8.2) implies that

$$c(G\langle x, y \rangle) = c(G).$$

QED

Corollary 8.1:   If $c(G) = f(n)$, $n \geqslant 5$, then for every vertex x in G, $\alpha(x) = 0$.

Proof: This follows immediately from Lemmas 8.4 and 8.6.

QED

Now, let $G(V, E)$ be a graph which satisfies $|V| = n \geqslant 5$ and $c(G) = f(n)$. Let x be a vertex of G and $y_1, y_2, \ldots, y_l$ be the vertices of G which are not connected by an edge to x. Form $G^{(1)} = G\langle y_1, x \rangle$. By Lemma 8.6, $c(G^{(1)}) = c(G)$, and still x is not connected by an edge to $y_2, y_2, \ldots, y_l$. We continue by constructing $G^{(i)} = G^{(i-1)}\langle y_i, x \rangle$ for $2 \leqslant i \leqslant l$. By induction

$$c(G^{(l)}) = c(G) = f(n),$$

and in $G^{(l)}$ none of $x, y_1, y_2, \ldots, y_l$ are connected to each other by an edge and

$$\Gamma^{(l)}(x) = \Gamma^{(l)}(y_1) = \cdots = \Gamma^{(l)}(y_l) = V - \{x, y_1, y_2, \ldots, y_l\}.$$

We can now take another set of vertices, $x', y'_1, y'_2, \ldots, y'_t$, where, again, none of the y's is connected by an edge to x', and end up with a new graph in which no two of them are connected by an edge, each one of them is connected by an edge to the same vertices and the number of cliques is still $f(n)$. We repeat this process until we end up with a graph G' whose vertices are partitioned into $B_1, B_2, \ldots, B_p$ such that no two vertices in one block are connected by an edge; every two vertices from distinct blocks are connected by an edge; $c(G') = f(n)$. Thus,

$$c(G') = \prod_{j=1}^{p} b_j,$$

where $b_j = |B_j|$.

Thus, the question of what is $f(n)$ reduces to the following combinatorial problem: What is the maximum of

$$\prod_{j=1}^{p} b_j \tag{8.4}$$

if all b_j's are positive integers and

$$\sum_{j=1}^{p} b_j = n. \tag{8.5}$$

Naturally, we denote the maximum of (8.4) subject to (8.5), over all the possible p's, by $f(n)$.

Lemma 8.7: If $(b_1, b_2, \ldots, b_p)$ yields the maximum $f(n)$ of the above combinatorial problem, then $b_j < 5$ for all j.

Proof: If for some j, $b_j \geq 5$, replace b_j by $b'_j = b_j - 2$ and $b''_j = 2$ (the new vector has $p + 1$ terms). Now

$$\sum_{i \neq j} b_i + b'_j + b''_j = \sum_{i=1}^{p} b_i = n$$

and

$$\left(\prod_{i \neq j} b_i \right) \cdot b'_j \cdot b''_j = \left(\prod_{i \neq j} b_i \right) \cdot (2b_j - 4) > \prod_{i=1}^{p} b_i.$$

QED

Lemma 8.8: If $(b_1, b_2, \ldots, b_p)$ is as in Lemma 8.7, then one of the following conditions must hold:

1. For all j, $b_j = 3$.
2. There is one i such that $b_i = 4$ and for every $j \neq i$, $b_j = 3$.
3. There are two indices i and j such that $b_i = b_j = 2$, and for all indices k, such that $k \neq i$ and $k \neq j$, $b_k = 3$.
4. There is one i such that $b_i = 2$ and for every $j \neq i$, $b_j = 3$.

Proof: By Lemma 8.7, for every i, either $b_i = 2$, or 3, or 4. If $\prod_{j=1}^{p} b_j$ is divisible by 8, then either we have two b's equal to 4, or one 4 and one 2, or three b's are 2. However, none is possible for

$$4 \cdot 4 < 3 \cdot 3 \cdot 2 \qquad \text{while } 4 + 4 = 3 + 3 + 2;$$

$$4 \cdot 2 < 3 \cdot 3 \qquad \text{while } 4 + 2 = 3 + 3;$$

$$2 \cdot 2 \cdot 2 < 3 \cdot 3 \qquad \text{while } 2 + 2 + 2 = 3 + 3.$$

Thus, $\prod_{j=1}^{p} b_j$ is not divisible by 8. The lemma follows.

QED

Theorem 8.1:

$$f(n) = \begin{cases} 3^{n/3} & \text{if } n \equiv 0 \ (\text{mod } 3); \\ 4 \cdot 3^{(n-4)/3} & \text{if } n \equiv 1 \ (\text{mod } 3); \\ 2 \cdot 3^{(n-2)/3} & \text{if } n \equiv 2 \ (\text{mod } 3). \end{cases}$$

Proof: If $n \equiv 0 \ (\text{mod } 3)$, then we must have case 1 of Lemma 8.8, and therefore

$$f(n) = 3^{n/3}.$$

If $n \equiv 1 \ (\text{mod } 3)$, then we can either have case 2 or case 3. In both cases,

$$f(n) = 4 \cdot 3^{(n-4)/3}.$$

If $n \equiv 2 \ (\text{mod } 3)$, then we must have case 4 and therefore

$$f(n) = 2 \cdot 3^{(n-2)/3}.$$

QED

The previous discussion answers the question of the maximum number of cliques a graph with n vertices can have and provides a graph H_n which achieves $f(n)$ as follows:

1. If $n \equiv 0 \pmod 3$, then H_n consists of $n/3$ triples of vertices. No two vertices in the same triple are connected by an edge, and every two vertices from distinct triples are connected by an edge.
2. If $n \equiv 1 \pmod 3$, we get two possible structures for H_n. Either it consists of one quadruple and $(n-4)/3$ triples, or it consists of two pairs and $(n-4)/3$ triples. The edges are as in 1.
3. If $n \equiv 2 \pmod 3$, then H_n consists of one pair and $(n-2)/3$ triples, with edges as in 1.

Moon and Moser [2] showed the interesting fact that these are the only graphs which achieve $f(n)$. I do not include this proof here, since I do not think that this fact is of much practical value.

8.2   An algorithm for generating all cliques of a given graph

In view of the possible exponential growth of the number of cliques of graphs with n vertices, it is desirable to have an efficient algorithm for their generation. It is most important to avoid generating in intermediate steps more items than the number of items we have to end up with. The algorithm to be described here was first described by Paull and Unger [3].

Assume that $G(V, E)$ is an undirected graph with $V = \{v_1, v_2, \ldots, v_n\}$.

Algorithm 8.1:   (For $n \geqslant 2$)
(1) Let $S_1 = \{\{v_1\}\}$ and $i = 1$.
(2) For every $t \in S_i$ form $\Gamma(v_{i+1}) \cap t$ and put $\{v_{i+1}\} \cup (\Gamma(v_{i+1}) \cap t)$ in a new set C_{i+1}. Thus, $C_{i+1} = \{s | s = \{v_{i+1}\} \cup (\Gamma(v_{i+1}) \cap t) \text{ for some } t \in S_i\}$.
(3) Compute $S'_{i+1} = C_{i+1} \cup S_i$.
(4) S_{i+1} is the set of all elements of S'_{i+1} (which are subsets of V) which are not subsets of other elements of S'_{i+1}. Thus,

$$S_{i+1} = \{s | s \in S'_{i+1} \text{ and } \forall t \in S'_{i+1} [t \supset s \Rightarrow t = s]\}.$$

(5) If $i + 1 = n$, stop; S_{i+1} is the set of all cliques of G. If not, increment i by one and go to step (2).

Clearly, after S'_{i+1} is computed there is no need to preserve C_{i+1} and S_i. However, $C_{i+1} \cap S_i = \emptyset$, for all elements of S_i are subsets of $\{v_1, v_2, \ldots, v_i\}$, while every element of C_{i+1} contains v_{i+1}. Thus, it pays to keep these two lists separate; no element of C_{i+1} is a subset of an element in S_i, and in the computation of S_{i+1} there is no need to check if elements of C_{i+1} are subsets of elements in S_i. Also, in this step there is no need to check if one element of S_i is a subset of another, for this has been checked in the formation of S_i.

In the generation of C_{i+1} some elements may be generated more than once. It may be more efficient to just list the elements as they come without trying to avoid these duplications and clean this up as part of step (4).

Once S_{i+1} is computed, there is no need to remember S_i or C_{i+1} or S'_{i+1}. Now $|C_{i+1}| \leqslant |S_i|$, and therefore the number of subsets of V to be remembered at one time is bounded by

$$\text{Max}\{2|S_1|, 2|S_2|, \ldots, 2|S_{n-1}|\}. \tag{8.6}$$

Let $G^i(V^i, E^i)$ be the vertex subgraph of G defined by $V^i = \{v_1, v_2, \ldots, v_i\}$; $\Gamma^i(x) = \Gamma(x) \cap V^i$.

Lemma 8.9: If S_i is the set of all cliques of G^i, then every element of S'_{i+1} is a completely connected set of vertices in G^{i+1}.

Proof: Assume that $s \in S'_{i+1}$. By step (3) either $s \in S_i$ or $s \in C_{i+1}$. If $s \in S_i$, by our hypothesis s is completely connected in G^{i+1}. If $s \in C_{i+1}$, then for some $t \in S_i$,

$$s = \{v_{i+1}\} \cup (\Gamma(v_{i+1}) \cap t).$$

Clearly, t is completely connected in G^{i+1}. Now, we add to it v_{i+1}, and those vertices of t which are not connected by an edge to v_{i+1} are eliminated. Therefore, s is completely connected in G^{i+1}.

$$\text{QED}$$

Lemma 8.10: If S_i is the set of all cliques of G^i, then every clique of G^{i+1} is in S'_{i+1}.

Proof: Assume that s is a clique of G^{i+1}. If $v_{i+1} \notin s$, then s is also a clique of G^i and belongs to S_i.

Now consider the case $v_{i+1} \in s$. The set $s \cap V^i$ is completely connected in G^i. Since S_i is the set of all cliques of G^i, there exists an element $t \in S_i$ such that $t \supset (s \cap V^i)$. Clearly $s = \{v_{i+1}\} \cup (\Gamma(v_{i+1}) \cap t)$ and thus $s \in C_{i+1}$.

QED

Theorem 8.2: Each S_i generated by Algorithm 9.1 is the set of all cliques of G^i.

Proof: The proof is by induction on i. Obviously, the theorem holds for $i = 1$.

Assume that the theorem is true for $1 \leqslant i < n$. By Lemma 8.10, all the cliques of G^{i+1} are in S'_{i+1}. By Lemma 8.9, only completely connected sets of vertices of G^{i+1} are included in S'_{i+1}. Thus, in step (4) the nonmaximal completely connected sets are eliminated, and the cliques remain.

QED

It follows that the last S_i, namely, S_n, is the set of all cliques of $G (= G^n)$. Let us consider the following graph, which is specified by its connection matrix. The set of vertices is $1, 2, \ldots, 6$; the matrix has a 1 in the i, j place if vertix i and vertex j are connected by an edge, and has a 0 if they are not. The connection matrix is

	1	2	3	4	5	6
1	0	1	1	1	1	0
2	1	0	1	1	1	0
3	1	1	0	1	0	1
4	1	1	1	0	0	1
5	1	1	0	0	0	1
6	0	0	1	1	1	0

The sequence of S_i, C_{i+1}, and S'_{i+1} is as follows:

$$S_1 = \{\{1\}\},$$
$$C_2 = \{\{1, 2\}\},$$
$$S'_2 = \{\{1, 2\}, \{1\}\},$$
$$S_2 = \{\{1, 2\}\},$$
$$C_3 = \{\{1, 2, 3\}\},$$
$$S'_3 = \{\{1, 2, 3\}, \{1, 2\}\},$$

$$S_3 = \{\{1, 2, 3\}\},$$
$$C_4 = \{\{1, 2, 3, 4\}\},$$
$$S'_4 = \{\{1, 2, 3, 4\}, \{1, 2, 3\}\},$$
$$S_4 = \{\{1, 2, 3, 4\}\},$$
$$C_5 = \{\{1, 2, 5\}\},$$
$$S'_5 = \{\{1, 2, 5\}, \{1, 2, 3, 4\}\},$$
$$S_5 = S'_5,$$
$$C_6 = \{\{5, 6\}, \{3, 4, 6\}\},$$
$$S'_6 = \{\{5, 6\}, \{3, 4, 6\}, \{1, 2, 5\}, \{1, 2, 3, 4\}\},$$
$$S_6 = S'_6.$$

Next, it is shown that the number of sets stored at any stage of Algorithm 8.1 is never considerably larger than the number of sets in S_n.

Theorem 8.3:   The number of elements in S_i is not greater than the number of elements in S_{i+1}.

Proof: If $s \in S_i$, then for some $t \in S_{i+1}$, $t \supset s$. If both s_1 and s_2 are in S_i and the same $t \in S_{i+1}$ satisfies $t \supset s_1$ and $t \supset s_2$, then $s_1 \cup s_2$ is a completely connected set of G^i and since s_1 and s_2 are cliques, $s_1 = s_1 \cup s_2 = s_2$. Thus, each $s \in S_i$ has at least one $t \in S_{i+1}$ which contains it alone.

                                                                                          QED

8.3   The set-covering algorithm

The set-covering algorithm was developed in the 1950s by switching theorists who were trying to find an efficient algorithm for minimizing two level logic. (See, for example, McCluskey's book [4].) There are many variations of this algorithm, but we shall restrict our attention to the most basic problem and techniques.

The algorithm is not very efficient, since in essence it is a branching procedure and therefore the amount of work may grow exponentially with the size of the problem. However, in view of the difficulty of the problem, the algorithm seems to be close to the best possible.

	1	2	3	4	5	6	7	8	9	10
A		1	1	1		1			1	
B				1	1			1		1
C						1		1		
D	1		1				1			
E	1					1	1	1		
F	1			1		1		1		
G	1					1		1		1
H	1		1			1		1		
I		1			1	1	1			
J		1	1			1		1		
K		1			1		1	1		1
L		1	1			1	1			

Figure 8.3

Assume that we have a finite set S and a family of subsets $B_1, B_2, \ldots, B_m$ of S. Our problem is to find a minimum number of B's whose union is S itself.

We shall demonstrate the algorithm by means of an example.

Assume that $S = 1, 2, \ldots, 10$ and assume that we have 12 subsets A through L specified in the table of Fig. 8.3. The elements in each subset are specified by the ones in the proper columns. For example, $A = \{2, 3, 4, 6, 9\}$.

First we look for redundant subsets. A subset is redundant if it is contained in another one. For example, $C \subset A$ and $J \subset A$. Now, C and J may be eliminated from consideration, since any minimum solution which includes C or J can have A instead, and all we want is to find one minimum. (If all minima are to be found, this type of elimination is not allowed.) This operation is called *row elimination.* After (or before) we have carried out all possible row eliminations, we consider the columns. If a certain column is covering another (has a one in every row that the other column has), it can be dropped from consideration, for it will be "automatically covered." For example, the column of 6 covers the column of 9 and the column of 8 covers that of 10 (in fact, they are identical). Thus, if 9 will be in one of our selected subsets, 6 will be there, too; and so on. Our new table is shown in Fig. 8.4. We reexamine the rows and discover that now $K \supset I$. After eliminating I, column 8 covers 5 and is eliminated.

It is important to note that after a column elimination, new row elimination may become possible, and after a row elimination, new column eliminations

	1	2	3	4	5	7	8	9
A		1	1	1				1
B				1	1		1	
D	1		1			1		
E	1					1		1
F	1			1				1
G	1						1	
H	1		1					1
I	1	1			1	1		
K		1			1	1	1	
L		1	1			1		

Figure 8.4

may be possible. Thus, we go to the next step only when neither is possible. Now row G is eliminated ($D \supset G$). The resulting table is shown in Fig. 8.5 and no further eliminations exist. Next, we look for columns with a single 1, for these force a selection of a row. In our case, there are none (this situation will be demonstrated shortly) and therefore we *branch*. That is, we divide the search into two different searches, one in which we assume that, say A, is selected, and one in which we assume that A is not selected. If A is selected, it takes care of columns 2, 3, 4, and 9 and therefore they may be dropped from further consideration. We still have to cover 1, 5, and 7 by a minimum number of rows among B, D, E, F, H, K, and L. The present table is shown in Fig. 8.6(a).

Now, $K \supset B$, $D \supset E$, $D \supset F$, $D \supset H$, and $K \supset L$. The reduced table is shown in Fig. 8.6(b). Now column 7 is redundant. We next observe that there

	1	2	3	4	5	7	9
A		1	1	1			1
B				1	1		
D	1		1			1	
E	1					1	1
F	1			1			1
H	1		1				1
K		1			1	1	
L		1	1			1	

Figure 8.5

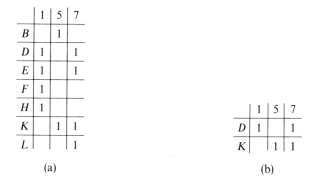

(a)   (b)

Figure 8.6

is a single 1 in column 1 and in column 5. Thus, rows D and K have to be selected, and we have found a cover consisting of the subsets A, D, and K.

Now, if A is not selected, we drop it out of Fig. 8.5. In the resulting table, column 7 is redundant (it covers column 2) and column 1 is redundant (it covers column 9). The resulting table is shown in Fig. 8.7(a). Now, $H \supset D$ and $H \supset E$. The resulting table is shown in Fig. 8.7(b). Again, no reductions or forced selection exist and we branch. (In fact, in this case, it is already clear that the cover A, D, K is minimum, for we shall need at least three rows to cover 2, 3, 4, 5, and 9.) If we select B, the resulting table, shown in Fig. 8.8(a), has two redundant rows (F and K) and in the resulting table the selection of H and L is indicated. Thus, we end up with the cover B, H, L. If we do not select B, the resulting table (derived from Fig. 8.7(b)) is shown in Fig. 8.8(b). Here, the selection of F and K is indicated, and then is leading to the table of Fig. 8.8(c). Thus, we get the cover F, K, H (or F, K, L).

	2	3	4	5	9
B			1	1	
D		1			
E					1
F		1			1
H		1			1
K	1			1	
L	1	1			

(a)

	2	3	4	5	9
B			1	1	
F			1		1
H		1			1
K	1			1	
L	1	1			

(b)

Figure 8.7

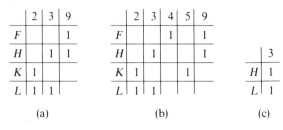

Figure 8.8

There are many improvements on the above algorithm; the most obvious of these is not to continue a search which already assumes the selection of the same number of subsets as a known cover. However, all these improvements do not eliminate the branching and therefore cannot be considered efficient. Special cases, for which more efficient covering algorithms exist, will be discussed in the following chapters.

8.4 Dominating sets and graph coloration

A *dominating set* of a graph $G(V, E)$ is a set of vertices S such that every vertex of G is either in S or is reachable from some vertex of S through an edge. Thus,

$$S \cup \Gamma(S) = V.$$

Here, $\Gamma(S)$ is the set of vertices v which are connected to vertices in S by an edge, and in case of directed graphs, by an edge from a vertex of S to v.

A dominating set is called *minimal* if no proper subset of it is a dominating set.

Theorem 8.4: Every maximal independent set of an undirected graph $G(V, E)$ is a minimal dominating set.

Proof: Assume that S is a maximal independent set. If $S \cup \Gamma(S) \neq V$, then a vertex s, not in $S \cup \Gamma(S)$, exists, and $S \cup \{s\}$ is independent. Thus S is a dominating set. However, if any vertex $s \in S$ is deleted, $s \notin \Gamma(S - \{s\})$, since S is independent, and therefore S is a minimal dominating set.

QED

In certain applications it is necessary to find a minimum dominating set of a given directed or undirected graph. In the absence of a known useful structure to the graph, we can use the following procedure.

For every $v \in V$, define the subset $B_v = \{v\} \cup \Gamma(v)$. Solve a set-covering problem, in an attempt to cover V with as few B's as possible. The set of vertices whose B's constitute a minimum cover of V is a minimum dominating set.

A partition of V of an undirected graph $G(V, E)$ into disjoint independent subsets $B_1, B_2, \ldots, B_k$ is called a *coloration*. All vertices of one B_i are assumed to have the same color, which is different from the color of all the other vertices. The minimum k for which a coloration exists is called the *chromatic number* of G. Clearly, if G is k chromatic, there exists a cover of V by means of k independent sets. Also, if V is coverable by k independent sets $A_1, A_2, \ldots, A_k$, then a k coloration can be obtained as follows:

$$B_1 = A_1$$
$$B_2 = A_2 - A_1$$
$$B_3 = A_3 - (A_1 \cup A_2)$$
$$\vdots$$
$$B_k = A_k - (A_1 \cup A_2 \cup \cdots \cup A_{k-1}).$$

That is, we put in B_2 those elements of A_2 which are not in A_1. In general, we put in B_i all the elements of A_i which were not in $B_1, B_2, \ldots, B_{i-1}$.

This suggests the following minimum coloration procedure for finite undirected graph $G(V, E)$. First, we use Algorithm 8.1 to find all maximal independent sets of $G(V, E)$ which are the cliques of $G'(V, E')$. Next, we use the set-covering algorithm to find a minimum cover of V by the least number of independent sets of $G(V, E)$. Finally, we translate this cover into coloration.

This procedure is far from being ideal, but in the absence of additional knowledge about the structure of G it is the best available procedure.

The interested reader can find additional information about the subjects of this chapter in many books and articles. See, for example, references 5 and 6.

EXERCISES

8.1 Describe a procedure for designing a directed tree with e edges which minimizes the probability of a mouse reaching a "cheese" vertex in the tree, if the mouse starts its search in the root and selects the next edge to walk on by some random process, where all available edges have the same probability to be entered; clearly this kind of choice repeats at each nonterminal vertex. (The mouse is allowed to walk on the edges, only in their given direction.)

8.2 Prove that, in case $n = 0 \pmod 3$, that H_n is the only graph with $3^{n/3}$ cliques. (This is a fairly hard problem. The reader who finds it too difficult can find an outline in reference 2.)

8.3 Find all cliques of the graph described by the following connection matrix:

0	1	1	0	1	1
1	0	0	1	1	1
1	0	0	1	0	1
0	1	1	0	1	0
1	1	0	1	0	1
1	1	1	0	1	0

8.4 Find a minimum dominating set in the following graph:

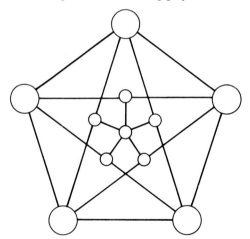

8.5 Find a minimum coloration of the graph of Exercise 8.4. (This is a graph with no triangles with a chromatic number 4. For a general construction of graphs with no triangles which require an arbitrarily large number of colors, see Mycielski [7]. A more general result is reported by Lovász [8].) Try to construct a family of graphs, $G_1, G_2, \ldots$, such that G_i has a chromatic number i and has no triangles.

8.6 Define the direct product, $G \times H$, of two undirected graphs $G(V_G, E_G)$ and $H(V_H, E_H)$, with no parallel edges as follows:

$$V_{G \times H} = \{(a, b) | a \in V_G \quad \text{and} \quad b \in V_H\}.$$

There is an edge connecting (a, b) with (c, d) in $G \times H$ if and only if a is adjacent to c in G and b is adjacent to d in H.

(a) Describe the direct product of the following two graphs:

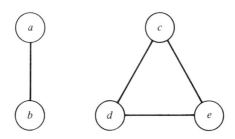

(b) Let $\beta(G)$ denote the maximum number of vertices in an independent set of G. Let $\gamma(G)$ denote the chromatic number of G. Prove that if $|V_G| = n$, then

$$\beta(G) \cdot \gamma(G) \geqslant n.$$

(c) Prove that if each vertex in G and H has a self-loop, then

$$\gamma(G \times H) \leqslant \gamma(G) \cdot \gamma(H)$$

and

$$\beta(G \times H) \geqslant \beta(G) \cdot \beta(H).$$

REFERENCES

1. Miller, R. E., and Muller, D. E., "A Problem of Maximum Consistent Subsets," *IBM Research Report RC-240*, J. T. Watson Research Center, Yorktown Heights, N.Y., 1960.
2. Moon, J. W., and Moser, L., "On Cliques in Graphs," *Israel J. Math.*, 1965, pp. 23–8.
3. Paull, M. C., and Unger, S. H., "Minimizing the Number of States in Incompletely Specified Sequential Functions," *IRE Trans. Electronic Computers*, Vol. EC-8, September 1959, pp. 356–67.
4. McCluskey, E. J., Jr., *Introduction to the Theory of Switching Circuits*, McGraw-Hill, New York, 1965.
5. Ore, O., *Theory of Graphs*, American Mathematical Society, Providence, R.I., 1962, Chaps. 13 and 14.
6. Harary, F., *Graph Theory*, Addison-Wesley, Reading, Mass., 1969, Chaps. 10 and 12.
7. Mycielski, J., "Sur le Coloriage des Graphes," *Colloq. Math.*, Vol. 3, 1955, pp. 161–62.
8. Lovász, L., "On Chromatic Number of Finite Set-Systems," *Acta Math. Acad. Sci. Hungar*, Vol. 19, 1968, pp. 59–67.

9

TRANSITIVE
AND PERMUTATION
GRAPHS

9.1   Maximum cliques and minimum coloration of transitive graphs

The directed graphs to be discussed in this chapter are all finite, having no parallel edges and no directed circuits. Clearly, the exclusion of directed circuits implies that there are no self-loops.

A graph $G(V, E)$ is called *transitive* if the existence of edges $a \rightarrow b$ and $b \rightarrow c$ implies the existence of $a \rightarrow c$. Here E is a relation, in the algebraic sense, and the transitivity with the absence of directed circuits makes it a strong partial order. Thus, this section may be considered to deal with finite strong partial orders.

As we have seen in Chapter 8, the problems of finding a maximum clique and minimum coloration are usually hard to solve. Our aim is to show that if $\tilde{G}$ is the undirected underlying graph of some directed transitive graph G, then it is easy to solve these two problems for $\tilde{G}$.

For the sake of convenience, let us first rename the vertices of the directed transitive graph G to be $1, 2, \ldots, n$ in such a way that edges always go from low to high. This can be done as follows: Since G is circuit-free and finite, it must have at least one source (a vertex with no incoming edges). Let v be any one of G's sources; rename it 1; remove it and adjacent edges from G to form $\bar{G}^1$. Now $\bar{G}^1$ is also circuit-free; call one of its sources 2 and form $\bar{G}^2$; and so on. Finally, $\bar{G}^n$ will be empty and all vertices have been renamed. It is obvious that this renaming satisfies the condition that if $i \to j$, then $i < j$. (All we have done here is embed the partial order in a full order.) Now our graph is $G(N, E)$, where $N = \{1, 2, \ldots, n\}$ and E has been changed as indicated.

Assume that S is a clique of $\tilde{G}$. The vertex subgraph $G'(S, E')$ of G has exactly one source—the least vertex; for if there were more than one there could not have been an edge connecting them. After eliminating this vertex and its adjacent edges from G' there is again one source; and soon. This proves that there is a directed path in G' which contains all its vertices. The converse of this statement follows directly from the definition of transitivity: The vertices on a directed path in G form a completely connected set of vertices of $\tilde{G}$, and, if the path is maximal, the set of its vertices is a clique.

Assume now that for some $1 \leqslant m < n$, S is a clique of the vertex subgraph $\tilde{G}^m$ defined by the vertices $1, 2, \ldots, m$. Let k be the highest vertex in S. It is now observed that $S \cup \{m + 1\}$ is a clique of $\tilde{G}^{m+1}$ if and only if $k \to m + 1$ in G. This provides an immediate simplification of the Paull and Unger procedure (Section 8.2), since intersection of subsets becomes unnecessary, and is replaced by searching the highest vertex of S which is connected by an edge to $m + 1$.

However, a much more impressive result is provided by the above-mentioned observation for finding a maximum clique. Let us construct a sequence of n integers $c(1), c(2), \ldots, c(n)$, where $c(i)$ is the number of vertices in the largest clique of $\tilde{G}^i$ to which i belongs. Clearly, $c(1) = 1$; next, if $1 \to 2$ in G, then $c(2) = 2$; if not, $c(2) = 1$. In general, when $c(1), c(2), \ldots,$ $c(i - 1)$ are known, let $\Gamma^{-1}(i)$ be the set of vertices j such that $j \to i$ in G. Clearly, in our case $\Gamma^{-1}(i)$ is a subset of $\{1, 2, \ldots, i - 1\}$. If $\Gamma^{-1}(i) = \varnothing$, let $c(i) = 1$; otherwise,

$$c(i) = 1 + \underset{j \in \Gamma^{-1}(i)}{\mathrm{Max}}\ c(j).$$

The size of the largest clique of $\tilde{G}$ is $\mathrm{Max}_{j \in N}\ c(j)$.

After all $c(i)$'s have been obtained, a traceback operation can be used to group all the vertices of a maximum clique. We locate first a j for which $c(j)$ is maximum. Thus, j participates in a maximum clique and is, in fact, the highest vertex in it. After gathering vertices $j = i_1 > i_2 \cdots > i_m$ and if $c(i_m) > 1$, we locate a next vertex i_{m+1} such that $i_{m+1} \to i_m$ in G and $c(i_m) = 1 + c(i_{m+1})$. This continues until for some $m, c(i_m) = 1$. Then, $\{i_1, i_2, \ldots, i_m\}$ is a maximum clique.

This dynamic programming approach can be extended to a weighted graph, where weight w_i is assigned to vertex i, and where we look for a clique with the maximum weight sum of its vertices. In this case the maximum clique weights are generated by

$$c(i) = \begin{cases} w_i & \text{if } \Gamma^{-1}(i) = \varnothing \\ w_i + \underset{j \in \Gamma^{-1}(i)}{\text{Max}} c(j) & \text{if } \Gamma^{-1}(i) \neq \varnothing. \end{cases} \tag{9.1}$$

Let us demonstrate the construction on the graph shown in Fig. 9.1, where we assume that $w_i = 1$ for all i. First we have $c(1) = 1$, and since $1 \not\to 2$ (1 is not connected to 2), $c(2) = 1$. Now $1 \to 3$; thus $c(3) = 1 + c(1) = 2$. Similarly, $c(4) = 2$. Vertex 5 is connected to 1, 2, 3, 4 ($\Gamma^{-1}(5) = \{1, 2, 3, 4\}$). Thus, $c(5) = 1 + \text{Max}_{j \in \Gamma^{-1}(5)} c(j) = 1 + 2 = 3$. Also, $\Gamma^{-1}(6) = \{2, 4\}$ and $c(6) = 3$. Finally, $\Gamma^{-1}(7) = \{2, 4, 6\}$ and $c(7) = 1 + 3 = 4$. We now know that a maximum clique is of size 4 and its largest vertex is 7 ($i_1 = 7$). Next, $i_2 = 6$, $i_3 = 4$, and $i_4 = 2$. A maximum clique is then $\{7, 6, 4, 2\}$.

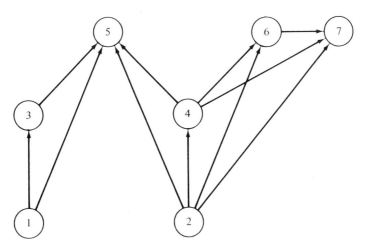

Figure 9.1

Next, we describe a minimum coloration algorithm for $\tilde{G}$. At the kth stage we generate a minimum coloration for the vertex subgraph $\tilde{G}^k$. We denote this coloration by $D_k = (S_1^k, S_2^k, \ldots, S_{m_k}^k)$, where each S_i^k is an independent set. Clearly $D_1 = (\{1\})$. Having derived D_k we add vertex $k + 1$ to the coloration by the following rule: Locate the first S_i^k to which vertex $k + 1$ can be joined without destroying its independence (that is, such a set that none of its members is connected to $k + 1$). We then add $k + 1$ to that first possible recipient. If none exists, a new monochromatic set is generated, containing vertex $k + 1$ alone. After the nth step we have $N = S_1^n \cup S_2^n \cup \cdots \cup S_{m_n}^n$. It is claimed that this decomposition is a minimum one. For, take any element of $S_{m_n}^n$. The reason that it was not put into S_{m_n-1} when it was introduced is that a previous and therefore smaller member in S_{m_n-1} is connected to it. Consider now this member of S_{m_n-1}; it must be connected to a member of S_{m_n-2}. We can thus display a directed path with m_n vertices which by transitivity is a clique. It is therefore clear that any chromatic decomposition must have at least m_n sets.

For example, consider again the graph of Fig. 9.1. First, $D_1 = (\{1\})$. Now $1 \not\to 2$; thus, $D_2 = (\{1, 2\})$. Since $1 \to 3$, we must put 3 in a new monochromatic set; thus, $D_3 = (\{1, 2\}, \{3\})$. Since $2 \to 4$ and $3 \not\to 4$ we get

$$D_4 = (\{1, 2\}, \{3, 4\}).$$

This is followed by

$$D_5 = (\{1, 2\}, \{3, 4\}, \{5\}),$$
$$D_6 = (\{1, 2\}, \{3, 4\}, \{5, 6\}),$$
$$D_7 = (\{1, 2\}, \{3, 4\}, \{5, 6\}, \{7\}).$$

In view of the existence of these efficient techniques for transitive graphs, a natural approach is the following: When presented with an undirected graph H for which we have to find a maximum clique or a minimum coloration, let us try to orient it into a directed graph G, such that $\tilde{G} = H$, and where G is circuit-free and transitive. If we succeed in this, our problem is then very easy to solve. Clearly, we should consider the difficulty involved in the orientation and the fact that not all undirected graphs are transitively orientable. But as we shall see in the next section, there exists a fairly efficient algorithm for testing whether a given undirected graph is transitively orientable, and find such an orientation if one exists.

9.2   Transitive orientation of undirected graphs

Let $G(V, E)$ be an undirected graph with no parallel edges and no self-loops, and assume that V, the set of vertices, is a set of integers.

Start by assigning to one of the arcs an arbitrary direction. Proceed by assigning directions to additional arcs using the following two rules:

Rule R_1:   For ever $i, j, k \in V$,

$$i \rightarrow j, \; k - j, \; i \not{+} k \text{ implies that } k \rightarrow j.$$

If i is connected by a directed edge to j, k is connected by an edge (directed or undirected) to j and i is not connected by an edge of any type to k, then direct the edge between k and j into j. The reason for this direction is that if $i \rightarrow j$ and $i \not{+} k$, we cannot have $j \rightarrow k$, for transitivity would require that $i \rightarrow k$, and there is no edge between them. In Fig. 9.2(a) this rule is illustrated. Here the dashed lines from i to j indicate that there is no edge between them.

It may happen that $j - k$ is already directed in the reverse direction, namely, $j \rightarrow k$. In this case we say that rule R_1 leads to a *contradiction*.

Rule R_2:   For every $i, j, k \in V$,

$$j \rightarrow i, \; j - k, \; i \not{+} k \text{ implies that } j \rightarrow k.$$

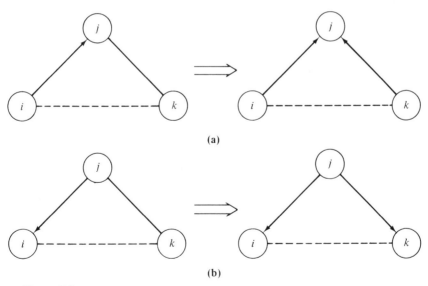

(a)

(b)

Figure 9.2

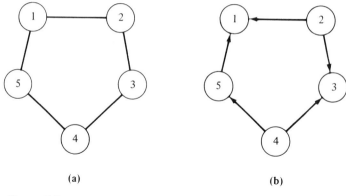

(a)   (b)

Figure 9.3

This rule is illustrated in Fig. 9.1(b) and may also lead to a contradiction.

Continue to assign direction and to check consistencies by rules R_1 and R_2 as long as they are applicable.

If a contradiction occurs, the process stops in failure.

If no contradiction occurs and rules R_1 and R_2 are no longer applicable, we examine the graph to see if all edges have been directed. If not, we reconsider the subgraph formed by deleting all the directed edges and proceed as before.

The algorithm will therefore terminate by either generating a contradiction, or directing all edges. We illustrate in Fig. 9.3 the two possible terminations of the algorithm. Consider the pentagon, shown in part (a). Assume that we start by directing $5 \to 1$. By R_1 this implies $2 \to 1$. By R_2 this implies $2 \to 3$, and so on; the sequence of implications is

$$5 \to 1 \Rightarrow 2 \to 1 \Rightarrow 2 \to 3 \Rightarrow 4 \to 3 \Rightarrow 4 \to 5 \Rightarrow 1 \to 5.$$

The first five directions are shown in Fig. 9.3(b). However, the last implication redirects the edge $1 — 5$ in the reverse direction; thus, the algorithm fails. And indeed, it is easy to see that there is no transitive orientation for the pentagon.

Consider the graph shown in Fig. 9.4(a). The first wave of directions may propagate as follows:

$$1 \to 2 \Rightarrow 1 \to 5 \Rightarrow 6 \to 5 \Rightarrow 6 \to 2 \Rightarrow 3 \to 2 \Rightarrow 3 \to 5.$$

The few more applications of the rules only confirm the existing directions and no contradiction arises. The subgraph of all undirected edges is shown in Fig. 9.4(c). Here the next wave of directions may propagate as follows (after arbitrarily directing $3 \rightarrow 4$):

$$3 \rightarrow 4 \Rightarrow 2 \rightarrow 4 \Rightarrow 1 \rightarrow 4 \Rightarrow 6 \rightarrow 4 \Rightarrow 5 \rightarrow 4.$$

Again no contradiction arises and the only edge remaining undirected is $1 — 3$. Assume that we direct it arbitrarily $3 \rightarrow 1$. The resulting direction for the whole graph is shown in Fig. 9.4(d).

Each time an edge is directed, all the edges adjacent to it on both sides have to be checked to see if one of the rules applies. Thus, the number of

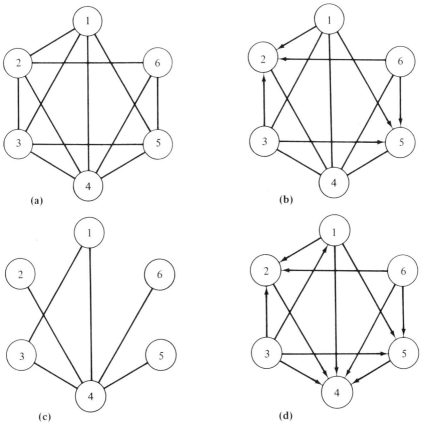

(a)

(b)

(c)

(d)

Figure 9.4

checks is bounded by $2md$, where m is the number of edges in the graph and d is the maximum degree of the vertices.

Our purpose is to show now that if the algorithm succeeds (that is, all edges are oriented and no contradiction arises), then this orientation is free of directed circuits and is transitive.

Consider a graph $G(V, E)$ in which phase 1 of the orientation algorithm has been successfully completed; that is, one arc has been arbitrarily oriented, and all possible consequences, by rules R_1 and R_2, have been followed without any contradictions. The set of edges directed in the first phase will be denoted by E'.

Lemma 9.1: After a successful completion of phase 1 it is impossible to have three vertices i, j, k such that $i \to j, j \to k$, while $i \not\to k$.

(Note that $i \not\to k$ means that either $i \leftarrow k$, or the edge $i — k$ is not directed, or there is no edge between i and k.)

Proof: First it is clear that there must be an edge between i and k; for if such an edge does not exist, then we immediately get a contradiction.

Assume now that forbidden situations, of the type $i \to j$ and $j \to k$ while $i \not\to k$, exist after phase 1. By the definition of phase 1 and the symmetry inherent in rules R_1 and R_2, there exists a derivation chain starting from $i \to j$ and leading to $j \to k$. (Actually it is in general true that if any of the edges directed in phase 1 is the first edge to be directed arbitrarily, the resulting phase 1 will yield the same directions to the same edges.) Consider now a shortest chain of derivations which leads to a forbidden situation. Such a chain must be longer than 2, because the only possible chains of derivations of length 2 are $i \to j \Rightarrow k \to j$ and $j \to i \Rightarrow j \to k$, and neither can be a forbidden situation. Therefore, a possible chain is of length $n > 2$:

$$(i \to j) \Rightarrow (\quad) \Rightarrow \cdots \Rightarrow (\quad) \Rightarrow (j \to k).$$
$$\alpha_1 \qquad\quad \alpha_2 \qquad\qquad\quad \alpha_{n-1} \qquad \alpha_n$$

We make now a second assumption about the selected path. We assume that among all the shortest chains of derivation we choose one with the minimum number of edges directed into k. Now α_{n-1} must be either $j \to j'$ for some j', or $k' \to k$ for some k'.

Case 1: Assume that α_{n-1} is $j \to j'$. First, it is clear that $j' \not\to k$, or rule R_2 would not apply for deriving α_n from α_{n-1}. Second, we must have $i \to j'$, for if $i \not\to j'$, we have a shorter chain of derivations which leads to a forbidden situation, contradicting the minimality of the length of our chain.

But if $i \to j'$ and $j' \not\to k$, then we direct $i \to k$, again contradicting our assumption that $i \not\to k$.

Case 2: Assume that α_{n-1} is $k' \to k$. First, it is clear that $j \not\to k'$. Second, there must be an edge $i - k'$, or $k' \to k$ would imply that $i \to k$. Furthermore, this edge must be directed $i \to k'$ by $i \to j$ and $j \not\to k'$. If we now start the chain with $i \to k'$, we get a chain

$$(i \to k') \Rightarrow (i \to j) \Rightarrow (\quad) \Rightarrow \cdots \Rightarrow (\quad) \Rightarrow (k' \to k).$$
$$\qquad\quad \alpha_1 \qquad\qquad \alpha_2 \qquad\qquad\quad \alpha_{n-2} \qquad \alpha_{n-1}$$

However, we assumed that $i \not\to k$, and therefore this is a chain of shortest length leading to a forbidden situation, but with one less edge entering k. This contradicts our second assumption about the selection of the chain.

QED

Corollary 9.1: The subgraph $\vec{G}(V, \vec{E'})$ of the oriented edges after the completion of phase 1 is transitive.

This follows directly from Lemma 9.1.

Theorem 9.1: If the orientation algorithm terminates successfully, it provides a transitive orientation.

Proof: By induction on the number of phases in the algorithm.

If the whole graph is oriented in phase 1, then by Corollary 9.1 the resulting orientation is transitive.

Let the graph be oriented in n phases, where E' is the set of edges oriented in phase 1. Then $G(V, E - E')$ is orientable in $n - 1$ phases and by the inductive hypothesis this orientation is transitive. By Corollary 1, $\vec{G}(V, \vec{E'})$ is transitive. Consider now the orientation of the whole graph induced by these two subgraphs. If we have any i, j, k such that $i \to j, j \to k$, but $i \not\to k$, we cannot have both $i \to j$ and $j \to k$ belong to $\vec{E'}$ or to $\vec{E} - \vec{E'}$, since each is transitive. If $i \to j$ belongs to $\vec{E'}$ and $j \to k$ belongs to $\vec{E} - \vec{E'}$, there must be an edge $i - k$ in E, or $i \to j \overset{R_1}{\Rightarrow} k \to j$. And if this edge is directed $k \to i$

in phase 1 (in the later phases), then $\vec{G}(V, \vec{E}')$ is not transitive $(\vec{G}(V, \vec{E} - \vec{E}')$ is not transitive).

QED

Theorem 9.2: If a finite undirected graph $G(V, E)$ with no parallel edges and no self-loops is transitively oriented into $\vec{G}(V, \vec{E})$, then $\vec{G}(V, \vec{E})$ has no directed circuits.

Proof: Assume that $\vec{G}(V, \vec{E})$ has directed circuits. Let $v_1 \to v_2 \to v_3 \to \cdots \to v_k \to v_1$ be a minimal-length directed circuit. By the transitivity $v_1 \to v_2$ and $v_2 \to v_3$ imply that $v_1 \to v_3$, thus shortening the circuit: a contradiction. The cases $k = 1$ and $k = 2$ are ruled out by the absence of self-loops and parallel edges in $G(V, E)$.

QED

Thus, we have established that if our algorithm terminates successfully, then it produces a transitive orientation in which there are no directed circuits. It remains to be shown that if a transitive orientation exists, then our algorithm will not fail.

Let $G(V, E)$ be a transitively orientable graph. It is clear that if we reverse all directions, then the resulting orientation is still transitive. We may therefore pick an arc and direct it in an arbitrary way, knowing that it coincides with a complete transitive orientation. All implications derived by rules R_1 and R_2 are compulsory in all possible orientations which agree with the first edge directions. Therefore, after completion of phase 1 we have directed some of the edges in a way which agrees with some transitive orientation of the graph and no contradictions could arise. Let us refer to this process as *marking* the directions of the underlying orientation. The set of marked edges, after phase 1, is therefore E'.

Define a set of *marked vertices* V' as follows: A vertex v is marked if it is adjacent to some marked edge; other edges adjacent to v may be unmarked.

Lemma 9.2: It is impossible to have three marked vertices i, j, k for which $i - j$ and $j - k$ are unmarked and $i - k$ is marked.

Note that all edges are directed, and we use $i - j$ because the direction does not matter.

Proof: Assume that such forbidden situations exist; namely, one could find triples i, j, k where $i - j$ and $j - k$ are unmarked and $i - k$ is marked. For

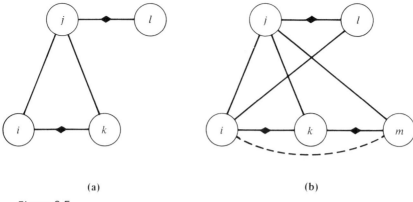

(a)   (b)

Figure 9.5

each such triple, since j is a marked vertex, there exists a marked edge $j — l$, for some l. Thus, as in the proof of Lemma 9.1, there is a chain of derivations leading from marking $i — k$ to marking $j — l$. Take a forbidden situation with a shortest chain of derivations of this type. In Fig. 9.5(a) the pertaining vertices are shown with the connections established so far. A diamond on the edge means that it is marked and a dashed line means that there is no such edge. The next marked edge after $i — k$ in the shortest chain is either $i — m$ or $k — m$, for some m. The two cases are similar enough, and we will discuss only the case $k — m$. Therefore $i \nmid m$, and also m and l must be distinct, since we must have $i — l$ or $i — j$ would have been marked. Also we must have $j — m$, or $j — k$ would have been marked. The established relations are shown in Fig. 9.5(b). Now $j — m$ cannot be marked, for marking it would have implied marking $i — j$. Thus, we have another forbidden situation: k, j, m with $k — j$ and $j — m$ unmarked and $k — m$ marked, with a shorter chain from $k — m$ to $j — l$.

QED

Lemma 9.3: $G(V, E - E')$ is transitively orientable.

Proof: First observe that $G(V', E')$ is connected. This is a result of the property of rules R_1 and R_2 of marking adjacent vertices only.

Consider now a vertex $v \in V - V'$. If v is connected by an edge (in $G(V, E)$) to one vertex $v' \in V'$, then it must be connected by an edge to all vertices of V'. This statement follows from the connectivity of $G(V', E')$, the fact that no edge incident with v is marked and the nature of rules R_1 and R_2.

We may partition $V - V'$ into four sets of vertices as follows:

$A = \{i|\ i \in V - V' \text{ and for all } j \in V'\ i \to j \text{ in the underlying orientation}\}$,

$B = \{i|\ i \in V - V' \text{ and for all } j \in V'\ j \to i \text{ in the underlying orientation}\}$,

$C = \{i|\ i \in V - V' \text{ and for all } j \in V'\ i \nleftrightarrow j\}$,

$D = V - (V' \cup A \cup B \cup C)$.

Thus, C consists of all vertices of $V - V'$ which are not adjacent to any vertex of V', and D consists of all vertices of $V - V'$ which are connected to all vertices of V', but the directions of all the connecting edges are not the same. These relations are schematically shown in Fig. 9.6(a).

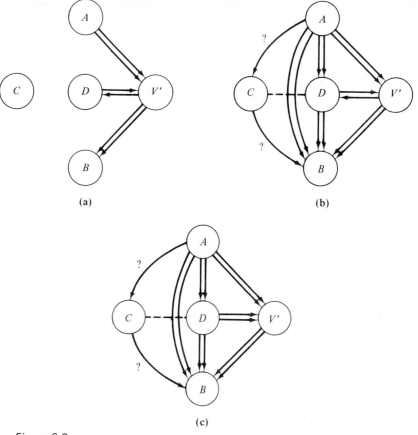

(a)   (b)

(c)

Figure 9.6

By transitivity of the underlying orientation we infer the following connections between the different sets:

1. For every $i \in A, j \in D, k \in B$ we have $i \rightarrow j, j \rightarrow k$, and $i \rightarrow k$.
2. No vertex of C is adjacent to a vertex of D.
3. All edges between A and C are directed from A to C.
4. All edges between B and C are directed from C to B.

The concluded situation is schematically shown in Fig. 9.6(b). Let us now reverse the direction of all edges leading from V' to D so that now all edges lead from D to V'. The resulting orientation is schematically shown in Fig. 9.6(c). We claim that the resulting orientation is still transitive.

To disprove this claim one has to display i, j, k such that $i \rightarrow j, j \rightarrow k$, but $i \nrightarrow k$. Since the original orientation was transitive, this is possible only if one or two of these three edges have been reversed. This leaves only three possibilities:

1. $i \in D, j \in V'$. In this case k must be in V' or in B, but i is connected to all these vertices. Thus, $i \rightarrow k$.
2. $j \in D, k \in V'$. In this case i must be in A or D, but i is connected to all the vertices of V'. Thus, $i \rightarrow k$.
3. $i \in V', k \in D$. In this case j must be in V' or B, and there is no way to connect j to k.

Our next operation is to delete all marked edges from the transitively directed graph. We claim again that transitivity is maintained. For assume that i, j, k are such that $i \rightarrow j, j \rightarrow k$, and $i \nrightarrow k$. Since the previous orientation was transitive and the only edges deleted are those of $\vec{G}(V', \vec{E}')$, we must have $i, j, k \in V'$ (observe that there is no vertex j outside V' which has both an edge from V' into it, and from it into V'). But this would imply that i, j, k are marked, $i - j$ and $j - k$ are unmarked, and $i - k$ is marked. By Lemma 9.2 this is impossible.

QED

9.3   Permutation graphs

Let $P = [P(1), P(2), \ldots, P(n)]$ be a permutation of the positive integers $1, 2, \ldots, n$. Then let $N = \{1, 2, \ldots, n\}$ and Π be a subset of $N \times N$ defined as in the following equations.

$$\Pi = \{(i, j) | i < j \quad \text{and} \quad P^{-1}(i) > P^{-1}(j)$$

or

$$i > j \quad \text{and} \quad P^{-1}(i) < P^{-1}(j)\}$$

where $P^{-1}(i)$ is the element of N which P maps into i. In a more pictorial way: Draw a matching diagram for the given permutation. This is done for $P = [2, 5, 4, 1, 3]$ in Fig. 9.7. In the diagram the line connecting the two i's intersects the line connecting the two j's if and only if $(i, j) \in \Pi$.

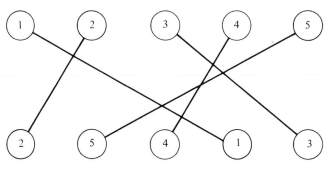

Figure 9.7

We now define the *permutation graph* of P to be $G(N, \Pi)$; that is, G is an undirected graph whose vertices are $1, 2, \ldots, n$ and its edges are specified by the symmetric relation Π. Clearly, G has no self-loops and no parallel edges. The permutation graph of $P = [2, 5, 4, 1, 3]$ is shown in Fig. 9.8.

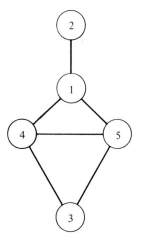

Figure 9.8

Our first aim is to characterize the graphs $G(N, R)$ which are permutation graphs of some P, and to devise an algorithm for finding a P if such exists. Notice that we assume that the vertices of the graph are labeled $1, 2, \ldots, n$, and our present question is with reference to this given labeling. We shall later discuss the question of whether a given graph can be relabeled to become a permutation graph.

Let us introduce a few additional terms. Assume that $G(N, R)$ is a given undirected graph, with no self-loops and no parallel edges; namely, R is an irreflexive symmetric relation. Define R' to be $N \times N - \{(i, i) | i \in N\} - R$. The graph $G'(N, R')$ is, therefore, the complementary undirected graph of $G(N, R)$. Now define

$$\vec{R} = \{(i, j) | i < j \quad \text{and} \quad (i, j) \in R\}.$$

Thus $\vec{G}(N, \vec{R})$ is actually $G(N, R)$, where all its edges are now directed from low to high. Similarly, define

$$\overleftarrow{R}' = \{(i, j) | i > j \quad \text{and} \quad (i, j) \in R'\}.$$

Therefore, $\overleftarrow{G}'(N, \overleftarrow{R}')$ is actually $G'(N, R')$, where all its edges are now directed from high to low. Finally, define

$$\overleftrightarrow{R} = \vec{R} \cup \overleftarrow{R}',$$

and $\overleftrightarrow{G}(N, \overleftrightarrow{R})$ is now the "union" of $\vec{G}$ and $\overleftarrow{G}'$. It consists of all the edges of G, directed from low to high, and of all edges missing from G (except the self-loops) now added and directed from high to low.

Lemma 9.4: Let $\vec{G}_1(V, \vec{E}_1)$ and $\vec{G}_2(V, \vec{E}_2)$ be transitive orientations of $G_1(V, E_1)$ and $G_2(V, E_2)$, where $E_1 \cap E_2 = \varnothing$ and $G(V, E_1 \cup E_2)$ is a completely connected graph with no parallel edges and no self-loops. The graph $\vec{G}(V, \vec{E}_1 \cup \vec{E}_2)$ has no directed circuits.

Proof: Assume that $\vec{G}$ contains simple directed circuits. Let $v_1 \to v_2 \to v_3 \to \cdots \to v_k \to v_1$ be a simple directed circuit of minimum length. If $k > 3$, consider the edge $v_1 - v_3$. If it is directed $v_1 \to v_3$, then this circuit is not minimum; but, $v_3 \to v_1$ leads to the same contradiction. Thus, $k = 3$. Without loss of generality we may assume that $v_1 \to v_2$ and $v_2 \to v_3$ belong to

$\vec{G}_1$. Thus, by $\vec{G}_1$'s transitivity $v_1 \rightarrow v_3$ belongs to $\vec{G}_1$, too. Again a contradiction. Therefore, $\vec{G}$ contains no directed circuits.

QED

Theorem 9.3: $G(N, R)$ is a permutation graph if and only if $\vec{G}(N, \vec{R})$ and $\overleftarrow{G}'(N, \overleftarrow{R}')$ are transitive.

Proof: Assume that $G(N, R)$ is a permutation graph and that $(i, j) \in \vec{R}$ and $(j, k) \in \vec{R}$. By the definition of $\vec{R}$ it follows that

$$i < j \quad \text{and} \quad (i, j) \in R$$

and

$$j < k \quad \text{and} \quad (j, k) \in R.$$

But $G(N, R)$ is assumed to be a permutation graph; therefore,

$$(i, j) \in R \Rightarrow \text{either } i < j \quad \text{and} \quad P^{-1}(i) > P^{-1}(j)$$
$$\text{or} \quad i > j \quad \text{and} \quad P^{-1}(i) < P^{-1}(j)$$

and a similar statement holds for (j, k). Thus,

$$i < j \quad \text{and} \quad P^{-1}(i) > P^{-1}(j)$$

and

$$j < k \quad \text{and} \quad P^{-1}(j) > P^{-1}(k).$$

It follows that $i < k$ and $P^{-1}(i) > P^{-1}(k)$, and (i, k) is an edge in both G and $\vec{G}$. This proves the transitivity of $\vec{G}(N, \vec{R})$.

Now assume that $(i, j) \in \overleftarrow{R}'$ and $(j, k) \in \overleftarrow{R}'$. By the definition of $\overleftarrow{R}'$ it follows that

$$i > j \quad \text{and} \quad (i, j) \in R'$$

and

$$j > k \quad \text{and} \quad (j, k) \in R'.$$

However,

$$(i, j) \in R' \Rightarrow \text{ either } i < j \quad \text{ and } \quad P^{-1}(i) < P^{-1}(j)$$

$$\text{or} \quad i > j \quad \text{ and } \quad P^{-1}(i) > P^{-1}(j),$$

and a similar statement holds for (j, k). Thus,

$$i > j \quad \text{ and } \quad P^{-1}(i) > P^{-1}(j)$$

and

$$j > k \quad \text{ and } \quad P^{-1}(j) > P^{-1}(j).$$

It follows that $i > k$ and $P^{-1}(i) > P^{-1}(k)$, and therefore, $(i, k) \in R'$ and $(i, k) \in \bar{R}'$. This proves the transitivity of $\overleftrightarrow{G}'(N, \bar{R}')$, and the proof of the "only if" part of the theorem is complete.

Now assume that both $\overleftrightarrow{G}(N, \bar{R})$ and $\overleftrightarrow{G}'(N, \bar{R}')$ are transitive. By Lemma 9.4 $\overleftrightarrow{G}(N, \bar{R})$ is circuit-free. Thus, it contains a sink, namely, a vertex s_1 for which $d_0(s_1) = 0$. Clearly it cannot have more than one sink; consider the edge connecting two vertices, both of which are supposed to be sinks.

Let $N_1 = N - \{s_1\}$. The vertex subgraph $\overleftrightarrow{G}_1(N_1, \bar{R}_1)$ of $\overleftrightarrow{G}(N, \bar{R})$ is also completely connected and circuit-free. Therefore, $\overleftrightarrow{G}_1$ contains a unique sink s_2, too. We now define $N_2 = N_1 - \{s_2\}$ and $\overleftrightarrow{G}_2(N_2, \bar{R}_2)$; and so on.

Consider now the sequence of successive sinks $s_1, s_2, \ldots, s_n$, obtained as above. It is clear that $\vec{R}$ is the set of all ordered pairs (s_i, s_j) for which $i > j$, and that $\vec{R}$ is the subset of $\vec{R}$ of all (s_i, s_j) which satisfy the condition $s_i < s_j$. Clearly $P = [s_1, s_2, \ldots, s_n]$ is a permutation of N with $P(i) = s_i$ and $P^{-1}(s_i) = i$. Thus, R is the set of all unordered pairs (s_i, s_j) for which either $s_i < s_j$ and $P^{-1}(s_i) > P^{-1}(s_j)$ or $s_j > s_i$ and $P^{-1}(s_i) < P^{-1}(s_j)$. Hence, $G(N, R)$ is a permutation graph.

QED

This proof implies an algorithm for deciding whether a given graph $G(N, R)$ is a permutation graph. The defining permutation is obtained by the sequence of sinks of $\overleftrightarrow{G}(N, \bar{R})$, when sinks are successively eliminated from the graph. In case one of the resulting graphs does not have a sink, the original graph is not a permutation graph.

Let us apply the suggested algorithm to the graphs of Fig. 9.9. First we construct $\overleftrightarrow{G}(N, \bar{R})$ for the graph given in Fig. 9.9(a). This is shown in Fig. 9.10,

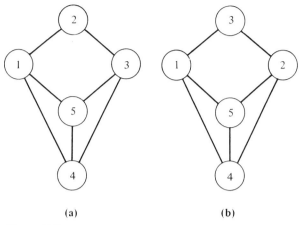

(a)   (b)

Figure 9.9

where the solid lines show the arcs of $\vec{G}$ and the dashed lines are those of $\bar{\bar{G}}'$. As is easily observed, this graph has no sinks, and therefore the graph of Fig. 9.9(a) is not a permutation graph.

The graph $\vec{\vec{G}}$ for the graph of Fig. 9.9(b) is shown in Fig. 9.11(a). Now vertex 3 is eliminated from the graph to yield the graph shown in Fig. 9.11(b). Vertex 5 is now a sink; thus, $P(2) = 5$. The successive steps are shown in Fig. 9.11(c) and (d). The resulting permutation is [3, 5, 4, 1, 2].

Let us now consider the harder problem, that of deciding whether the vertices of a given undirected graph $G(V, E)$ with no parallel edges and no self-loops can be relabeled in such a way that G becomes a permutation graph with respect to these labels.

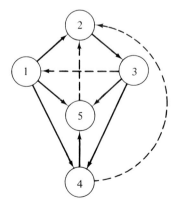

Figure 9.10

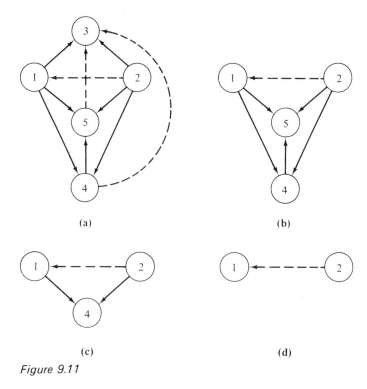

Figure 9.11

Theorem 9.4: A graph $G(V, R)$ is a permutation graph with respect to some labeling of the vertices if and only if both $G(V, R)$ and $G'(V, R')$ are transitively orientable.

Here $G'(V, R')$ is the complementary graph of $G(V, R)$ with respect to the completely connected graph on V.

Proof: Let $\vec{G}(V, \vec{R})$ and $\vec{G}'(V, \vec{R}')$ be transitive orientations of $G(V, R)$ and $G'(V, R')$. Construct the graph $\overleftrightarrow{G}(V, \overleftrightarrow{R})$, the merger of $\vec{G}(V, \vec{R})$ and $\vec{G}'(V, \vec{R}')$. By Lemma 9.4, $\overleftrightarrow{R}$ is circuit-free. Successively eliminate sinks to determine a "natural" ordering of the vertices. (The first sink is labeled n, where $n = |V|$; the next $n - 1$; and so on.) The set of vertices is now assumed to be $N = \{1, 2, \ldots, n\}$, and $G = G(N, R)$, $G' = G'(N, R')$ are defined in the obvious way. Clearly the edges in $\vec{G}(N, \vec{R})$ are now directed from low to high. Next, construct $\overleftarrow{G}'(N, \overleftarrow{R}')$ by reversing the direction of all the edges of $\vec{G}'$. Clearly $\overleftarrow{G}'$ is still transitive, and its edges are directed from high to low. By Theorem 9.3, $G(N, R)$ is a permutation graph.

The "only if" part of the theorem follows immediately from the "only if" part of Theorem 9.3.

QED

We now have an algorithm for deciding whether a given undirected unlabeled graph $G(V, R)$ can be labeled to become a permutation graph. It runs as follows:

1. Use the orientation algorithm of Section 9.2 to direct both $G(V, R)$ and $G'(V, R')$. If any contradiction arises $G(V, R)$ cannot be labeled to become a permutation graph.
2. Construct $\vec{\bar{G}}(V, \vec{\bar{R}})$ by merging $\vec{G}(V, \vec{R})$ and $\vec{G}'(V, \vec{R}')$ and eliminate sinks successively and use the new labels to define $\vec{G}(N, \vec{R})$ and $\vec{G}'(N, \vec{R}')$.
3. Merge $\vec{G}(N, \vec{R})$ and $\vec{\bar{G}}'(N, \vec{\bar{R}}')$ and eliminate sinks successively. The sequence of sinks provides the permutation defining $G(N, R)$.

Consider the graph shown in Fig. 9.12(a). The complementary graph is shown in Fig. 9.12(b). We apply the orientation algorithm to both. The algorithm is successful on both and possible orientations are shown in Fig. 9.12(c) and (d). The merger of the two oriented graphs is shown in Fig. 9.12(e); also the "natural" labeling is shown. The result of reversing the direction of all the edges of the complement is shown in Fig. 9.12(f). The resulting permutation is $P = [4, 2, 1, 5, 3]$.

9.4   Examples of applications

In this section we bring first an application of the maximum clique algorithm to the field of system programming. In a multiprogramming computer system environment the computer's memory holds at one time n programs, whose starting addresses are, respectively, $x_1, x_2, \ldots, x_n$.

After a certain time, some of these programs change their memory-space requirements, with the new length of the ith program being l_i. In order to satisfy these requirements, some of the programs are shifted bodily from one address to another to make new space.

With each program we associate a cost of transplantation ω_i which incurs if the program is shifted but is independent of the distance shifted. We stipulate that the shifts permitted preserve the order of the programs in memory, and also that the overall memory requirement fits the available space [1].

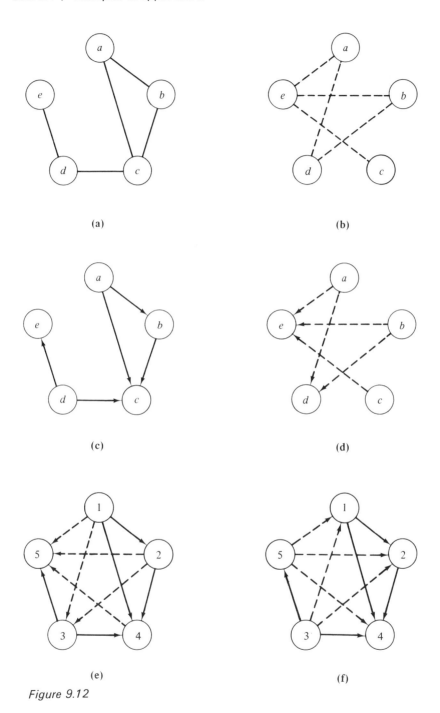

(a)

(b)

(c)

(d)

(e)

(f)

Figure 9.12

The problem is to minimize the reallocation costs. To tackle this problem, we define an undirected graph, $G(N, R)$, whose vertex i corresponds to the ith program. We draw an edge $(i, j) \in R$ if the local memory requirements are such that programs i and j can both start at the same initial addresses x_i and x_j, respectively. This is expressed for $i < j$ by

$$(i, j) \in R \Leftrightarrow \sum_{k=i}^{j-1} l_k \leq x_j - x_i$$

and similarly for $i > j$.

A maximum clique in the graph G corresponds to a set of programs that can be left in place simultaneously while the others must be shifted. Thus the cost-minimization problem is equivalent to the problem of finding a maximum clique (with the maximum sum of ω_i) in G.

We proceed to show that $\vec{G}(N, \vec{R})$ and $\overleftarrow{G}'(N, \overleftarrow{R}')$ are both transitive. Let $i < j < k$. If $(i, j) \in R$ and $(j, k) \in R$; then by definition

$$\sum_{m=i}^{j-1} l_m \leq x_j - x_i, \qquad \sum_{m=j}^{k-1} l_m \leq x_k - x_j.$$

Adding these two inequalities, we obtain

$$\sum_{m=i}^{k-1} l_m \leq x_k - x_i$$

and thus $(i, k) \in R$.

Similarly, by using the oppositely directed inequalities, we derive

$$(i, j) \in R' \quad \text{and} \quad (j, k) \in R' \quad \Rightarrow \quad (i, k) \in R'.$$

Thus, by Theorem 9.3, any memory reallocation of the type described generates a permutation graph. In particular it generates a transitive graph and we may use the maximum clique procedure of Section 9.1 for finding an optimal reallocation.

To ensure that the programs are not shifted out of memory, we modify our description by requiring that programs 1 and n, which are dummy programs, never require additional space and are not to be moved. This can be taken care of by either directly looking for the maximum clique which contains vertices 1 and n, or indirectly, by assigning them very high shift costs ω_1 and ω_n.

In the table shown we summarize a reallocation problem and its solution. We assume that programs 1 and 8 are dummy programs and should not be moved. Also, we assume that all programs have the same cost of transplantation. Therefore, the problem reduces to that of finding a maximum (in number of vertices in it) clique among those which contain both vertex 1 and vertex 8.

Program Number	Start Address x_i	Length Required l_i	Size of a Largest Clique (containing 1) Whose Highest Vertex Is i
1	0	0	1
2	0	300	2
3	200	100	0
4	600	600	3
5	1000	200	3
6	1100	100	0
7	1500	300	4
8	1700	0	4

The graph $G(N, R)$ of our example is shown in Fig. 9.13. There is a unique clique of maximum size which contains both 1 and 8 : $\{1, 2, 5, 8\}$. As the reader

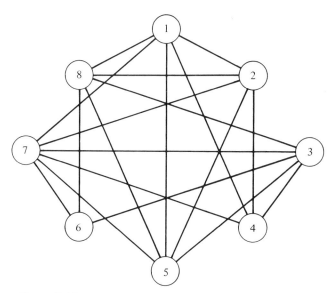

Figure 9.13

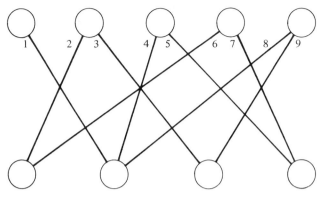

Figure 9.14

can establish for himself, there is no need to construct $G(N, R)$ and the last column of the table can be computed directly.

It can be shown that every permutation graph corresponds to some memory reallocation problem [2]. We now turn to a problem from a different area.

In his book *Introduction to Combinatorial Mathematics* [3], Liu describes a problem of realizing a connection board with the least number of planes. The original connection requirements are prescribed by a bipartite graph. For illustration consider the following example. Consider the connection requirements specified in Fig. 9.14, where the nodes are accessible on several parallel planes and the lines are made of conducting plated metal strips on any one of the planes. In order to determine the least number of planes in which these connections can be realized, without two connections intersecting in one plane, Liu constructs a new undirected graph in which the vertices correspond to the lines (connections) of the original problem. Two vertices are connected by an edge if and only if the corresponding lines intersect. It is then observed that the chromatic number of the resulting graph is the same as the required number of planes and that a coloration prescribes an assignment of lines to planes. However, the situation can be further improved by observing that in essence we have a permutation graph. In our example, simply "trim" the vertices above and below. The result is shown in Fig. 9.15.

The defining permutation is $P = [2, 6, 1, 4, 8, 3, 9, 5, 7]$. Now, instead of using any of the conventional algorithms for coloration, all of which are comparatively inefficient, we can use the algorithm in Section 9.1:

$$D_1 = (\{1\}),$$
$$D_2 = (\{1\}, \{2\}),$$
$$D_3 = (\{1, 3\}, \{2\}),$$
$$D_4 = (\{1, 3\}, \{2, 4\}),$$
$$D_5 = (\{1, 3, 5\}, \{2, 4\}),$$
$$D_6 = (\{1, 3, 5\}, \{2, 4\}, \{6\}),$$
$$D_7 = (\{1, 3, 5, 7\}, \{2, 4\}, \{6\}),$$
$$D_8 = (\{1, 3, 5, 7\}, \{2, 4, 8\}, \{6\}),$$
$$D_9 = (\{1, 3, 5, 7\}, \{2, 4, 8, 9\}, \{6\}).$$

Also, the chromatic number of this graph could be determined directly by the maximum clique procedure of Section 9.1.

Finally, we want to mention a slightly different way of finding a minimum coloration of a permutation graph. The blocks (subsets) are constructed directly from P. Let us illustrate on P mentioned above. The first block contains 2, next is 6 (which is greater than 2 and to its right in P and therefore not connected to it), next is 8, and finally 9. Thus, the first block is $\{2, 6, 8, 9\}$. It is clear that we always adjoin the first element which can be adjoined to the present set. The procedure is continued on the remaining sequence: $[1, 4, 3, 5, 7]$. We derive the block $\{1, 4, 5, 7\}$. The last block is $\{3\}$.

The proof of validity of this algorithm is left as an exercise (see Exercise 9.7).

This chapter is based on two papers by Pnueli, Lempel, and Even [2, 4].

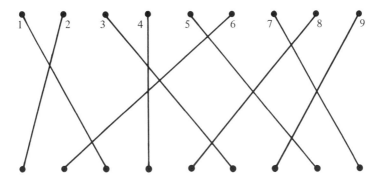

Figure 9.15

EXERCISES

9.1   Prove that if G is a circuit-free directed finite graph, then G has at least one source.

9.2   Which of the following three graphs is transitively orientable? Which is a permutation graph with respect to some relabeling of the vertices?

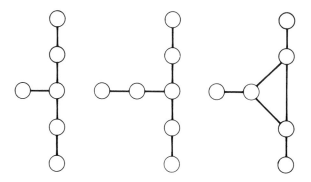

9.3   In the following reallocation problem, find the maximum number of programs which can stay in their previous place. Assume that negative addresses are not allowed.

i	1	2	3	4	5	6	7
x_i	900	1000	1800	2400	2600	3100	3500
l_i	200	400	300	500	800	100	700

9.4   Find the minimum number of planes for realization of the following connection board, and describe the connections on each plane in such a realization.

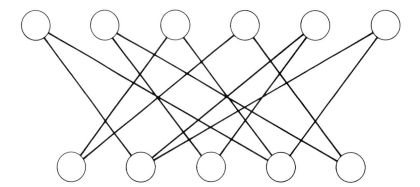

9.5 Prove that if a labeled graph $G(N, R)$ is a permutation graph, then its complement $G'(N, R')$ is also a permutation graph. What is the relation between the permutation P which corresponds to G, and P' which corresponds to G'?

9.6 Prove that the permutation graph of the permutation P is isomorphic to the permutation graph of the permutation P^{-1}. (Two graphs are isomorphic if renaming the vertices of one makes it identical with the other.)

9.7 Prove the validity of the coloration algorithm described at the end of Section 9.4.

The following set of exercises follows some of the results of references 5, 6, and 7.
Let G be an undirected finite graph with no parallel edges and no self-loops. An orientation of its edges into $\vec{G}$ is called an *R-orientation* if (1) $\vec{G}$ has no directed circuits; (2) if $b \to a$ and $c \to a$, then $b - c$ (that is, either $b \to c$ or $c \to b$).

9.8 Describe and prove the validity of an algorithm for finding an R-orientation if one exists. (*Hint :* Look for a vertex v, for which $\Gamma(v)$ is completely connected.)

9.9 Prove that a set of vertices S is completely connected in G if and only if for some vertex v, $S \subset \{v\} \cup \Gamma^{-1}(v)$, where Γ^{-1} is with respect to $\vec{G}$. Describe an algorithm for finding a maximum clique of an R-orientable G. Assume that the set of vertices of $\vec{G}$ is $N = \{1, 2, \ldots, n\}$ and all edges are directed from low to high (show that such a relabeling is always possible).

9.10 Prove that the algorithm of Section 9.1 for coloring transitively oriented graphs finds a minimum coloration for $\vec{G}$ (which is R-oriented, but may not be transitive.)

9.11 Find a graph which is transitively orientable but is not R-orientable, and a graph which is R-orientable but is not transitively orientable.

9.12 Construct a sequence of vertices of $\vec{G}$ in the following way: $v_1 = n$, v_2 is the highest vertex not in $\{v_1\} \cup \Gamma^{-1}(v_1)$, and in general v_i is the highest vertex not in

$$\{v_1, v_2, \ldots, v_{i-1}\} \cup \Gamma^{-1}(v_1) \cup \Gamma^{-1}(v_2) \cup \cdots \cup \Gamma^{-1}(v_{i-1}).$$

Let $v_1, v_2, \ldots, v_t$ be the resulting sequence.
(a) Prove that the set $\{v_1, v_2, \ldots, v_t\}$ is independent in G.
(b) Prove that the family $S_1, S_2, \ldots, S_t$, where $S_i = \{v_i\} \cup \Gamma^{-1}(v_i)$, is a cover of N by t completely connected sets.
(c) Conclude that $\{v_1, v_2, \ldots, v_t\}$ is a maximum independent set and t is the minimum number of cliques which cover N.

REFERENCES

1. Knuth, D. E., *The Art of Computer Programming*, Vol. 1, Fundamental Algorithms, Addison-Wesley, Reading, Mass., 1968, Sec. 2.2.2.

2. Even, S., Pnueli, A., and Lempel, A., "Permutation Graphs and Transitive Graphs," *J. ACM*, Vol. 19, 1972, pp. 400–10.

3. Liu, C. L., *Introduction to Combinatorial Mathematics*, McGraw-Hill, New York, 1968, Chap. 9, Ex. 9-5.

4. Pnueli, A., Lempel, A., and Even, S., "Transitive Orientation of Graphs and Identification of Permutation Graphs," *Can. J. Math.*, Vol. 23, No. 1, 1971, pp. 160–75.

5. Berge, C., "Some Classes of Perfect Graphs," in *Graph Theory and Theoretic Physics*, F. Harary (ed.), Academic Press, New York, 1967.

6. Rose, D. J., "Triangulated Graphs and the Elimination Process," *J. Mathematical Analysis and Applications*, Vol. 32, 1970, pp. 597–609.

7. Gavril, F., "Algorithm for Minimum Coloring, Maximum Clique, Minimum Covering by Cliques and Maximum Independent Set of a Chordal Graph," to appear in *J. SIAM* on Computing.

10

MAXIMUM FLOW
IN A GRAPH

10.1 Graphs with a source, a sink, and upper bounds on the flow
in the edges

All the graphs of interest in this section are finite, directed, have no self-loops, and no parallel edges. Each such graph, $G(V, E)$, has one vertex, s, called the *source* and one vertex, t, called the *sink*. These two vertices are not necessarily a source and a sink as previously defined; that is, s may have incoming edges; t, outgoing edges. Although we allow these edges to exist, they are actually of no interest.

Each one of the edges, e, of G is assigned an upper bound $c(e) \geq 0$ called its *capacity*. A function $\phi(e) \geq 0$ defined for each edge e is called a *flow* if it satisfies the following two conditions:

1. For every edge e $\phi(e) \leq c(e)$.
2. Let $e_1, e_2, \ldots, e_p$ and $e'_1, e'_2, \ldots, e'_q$ be the outgoing edges and incoming

edges, respectively, to some vertex v. If $v \neq s$ and $v \neq t$, then

$$0 = \sum_{i=1}^{p} \phi(e_i) - \sum_{i=1}^{q} \phi(e_i'). \qquad (10.1)$$

Rule 2 is called the *conservation rule*. It means that the total incoming flow to the vertex v is equal to the total outgoing flow from v. That is, in vertices, other than the source and the sink, there is no generation of flow and no absorption of flow.

The *value of the flow* ϕ, designated Φ, is defined as

$$\Phi = \sum_{i=1}^{p} \phi(e_i) - \sum_{i=1}^{q} \phi(e_i'), \qquad (10.2)$$

where $e_1, e_2, \ldots, e_p$ and $e_1', e_2', \ldots, e_q'$ are the outgoing and incoming edges of s.

A flow ϕ is called *maximum* if its value Φ is the maximum of all the possible values of flows. Our aim is to describe an efficient algorithm for finding a maximum flow.

Let $S \cup \bar{S} = V$, while $S \cap \bar{S} = \phi$. We denote by $(S; \bar{S})$ the set of all edges $a \xrightarrow{e} b$, where $a \in S$ and $b \in \bar{S}$. Also, $c(S; \bar{S})$ is defined by

$$c(S; \bar{S}) = \sum_{e \in (S; \bar{S})} c(e). \qquad (10.3)$$

Let us define the value of ϕ at $(S; \bar{S})$, $\phi(S; \bar{S})$ by

$$\phi(S; \bar{S}) = \sum_{e \in (S; \bar{S})} \phi(e) - \sum_{e \in (\bar{S}; S)} \phi(e). \qquad (10.4)$$

Clearly,

$$\Phi = \phi(\{s\}; V - \{s\}). \qquad (10.5)$$

A set $(S; \bar{S})$ is called a *cut* if $s \in S$ and $t \in \bar{S}$; the quantity $c(S; \bar{S})$ is then called the *value of the cut*. We observe that if $(S; \bar{S})$ is a cut, then

$$\Phi = \phi(S; \bar{S}). \qquad (10.6)$$

This is easily shown by summing up (10.2) and (10.1) for every vertex $v \in S$. Every edge $a \rightarrow b$, where both $a \in S$ and $b \in S$, appears twice in the resulting equation and its flow is canceled out. The remaining terms yield

$$\Phi = \sum_{e \in (S; \bar{S})} \phi(e) - \sum_{e \in (\bar{S}; S)} \phi(e). \tag{10.7}$$

By (10.4) we get (10.6).

Since $(V - \{t\}; \{t\})$ is a cut, (10.6) implies that

$$\Phi = \phi(V - \{t\}; \{t\}). \tag{10.8}$$

By condition 1, $\phi(e) \leq c(e)$ for every e. Therefore,

$$\sum_{e \in (S; \bar{S})} \phi(e) \leq \sum_{e \in (S; \bar{S})} c(e) = c(S; \bar{S}).$$

Also,

$$\sum_{e \in (\bar{S}; S)} \phi(e) \geq 0.$$

Thus, by (10.6) we get

$$\Phi \leq c(S; \bar{S}) ; \tag{10.9}$$

namely, the value of every cut is an upper bound on the value of the flow, and the value of every flow is a lower bound on the values of the cuts. Thus, if we succeed in achieving a flow with a value equal to a value of some cut, then the flow is maximum and the cut is minimum.

We shall now describe the labeling procedure of Ford and Fulkerson [1] for finding a maximum flow (and a minimum cut). The algorithm consists of two phases. In the first phase we attempt to determine whether the present Φ is maximum. In case it is not, we apply the second phase, in which we use the labels generated in the first phase to increase Φ, and we repeat the first phase. Otherwise, a cut is determined with a value equal to Φ.

The labels assigned in the first phase are of the form (d_v, Δ_v) for vertex v, where d_v is the direction from which this label has reached v, and Δ_v is a positive number which is an additional quantity which can be made available at vertex v. The form of d_v, where $v \neq s$ is either u^+ or u^-, where u is the vertex by which this additional quantity is made available; the symbol u^+ is used in case this can be done through an increase in flow in the edge $u \to v$, and u^- is used if this can be done through a decrease in flow in the edge $v \to u$.

In the first phase each vertex is labeled at most once. If t receives a label, the d_v symbols are used to trace back a path on which the value of Φ can be increased by Δ_t.

A *forward labeling* from vertex u to vertex v on the edge $u \xrightarrow{e} v$ is applicable if

1. u is labeled and v is not;
2. $c(e) > \phi(e)$.

The label that v gets is (u^+, Δ_v), where

$$\Delta_v = \text{Min}\{\Delta_u, c(e) - \phi(e)\}.$$

A *backward labeling* from vertex u to vertex v on the edge $u \xleftarrow{e} v$ is applicable if

1. u is labeled and v is not;
2. $\phi(e) > 0$.

The label that v gets is (u^-, Δ_v), where

$$\Delta_v = \text{Min}\{\Delta_u, \phi(e)\}.$$

Algorithm 10.1
(1) Assign the edges some legal flow; an assignment $\phi(e) = 0$ for every edge e will do.
(2) Label s by $(-, \infty)$; the value of d_s is irrelevant.
(3) Search for a vertex v which can be labeled through either forward or backward labeling. If none exist, the present flow is maximum; stop. If such v exists, label it. If $v = t$, go to step (4); otherwise repeat step (3).
(4) Let the label of t be (d_t, Δ_t). If $d_t = v^+$, increase the flow on $v \to t$ by Δ_t. If $d_t = v^-$, decrease the flow on $v \leftarrow t$ by Δ_t. (If the initial flow has no flow coming out of t, none will be generated in our procedure and $d_t = v^-$ will never occur.)
(5) If $v = s$, erase all labels and go to step (2).
(6) Let the label of v be (d_v, Δ_v). If $d_v = u^+$, increase the flow on $u \to v$ by Δ_t, let u assume the task of v, and go to step (5). In case $d_v = u^-$, decrease the flow on $u \leftarrow v$ by Δ_t, let u assume the task of v, and go to

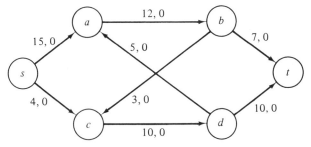

Figure 10.1

step (5). (If the initial flow has no flow entering s, none will be generated in our procedure, and $d_v = s^-$ will never occur. In this case, if $d_v = u^-$ we can go directly to (6) instead of (5).)

As an example, consider the graph shown in Fig. 10.1. Next to each edge e we write $c(e)$, $\phi(e)$ in this order. We take as an initial flow $\phi(e) = 0$ in all edges, as suggested in step (1). A first wave of label propagation might be

$$s:(—, \infty),$$
$$c:(s^+, 4),$$
$$d:(c^+, 4),$$
$$a:(d^+, 4).$$
$$b:(a^+, 4),$$
$$t:(b^+, 4).$$

The last application of step (3) sends us to step (4). Here, going through the loop (4) $\rightarrow$ (5) $\rightarrow$ (6) and back to (5), v becomes b, then a, d, c, s. Thus, we are backtracking a path through which Φ is increased to 4. The resulting flow is shown in Fig. 10.2. A next wave of label propagation can be as that in the

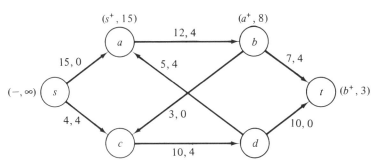

Figure 10.2

diagram. This time Φ is increased to 7. The new flow is shown in Fig. 10.3(a), where a new wave of labeling is shown. Again the flow is increased by 3 to 10. The new flow and the wave of labeling is shown in Fig. 10.3(b). Now the flow is increased by 4 to 14. The resulting flow is shown in Fig. 10.3(c).

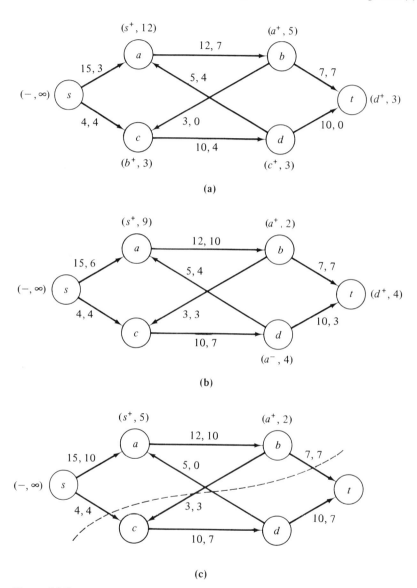

Figure 10.3

This time, as shown, the label propagation does not reach t. The algorithm stops at step (3).

First, let us show that the algorithm will stop if all capacities and initial flows in all edges are integral. Each time the labeling reaches t the flow is increased by at least one unit. Since there is an upper bound on the flow (any cut will do, by (10.9)), the number of times the labeling can reach t is bounded. Also, each labeling wave is finite, since each vertex is labeled at most once, and the number of vertices is finite. In case the bounds are not integral, this argument fails. In fact, Ford and Fulkerson found that the algorithm may fail. Their counterexample (reference 2, p. 21) displays an infinite sequence of flow augmentations. The flow converges (in infinitely many steps) to a value which is one fourth of the maximum value of the flow. We shall not bring their example here, because it is no longer that important. In a recent paper, Edmonds and Karp [2] have shown that a slight modification of Algorithm 10.1 will ensure termination for any real capacities. This will be discussed in the next section.

One could have argued that for all practical purposes, we may assume that the algorithm is sure to halt. This follows from the fact that our computations are usually through a fixed radix (decimal, binary, and so on) number representation with a bound on the number of digits used; in other words, all figures are multiples of a fixed quantum and the termination proof works here as it does for integers. However, a simple example shows the weakness of this argument. Consider the graph shown in Figure 10.4. Assume that M is a very large integer. If the algorithm starts with $\phi(e) = 0$ for all e, and alternately one uses $s \to a \to b \to t$ and $s \to b \to a \to t$ as augmenting paths, in accord with Algorithm 10.1, it will take $2M$ augmentations before $\Phi = 2M$

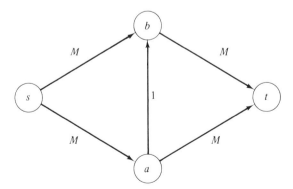

Figure 10.4

is achieved. The Edmonds and Karp modification makes sure that this kind of trouble will not occur.

Now let us show that when the algorithm stops we have a maximum flow (and a minimum cut). In the last labeling, let S be the set of labeled vertices. Clearly, s is labeled. Also, every edge $a \rightarrow b$, where $a \in S$ (labeled) and $b \in \bar{S}$ (unlabeled) must be saturated; that is, $\phi(e) = c(e)$. For if $\phi(e) < c(e)$, by step (3) b would have been labeled. Similarly, every edge $a \leftarrow b$, where $a \in S$ and $b \in \bar{S}$, must carry no flow; that is, $\phi(e) = 0$. For if $\phi(e) > 0$, by step (3) b would have been labeled. Thus, by (10.7) and (10.3) we get

$$\phi = c(S; \bar{S}).$$

Now (10.9) and the discussion following it imply that the particular Φ that we end up with is maximum and the cut we have is minimum. In the example of Fig. 10.3(c), $S = \{s, a, b\}$ and the cut $(S, \bar{S})$ is shown by a dashed line. As is easily seen, the value of this cut is 14, as is the total flow.

The fact that in the type of graph we have discussed there exists a maximum flow which is equal to a minimum cut is known as the maximal flow–minimal cut theorem.

It should be reemphasized that if all the capacities are integral, and the initial flow is integral, then no fractions are ever introduced by Algorithm 10.1. Since we can always use the all-zero as an initial flow, this proves that the maximum flow, in this case, is always integral, and no fractional flows in the edges are necessary to achieve maximality. This stands in a clear contrast to the situation in linear programming; there, even if integral optimal solutions exist, it may be necessary to invest additional effort to find one.

10.2 Improvement of the algorithm with a bound on the number of steps in the computation

In this section we shall modify the maximum-flow algorithm slightly and show that this change guarantees that the computation will terminate within a specified number of steps, independent of the nature of the capacities. We follow the recent work of Edmonds and Karp [2].

Note that the labeling procedure of Algorithm 10.1 identifies an augmenting path from s to t, if one exists. The value Δ_t is the least of all values

$\varepsilon_1, \varepsilon_2, \ldots, \varepsilon_p$ defined in the following way. Let

$$s = u_0 \overset{e_1}{-\!\!-} u_1 \overset{e_2}{-\!\!-} u_2 \overset{e_3}{-\!\!-} \cdots \overset{e_p}{-\!\!-} u_p = t$$

be the augmenting path. Some of its edges are directed forward, and some are directed backward. If e_i is directed forward, $u_{i-1} \overset{e_i}{\to} u_i$, then

$$\varepsilon_i = c(e_i) - \phi(e_i) > 0.$$

If e_i is directed backward, $u_{i-1} \overset{e_i}{\leftarrow} u_i$, then

$$\varepsilon_i = \phi(e_i) > 0.$$

Clearly,

$$\Delta_t = \underset{1 \leq i \leq p}{\text{Min}} \ \varepsilon_i > 0.$$

Thus, $\Delta_t = \varepsilon_i$ for some i. Such an edge, e_i, is called a *bottleneck*.

Assume that we start with an initial flow ϕ_0. (This may be an assignment of $\phi(e) = 0$ for every edge e in the graph.) After finding a first augmenting path, the flow changes to be ϕ_1, and so on. Assume that $\phi_0, \phi_1, \phi_2, \ldots$ is the sequence of such flows.

Lemma 10.1: If $k < m$ and e is a bottleneck used in the forward (backward) direction in both the augmenting path which changes ϕ_k into ϕ_{k+1} and in the augmenting path which changes ϕ_m into ϕ_{m+1}, then there exists an l, $k < l < m$, such that e is used in the backward (forward) direction in the augmenting path which changes ϕ_l into ϕ_{l+1}.

Proof: Since e is a bottleneck used in the forward direction in the augmenting path which changes ϕ_k into ϕ_{k+1}, it is saturated ($\phi_{k+1}(e) = c(e)$) in ϕ_{k+1}. Thus, it cannot be used in the forward direction in a later augmenting path unless in an intermediate augmenting path its flow has been reduced; that is, it has been used in the backward direction. A similar argument proves the alternative statement.

QED

The change that Edmonds and Karp make in the Ford and Fulkerson algorithm is as follows: Use the "first-labeled, first scanned" principle. That is, first label the source s. Then label all unlabeled vertices which can be labeled from s. In every step we use a labeled vertex v to propagate new labels to all its unlabeled immediate neighbors, either by forward or by backward labeling; this action is referred to as *scanning v*. If v has been labeled before u, then it is scanned before u.

It is easy to see that the labels will propagate now exactly as the labels of Algorithm 4.1 do. Thus, the augmenting path will always be a shortest path, if its length is measured in the number of edges (ignoring the direction of the edges used). Clearly, by shortest, we mean a shortest path among all possible augmenting paths. Let us denote by $\lambda(u, v)$ the length of the shortest path from vertex u to vertex v, where directions are ignored except that an edge can be used in the forward direction only if it is not saturated, and it can be used in the backward direction only if it carries nonzero flow; the length is measured by the number of edges on the path.

Lemma 10.2: If the "first-labeled, first-scanned" principle is used and if $k < l$ and e is used in the forward (backward) direction in the augmenting path which changes ϕ_k into ϕ_{k+1} and in the backward (forward) direction in the augmenting path which changes ϕ_l into ϕ_{l+1}, then

$$\lambda^l(s, t) \geqslant \lambda^k(s, t) + 2.$$

Here $\lambda^i(u, v)$ denotes the length of a shortest augmenting path from u to v when the flow is ϕ_i.

Proof: First, let us show that for every vertex v and every $k = 0, 1, 2, \ldots,$

$$\lambda^k(s, v) \leqslant \lambda^{k+1}(s, v). \tag{10.10}$$

If there is no path, with the flow ϕ_{k+1}, from s to v, then $\lambda^{k+1}(s, v)$ is assumed to be infinite and the statement follows trivially. Otherwise, assume that a shortest path from s to v with respect to ϕ_{k+1} is

$$s = u_0 \overset{e_1}{\text{---}} u_1 \overset{e_2}{\text{---}} u_2 \overset{e_3}{\text{---}} \cdots \overset{e_p}{\text{---}} u_p = v. \tag{10.11}$$

Clearly,

$$\lambda^k(s, u_0) = 0.$$

Assume that e_i is used in the forward direction in (10.11). Thus, $\phi_{k+1}(e_i)$ $< c(e_i)$. Therefore, either $\phi_k(e_i) < c(e_i)$ or e_i has been used in the backward direction in the augmenting path which has changed ϕ_k into ϕ_{k+1}. In the former case,

$$\lambda^k(s, u_i) \leqslant \lambda^k(s, u_{i-1}) + 1, \tag{10.12}$$

for one augmenting path from s to u_i is a shortest path to u_{i-1} followed by e_i in the forward direction. In the latter case, using the fact that e_i has been used in the backward direction in the augmenting path, we get

$$\lambda^k(s, u_{i-1}) = \lambda^k(s, u_i) + 1.$$

Thus, (10.12) holds in both cases. The proof in case e_i is used in the backward direction in the path (10.11) is similar.

By summing up the statements (10.12) for $i = 1, 2, \ldots, p$ we get

$$\lambda^k(s, u_p) \leqslant p.$$

But $p = \lambda^{k+1}(s, v)$. Thus, (10.10) follows. Clearly, a similar argument shows that for every vertex v and every $k = 0, 1, 2, \ldots,$

$$\lambda^k(v, t) \leqslant \lambda^{k+1}(v, t). \tag{10.13}$$

Assume now that $u \xrightarrow{e} v$, where e is as in the premise of the lemma. We have

$$\lambda^l(s, t) = \lambda^l(s, v) + 1 + \lambda^l(u, t)$$

since e is assumed to be used in the backward direction in augmenting ϕ_l. But

$$\lambda^l(s, v) \geqslant \lambda^k(s, v)$$

and

$$\lambda^l(u, t) \geqslant \lambda^k(u, t)$$

by (10.10). Furthermore,

$$\lambda^k(s, v) = \lambda^k(s, u) + 1$$

since e is used in the forward direction in augmenting ϕ_k. Thus,

$$\lambda^l(s, t) \geq \lambda^k(s, u) + 1 + 1 + \lambda^k(u, t)$$

or

$$\lambda^l(s, t) \geq \lambda^k(s, t) + 2.$$

QED

Theorem 10.1: (Edmonds and Karp). If, in the labeling procedure for finding a maximum flow in a graph $G(V, E)$, each flow augmentation is done along an augmenting path having fewest edges, then a maximum flow will be obtained after no more than $|E| \cdot (|V| + 2)/2$ augmentations.

Proof: Let $u \xrightarrow{e} v$ be any edge. Let us consider the sequence of flows $\phi_{k_1}, \phi_{k_2}, \ldots$, where $k_1 < k_2 < \cdots$ such that e is used in the forward direction in augmenting ϕ_{k_i} and is a bottleneck. By Lemma 10.1, there exists a sequence $l_1, l_2, \ldots$ such that

$$k_1 < l_1 < k_2 < l_2 < k_3 \cdots$$

and e is used in the backward direction in augmenting ϕ_{l_i}. By Lemma 10.2 we have

$$\lambda^{k_i}(s, t) + 2 \leq \lambda^{l_i}(s, t)$$

and

$$\lambda^{l_i}(s, t) + 2 \leq \lambda^{k_{i+1}}(s, t).$$

Thus,

$$\lambda^{k_1}(s, t) + 4(j - 1) \leq \lambda^{k_j}(s, t).$$

Since

$$\lambda^{k_j}(s, t) \leq |V| - 1$$

and

$$1 \leq \lambda^{k_1}(s, t),$$

we have

$$1 + 4(j - 1) \leqslant |V| - 1$$

or

$$j \leqslant \frac{|V| + 2}{4}.$$

Thus, e can be used as a bottleneck in the forward direction at most $(|V| + 2)/4$ times. A similar argument shows that it can be used as a bottleneck in the backward direction at most $(|V| + 2)/4$ times, too. Thus, each edge can serve as a bottleneck at most $(|V| + 2)/2$ times. Since the number of edges is $|E|$, the number of augmentations is at most $|E| \cdot (|V| + 2)/2$.

QED

It should be noticed that no assumption was made about the edge capacities except that they are nonnegative. Thus, the Edmonds and Karp variation of Algorithm 10.1 terminates in a finite number of steps for any real nonnegative capacities.

Since the number of checks in Algorithm 4.1 is at most $|E|$, the number of checks in the maximum-flow solution is at most $|E|^2 \cdot (|V| + 2)/2$. Thus, if $|V| = n$, the number of checks is at most $n^2(n - 1)^2(n + 2)/2$.

For further results on this subject see references 4 and 5.

10.3 Graphs with upper and lower bounds on the flow in the edges

In the previous sections we have assumed that the flow in the edges is bounded from above but the lower bound on all the edges is zero. The significance of this assumption is that the assignment of $\phi(e) = 0$, for every edge e, defines a legal flow, and the algorithm for improving the flow can be started without any difficulty.

In this section, in addition to the upper bound, $c(e)$, on the flow through e, we assume that the flow is also bounded from below by $b(e)$. Thus, ϕ must satisfy

$$b(e) \leqslant \phi(e) \leqslant c(e) \tag{10.14}$$

in every edge e. We still assume condition 2 (the conservation rule).

Thus, our problem of finding a maximum flow is divided into two. First, we want to check whether the given graph has legal flows, and if the answer is positive, we want to find one. Second, we want to increase the flow and find a maximum flow.

A simple example of a graph which has no legal flow is shown in Fig. 10.5. Here next to each edge e we write $b(e)$, $c(e)$.

Figure 10.5

We shall now describe an algorithm for testing whether a given graph has legal flows. In case of a positive answer, a flow will be found.

We modify the original graph $G(V, E)$ in the following way:

1. Add to the set of vertices two new vertices: $\bar{s}$, which is called the auxiliary source, and $\bar{t}$, which is called the auxiliary sink.

2. For every $v \in V$ construct an edge $v \overset{e}{\rightarrow} \bar{t}$ with an upper bound

$$c(e) = \sum_{i=1}^{p} b(e_i),$$

where $e_1, e_2, \ldots, e_p$ are the edges which emanate from v in G.

3. For every $v \in V$ construct an edge $\bar{s} \overset{e}{\rightarrow} v$ with an upper bound

$$\bar{c}(e) = \sum_{i=1}^{q} b(e_i'),$$

where $e_1', e_2', \ldots, e_q'$ are the edges which enter v in G.

4. For each edge e of G define an upper bound $\bar{c}(e) = c(e) - b(e)$.

5. Define a new edge $t \overset{e}{\rightarrow} s$ with a very high upper bound $\bar{c}(e) \, (= \infty)$.

The resulting auxiliary graph has a source $\bar{s}$, a sink $\bar{t}$ (s and t are regarded here as regular vertices which now have to conform to the conservation rule), and upper bounds on the edges. The lower bound, as in the previous sections, is assumed to be zero everywhere.

Let us demonstrate this construction on the graph shown in Fig. 10.6(a). The auxiliary graph is shown in Fig. 10.6(b). The upper bounds $\bar{c}(e)$ are shown next to the edges to which they apply.

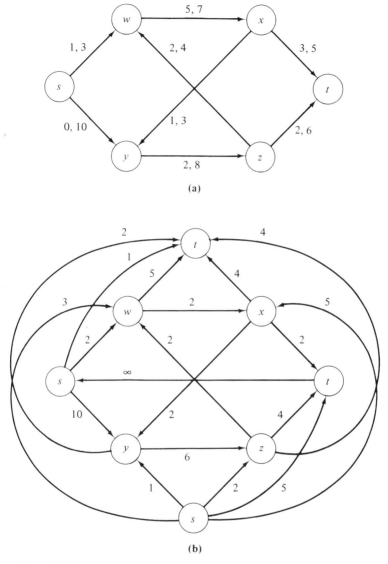

Figure 10.6

We may now use Algorithm 10.1 to find a maximum flow in the auxiliary graph.

Theorem 10.2: The original graph has a legal flow if and only if the maximum flow in the auxiliary graph is one in which all the edges which emanate from $\bar{s}$ are saturated.

Clearly, if all the edges which emanate from $\bar{s}$ are saturated, then so are all the edges which enter $\bar{t}$. This follows from the fact that each $b(e)$, of the original graph, contributes its value to the capacity of one edge emanating from $\bar{s}$ and to the capacity of one edge entering $\bar{t}$. Thus, the sum of capacities of edges emanating from $\bar{s}$ is equal to the sum of capacities of edges entering $\bar{t}$.

Proof: Assume that we find a (maximum) flow $\bar{\phi}$ of the auxiliary graph which saturates all edges which emanate from $\bar{s}$. Define the following flow ϕ for the original graph:

$$\phi(e) = \bar{\phi}(e) + b(e) \qquad \text{if } e \in E. \tag{10.15}$$

Since

$$0 \leqslant \bar{\phi}(e) \leqslant \bar{c}(e) = c(e) - b(e), \tag{10.16}$$

we have

$$b(e) \leqslant \phi(e) \leqslant c(e). \tag{10.17}$$

Now, if $e_1, e_2, \ldots, e_p$ are the original edges which emanate from v, where $v \in V - \{s, t\}$, $e'_1, e'_2, \ldots, e'_q$ are the original edges which enter v, σ is the auxiliary edge $\bar{s} \overset{\sigma}{\to} v$ and τ is the auxiliary edge $v \overset{\tau}{\to} \bar{t}$, then we have

$$\sum_{i=1}^{p} \bar{\phi}(e_i) + \bar{\phi}(\tau) = \sum_{i=1}^{q} \bar{\phi}(e'_i) + \bar{\phi}(\sigma), \tag{10.18}$$

$$\bar{c}(\tau) = \sum_{i=1}^{p} b(e_i), \tag{10.19}$$

$$\bar{c}(\sigma) = \sum_{i=1}^{q} b(e'_i), \tag{10.20}$$

and by assumption on $\bar{\phi}$,

$$\bar{\phi}(\tau) = \bar{c}(\tau) \tag{10.21}$$

and

$$\bar{\phi}(\sigma) = \bar{c}(\sigma). \tag{10.22}$$

Thus,

$$\sum_{i=1}^{p} \bar{\phi}(e_i) + \sum_{i=1}^{p} b(e_i) = \sum_{i=1}^{q} \bar{\phi}(e_i') + \sum_{i=1}^{q} b(e_i'). \tag{10.23}$$

By (10.15) this implies that

$$\sum_{i=1}^{p} \phi(e_i) = \sum_{i=1}^{q} \phi(e_i'). \tag{10.24}$$

Thus, ϕ is a legal flow of the original graph.

The steps of this proof are reversible, with minor modifications. If we assume that ϕ is a legal flow of the original graph, we can define a flow $\bar{\phi}$ for the auxiliary graph through an equation identical with (10.15). Since ϕ satisfies (10.17), we get (10.16). Namely, in all the edges of E, $\bar{\phi}$ is within the legal bounds.

Now, ϕ satisfies (10.24) for every $v \in V - \{s, t\}$, and therefore (10.23). Let us now define $\bar{\phi}(\tau)$ and $\bar{\phi}(\sigma)$, for every vertex $v \in V - \{s, t\}$ by (10.21) and (10.22). By (10.19), (10.20) (of the definition of the auxiliary graph), (10.21), (10.22), and (10.23) we get (10.18). Thus, $\bar{\phi}$ satisfies the conservation rule in every $v \in V - \{s, t\}$.

The flow that now enters $\bar{t}$ is equal to the flow which emanates $\bar{s}$ (and all these edges are saturated), and the net flow (of $\bar{\phi}$) into t is equal to the net flow out of s. Thus, the edge $t \to s$ can be assigned this value to make both conform to the conservation rule.

QED

A modification of the auxiliary graph which does not hamper its usefulness for testing the existence of a legal flow for the original graph can now be carried out. For each vertex $v \in V$, we consider the edges $\bar{s} \xrightarrow{\sigma} v$ and $v \xrightarrow{\tau} \bar{t}$. If $\bar{c}(\sigma) = \bar{c}(\tau)$, both can be dropped. If $\bar{c}(\sigma) > \bar{c}(\tau)$, we delete τ, and change the capacity of σ to be $\bar{c}(\sigma) - \bar{c}(\tau)$. If $\bar{c}(\tau) > \bar{c}(\sigma)$, we delete σ and change the capacity of τ to be $\bar{c}(\tau) - \bar{c}(\sigma)$. The modified graph for our example is shown in Fig. 10.7(a). Also, a maximum flow is displayed, and as we observe, all

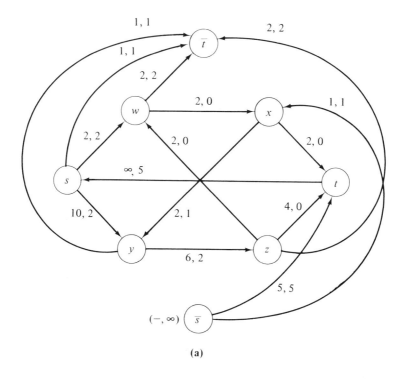

(a)

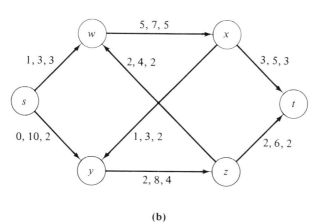

(b)

Figure 10.7

the edges out of $\bar{s}$ are saturated. Thus, the original graph has a legal flow. This is shown in Fig. 10.7b. In this diagram, next to each edge e we have the triple $b(e), c(e), \phi(e)$.

We turn now to the second part, that of finding a maximum flow once a legal flow has been established.

For this purpose we may modify the labeling procedure. In the backward labeling through $u \xleftarrow{e} v$, if u is labeled and v is not, and if $\phi(e) > b(e)$, then v is labeled (u^-, Δ_v), where

$$\Delta_v = \text{Min}\{\Delta_u, \phi(e) - b(e)\}. \tag{10.25}$$

The forward labeling does not change. With this change we can apply Algorithm 10.1 or its Edmonds and Karp variation.

Let us demonstrate this algorithm on the graph of Fig. 10.7(b). A first wave of labels is shown in Fig. 10.8(a). The improved flow is shown in Fig. 10.8(b),

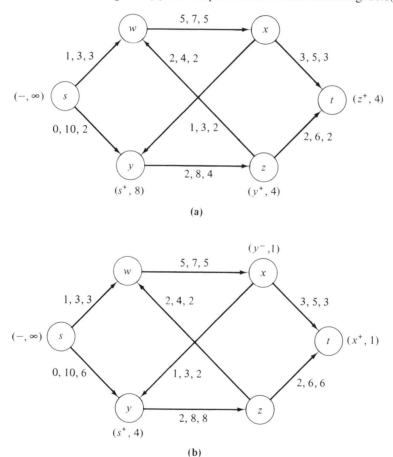

(a)

(b)

Figure 10.8

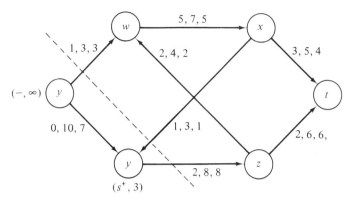

Figure 10.9

with a second wave of label propagation. Again, the improved flow is shown
in Fig.10.9 with the final wave of labels. The dashed line indicates the resulting
cut. It is clear that all edges from labeled vertices to unlabeled vertices are
saturated ($\phi(e) = c(e)$) and in all edges from unlabeled vertices to labeled
vertices the flow is at the lower bound ($\phi(e) = b(e)$). Indeed, the value of the
cut, in this case, is defined by

$$c(S;\bar{S}) = \sum_{e\in(S;\bar{S})} c(e) - \sum_{e\in(\bar{S};S)} b(e). \qquad (10.26)$$

If S is the set of vertices labeled in the last labeling, then it is clear that the
total flow Φ upon termination satisfies

$$\Phi = c(S;\bar{S})$$

and by an argument similar to that of Section 10.1, Φ is maximum and
$c(S;\bar{S})$ is a minimum cut.

10.4   Minimum flow in graphs with a source, a sink, and lower
bounds on the flow in the edges

Let us first assume that there is no upper bound on the flow in the edges and
that for every edge e, $b(e) > 0$. We can use the technique described in the
previous section to determine whether a legal flow exists, by using $c(e) = \infty$
for all edges. However, a simple necessary and sufficient condition for existence of a legal flow is that for every edge e either there exists a directed circuit

of which e is a part, or there exists a directed path from s to t of which e is a part (Exercise 10.5).

Once an initial flow has been found, we have to determine whether the total flow from s to t is bounded from below. Again, it is easy to prove that the total flow is bounded from below if and only if there is no directed path from t to s. For if such a path exists, the total flow from t to s is unbounded from above, and therefore the total flow from s to t is unbounded from below. If no such path exists, then if we define $\bar{S}$ to be the set of all vertices reachable from t, then S ($= V - \bar{S}$) is nonempty ($s \in S$) and there are no edges $u \to v$ where $u \in \bar{S}$ and $v \in S$. Thus, the total flow Φ must satisfy

$$\Phi \geqslant \sum_{e \in (S;\bar{S})} b(e), \qquad (10.27)$$

where the right-hand side may be called the value of the cut $(S;\bar{S})$.

One may use a variation of Algorithm 4.1 for directed graphs for testing whether s is reachable from t. Once it is established that legal flows exist and one is found, and after it is established that the flow is bounded from below, we may turn to the task of minimizing the flow. As in Algorithm 10.1, we shall use both forward labeling and backward labeling.

A forward labeling from x to y can be applied if x is labeled (d_x, Δ_x) and there exists an edge $x \xrightarrow{e} y$. The label for y is (x^+, Δ_y), where $\Delta_y = \Delta_x$.

A backward labeling from x to y can be applied if x is labeled (d_x, Δ_x) and there exists an edge $y \xrightarrow{e} x$ for which $\phi(e) > b(e)$. The label for y is (x^-, Δ_y), where

$$\Delta_y = \text{Min}\{\Delta_x, \phi(e) - b(e)\}.$$

We first label t $(-, \infty)$ and apply the forward and backward labeling as in Algorithm 10.1. If the vertex s is labeled, we increase the flow from t to s by Δ_s (decrease the total flow from s to t) and relabel. If the labeling stops with s unlabeled, then we have located a cut $(S;\bar{S})$ where $\bar{S}$ is the set of all labeled vertices. Clearly,

$$\Phi = \sum_{e \in (S;\bar{S})} b(e).$$

Thus, by (10.27) the total flow is minimum and the cut is maximum.

Finally, let us consider the case of finding a minimum flow in a graph where all edges have both upper and lower bounds. We first can use the

techniques of the previous section to find a legal flow, if one exists. There is
no need to consider whether the flow is bounded from below, since obviously
it is. Next, we can use a labeling procedure identical with that for maximizing
the flow, only that it is started from t. If the labeling does not reach s, we have
located a cut $(S; \bar{S})$, where $\bar{S}$ is the set of all labeled vertices. If $e \in (S; \bar{S})$,
then $\phi(e) = b(e)$, and if $e \in (\bar{S}; S)$, then $\phi(e) = c(e)$. Thus,

$$\Phi = \sum_{e \in (S; \bar{S})} b(e) - \sum_{e \in (\bar{S}; S)} c(e),$$

and therefore the total flow is minimum and the cut is maximum.

EXERCISES

10.1 Find a maximum flow in the graph.

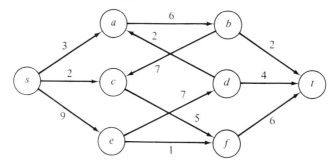

10.2 In the graph x_1, x_2, x_3 are all sources (of the same commodity). The supply at
x_1 is 5, at x_2 is 10, and at x_3 is 5. The vertices y_1, y_2, y_3 are all sinks. The supply
required at y_1 is 5, at y_2 is 10, and at y_3 is 5. Find out whether all requirements
can be met simultaneously. (*Hint:* One way of solving this type of problem is to
introduce an auxiliary source s and a sink t; connect s to x_i through an edge of

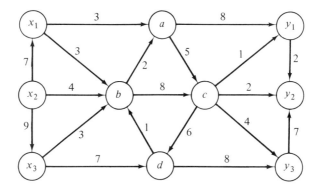

capacity equal to x_i's supply; connect each y_i to t through an edge of capacity equal to y_i's demand; find a maximum flow in the resulting network and observe if all the demands are met.)

10.3 In the graph, in addition to the capacities of the edges, each vertex other than s and t has an upper bound on the flow that may flow through it. These vertex capacities are written below the vertex labels. Find a maximum flow for this network. (*Hint*: One way of solving this type of problem is to replace each vertex v by two vertices v' and v'' with an edge $v' \xrightarrow{e} v''$, where $c(e)$ is the upper bound on the flow that may go through v in the original graph. All the edges which previously entered v are now entering v', and all the edges which previously emanated from v now emanate from v''.)

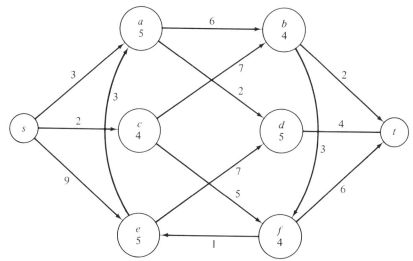

10.4 (a) Describe an alternative labeling procedure for maximizing the flow (like that of Algorithm 10.1), where the labeling starts at t and if it reaches s, the flow is improved.
   (b) Demonstrate your algorithm on the graph.

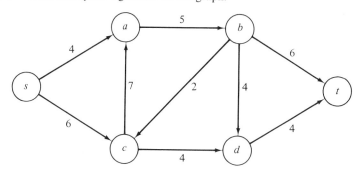

(c) Describe a method of locating an edge which has the property that increasing its capacity increases the maximum total flow in the graph. (*Hint :* One way of doing this is to use both source-to-sink and sink-to-source labelings.) Demonstrate your method on the graph of (b).

(d) Does an edge like this always exist? Prove your claim.

10.5 Prove that in a graph with a lower bound $b(e) > 0$ for every edge e, there exists a a legal flow if and only if for every edge e either e is in a directed circuit or e is in a directed path between s and t.

10.6 Find a minimum flow for the graph of Exercise 10.1, where all the numbers next to the edges are assumed to be lower bounds.

10.7 The two graphs shown have both lower and upper bounds on the flow through the edges. Which of the two graphs has no legal flow? Find a maximum flow if flows exist. If no legal flow exists, display a "cut" which points out the nonexistence of a legal flow, namely, a set of vertices which does not include the source and is required to produce flow, or a set of vertices which does not include the sink and is required to absorb flow.

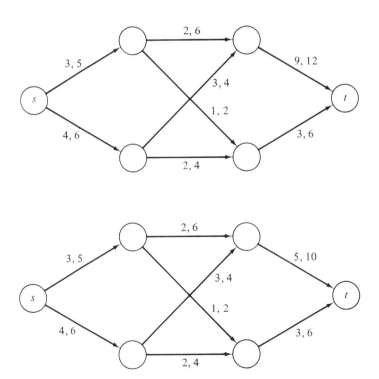

10.8 Prove that a graph with upper and lower bounds on the flow in the edges has no legal flow if and only if there exists a set of vertices with no assigned sources which is required to produce flow, or there exists a set of vertices with no assigned sinks which is required to absorb flow.

REFERENCES

1. Ford, L. R., Jr., and Fulkerson, D. R., *Flows in Networks*, Princeton University Press, Princeton, N.J., 1962.
2. Edmonds, J., and Karp, R. M., "Theoretical Improvements in Algorithmic Efficiency for Network Flow Problems," *J. ACM*, Vol. 19, 1972, pp. 248–64.
3. Hu, T. C., *Integer Programming and Network Flows*, Addison-Wesley, Reading, Mass., 1969.
4. Dinic, E. A., "Algorithm for Solution of a Problem of Maximal Flow in a Network with Power Estimation," *Sov. Math. Dokl.*, Vol. 11, 1970, 1277–80.
5. Zadeh, N., "Theoretical Efficiency of the Edmonds–Karp Algorithm for Computing Maximal Flows," *J. ACM*, Vol. 19, 1972, pp. 184–92.

11

MISCELLANIES

11.1 PERT* graphs

Consider a finite directed graph $G(V, E)$ with a vertex $s \in V$ called the *start vertex* and a vertex $t \in V$ called the *termination vertex*. Each edge e has a length $l(e)$. (This description is similar to that of Section 4.3.) Assume that each edge represents a process which takes $l(e)$ units of time from the moment it is started to the moment it is completed. The processes whose edges emanate from v can be started once all the processes whose edges enter v are completed.

The first problem we shall address ourselves to is that of finding the minimum time it takes from the moment the processes whose edges emanate from s are started to the moment all the processes whose edges enter t terminate.

*Program evaluation and review technique.

Clearly, in order to be able to start the system legally, there may be no edge entering s; that is, s is a true source in the graph-theoretic sense. Also, it is natural to assume that every edge e belongs to some directed path from s to t. For if there is no directed path from e to t, then e is of no interest and may be deleted; if there is an edge $x \xrightarrow{e} y$ where x is a source other than s, then we add an edge $s \xrightarrow{e'} x$ with $l(e') = 0$, thus making s the only source; if still for some edge $x \xrightarrow{e} y$ there is no directed path from s to x, then the process corresponding to e can never be started. This brings us to the most common overlook in a PERT graph: No directed circuits are allowed. For, if a directed circuit exists, none of the corresponding processes can ever start; in other words, they are "dead." Also, every vertex reachable from a dead vertex (an end point of a dead edge) by a directed path is also dead, and all processes whose edges emanate from it are dead.

To summarize, $G(V, E)$ is a *PERT* graph if

1. $G(V, E)$ is a directed and finite graph with no parallel edges.
2. Each $e \in E$ is assigned a *length* $l(e) \geqslant 0$.
3. $G(V, E)$ is circuit-free (has no directed circuits).
4. $G(V, E)$ has exactly one source s and one sink t.

It is easy to prove that if all these conditions are satisfied, then for every edge e in G there exists a directed path from s to t which includes e. (See Exercise 11.1.)

The testing of whether a given graph is circuit-free is easily done by successively eliminating sinks (as in Section 9.1); if no sink is found at some point before all vertices have been eliminated, then G contains a directed circuit.

The minimum time for completion of the whole system is found by the following algorithm:

Algorithm 11.1
(1) Assign s the label 0 ($\lambda(s) = 0$).
(2) Search for an unlabeled vertex v such that all vertices in $\Gamma^{-1}(v)$ are labeled. If such a vertex $\hat{v}$ exists, assign $\hat{v}$ the label $\lambda(\hat{v})$ determined by

$$\lambda(\hat{v}) = \text{Max}\{\lambda(v_i) + l(e_i)\},$$

where the maximization is over all edges $v_i \xrightarrow{e_i} \hat{v}$. If no such vertex exists, the graph contains a directed circuit.

(3) Is the vertex t labeled? if so, stop; $\lambda(t)$ is the minimal time of completing the whole system of processes. If not, go to step (2).

The reader can observe that this algorithm is similar to Algorithm 4.5. The difference is that there, in effect, we take the minimum, and here, the maximum. There the vertices perform an OR (disjunction) operation, while here they perform an AND (conjunction) operation. An in-between case is shown in Exercise 11.4.

We can now use an algorithm similar to Algorithm 4.2, to backtrack a directed path from s to t whose length is equal to $\lambda(t)$. We start from t, find a vertex u_1 such that $u_1 \overset{e_1}{\rightarrow} t$ and $\lambda(u_1) + l(e_1) = \lambda(t)$. Next, we look for $u_2 \overset{e_2}{\rightarrow} u_1$ such that $\lambda(u_2) + l(e_2) = \lambda(u_1)$, and so on, until we reach s. Such a path is called *critical*.* Clearly, there may be more than one critical path. If one wants to shorten the time, $\lambda(t)$, that the system requires, on each critical path at least one edge length must be shortened.

We shall now consider another problem concerning PERT graphs without referring to edge lengths. Assume that each of the processes, represented by the edges, occupies one processor for the length of time it takes to perform this process. Also assume that a number of processors is available, but all are similar to each other in all respects. We want to find a way of assigning the edges (processes) to processors in such a way that a processor will always be available when one is needed, so that the system is not slowed down by any waiting for a processor. Also, we would like to do this with the least number of processors. Notice that the assignment must satisfy these conditions, no matter how long the individual processes may take. Their duration may even vary from time to time.

We shall solve a minimum-flow problem on the graph assuming that $b(e) = 1$ for every edge. For example, assume that the graph is as shown in Fig. 11.1. The statement of Exercise 11.1 assures that a legal flow exists and such a flow is shown in Fig. 11.2(a). Also the labeling, which does not reach s, reveals that the flow is minimum, and a maximum cut is shown by the dashed line.

It is already clear that in a maximum cut all edges are *concurrent*; that is, it may happen, by assigning these edges long times, that all of them will have to be processed concurrently. Thus, it is clear that the number of processors required is not less than the value of a maximum cut (in our case, at least six).

Let us now demonstrate that we may "cover" all edges of the graph by a number of paths equal to the value of a minimum flow, and therefore equal

*The whole approach is sometimes called the critical path method (CPM).

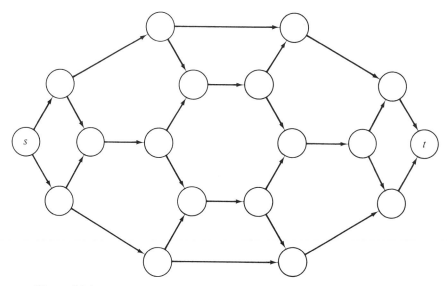

Figure 11.1

to the value of a maximum cut. All paths are directed, start at s, and end at t.
By "cover" we mean that each edge will belong to at least one of these paths.

We start at s and initiate for each $s \xrightarrow{e} u$, $\phi(e)$ paths whose first edge is e.
As long as we have not reached t with all our paths, we look for a vertex v
such that all vertices of $\Gamma^{-1}(v)$ have been processed. (There must be one, or
the graph contains a directed circuit.) We distribute the $\sum_{i=1}^{q} \phi(e_i')$ incoming
paths, where $e_1', e_2', \ldots, e_q'$ are the edges which enter v, to the emanating
edges $e_1, e_2, \ldots, e_p$ so that e_i takes $\phi(e_i)$ paths. The order in which they are
assigned is insignificant. One way of assigning the paths in our example is
shown in Fig. 11.2(b).

Now we may assign all the edges of one path to one processor. If an edge
belongs to more than one path, then one of these processors will perform the
task while the others will idle. It is clear that we are never short of processors,
and that we have the least number of processors which will assure this time-
independent mode of operation.

11.2   Connectivity in graphs

In this section we shall assume that $G(V, E)$ is a finite connected undirected
graph, with no self-loops. A set of vertices $S \subset V$ is said to be a *separating set*

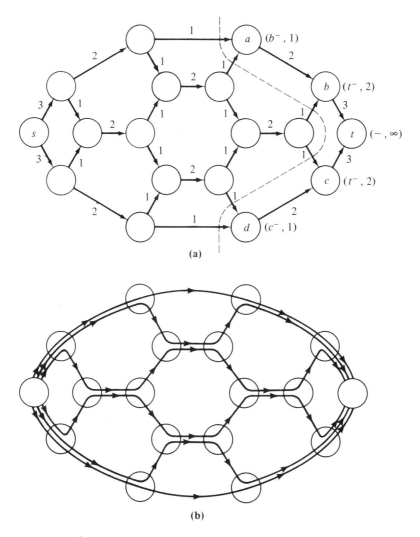

Figure 11.2

if $V - S$ can be partitioned into nonempty sets P and $\bar{P}$ in such a way that every path from a vertex of P to a vertex of $\bar{P}$ passes through at least one vertex of S, and no proper subset of S has this property. A vertex v such that $\{v\}$ is a separating set is called a *separating vertex*. A graph which is connected and has no separating vertices is called *nonseparable*. Clearly, the only connected graphs which have no separating sets are the completely connected graphs (where every two vertices are connected by an edge). A graph is said to be *k-connected* if one of the following two conditions hold:

1. The graph has separating sets, and the minimum number of vertices in such a set is k.
2. The graph has $k + 1$ vertices and is completely connected.

Assume that $x, y \in V$ and denote the number of the maximum vertex-disjoint paths that connect x with y by $N(x, y)$. (These paths have to be chosen simultaneously. Every two of these paths have only two vertices in common: x and y.)

The following two theorems are attributed to Menger [1]. Our approach is following Ford and Fulkerson [2].

Theorem 11.1: If $G(V, E)$ is a (finite, undirected) k-connected graph, then for every two vertices s and t $N(s, t) \geq k$.

Proof: Assume that $s \neq t$. Define an auxiliary flow graph $\tilde{G}(\tilde{V}, \tilde{E})$ as follows:

1. For every $v \in V$, let $\tilde{G}$ have two corresponding vertices v' and v''. Thus, $|\tilde{V}| = 2|V|$.
2. For every edge $x - y$ in G assign two edges in $\tilde{G}$: $x'' \rightarrow y'$ and $y'' \rightarrow x'$. These edges have no upper bound on the flow; that is, their capacity is infinite.
3. For every $v \in V$, there is an edge $v' \rightarrow v''$ in $\tilde{G}$ with unit capacity.

Now, consider the problem of maximizing the flow from s'' to t' in $\tilde{G}$. First, it is clear that this flow is bounded; the cut $(R; \bar{R})$ defined by

$$R = \{s''\} \cup \{v' | v \in V - \{t\}\}$$

has the capacity $c(R; \bar{R}) = |V| - 2$. Next, assume that a maximum flow has been found by Algorithm 10.1. Therefore, all edge flows are integral. The minimum cut $(S; \bar{S})$ located by the procedure may not contain an edge $x'' \rightarrow y'$, with $x'' \in S$ and $y' \in \bar{S}$, because all these edges have an infinite capacity. Thus, all the edges of $(S; \bar{S})$ are of the type $v' \rightarrow v''$, with $v' \in S$ and $v'' \in \bar{S}$, which have a unit capacity. The maximum flow is thus equal to the number of edges in $(S; \bar{S})$.

Every path from s'' to t' must go through at least one edge of $(S;\bar{S})$. There-fore, every path from s to t in G must go through at least one vertex which corresponds to one of the edges in $(S;\bar{S})$. Thus, $c(S;\bar{S}) \geqslant k$, and, therefore, the maximum flow Φ satisfies $\Phi \geqslant k$. However, the flow can be decomposed into paths (of unit flow) from s'' to t', as was done in the previous section. Except at s'' and t', there will be at most one path (and the same) going through v' and v''. These paths correspond to Φ vertex-disjoint paths from s to t in G.

The case $s \longrightarrow t$ can be handled as follows: First remove this edge. The connectivity of the resulting graph is at least $k - 1$. (The proof of this state-ment is left as Exercise 11.6.) Repeat the construction described above. This will produce at least $k - 1$ vertex-disjoint paths from s to t. Add the edge $s - t$, and now we have at least k such paths.

QED

Theorem 11.2: The minimum value $N(s, t)$ can have, over all possible choices of s and t, is less than or equal to the connectivity k.

Proof: Let S be a separating set with k vertices. Choose some $s \in P$ and $t \in \bar{P}$ (where $P, \bar{P}$ is a partition of $V - S$, and so on). Obviously $N(s, t) \leqslant k$. Thus,

$$\operatorname*{Min}_{s,t} N(s, t) \leqslant k.$$

QED

Corollary 11.1:

$$\operatorname*{Min}_{s,t} N(s, t) = k.$$

A similar study can be carried for paths which are edge-disjoint but may share vertices. The corresponding separating sets are sets of edges, and the minimum number of edges which has to be deleted in order to break the connectivity is called the edge connectivity of the graph. Analogous results hold. (See Exercise 11.7.)

Lemma 11.1: If $G(V, E)$ is nonseparable, $|V| > 2$ and $x \overset{e}{\longrightarrow} y$ in G, then the graph $\tilde{G}$ resulting from G by deletion of the edge e and adding a new vertex z with two edges $x \overset{e'}{\longrightarrow} z$ and $z \overset{e''}{\longrightarrow} y$ is also nonseparable.

Proof: No vertex of V is a separating vertex in G and therefore it is not a separating vertex in $\tilde{G}$ either. If z is a separating vertex in $\tilde{G}$, then either x or y is a separating vertex in G.

QED

Theorem 11.3: Let $G(V, E)$ be a finite undirected graph with no isolated vertices, no self-loops, and with $|V| > 2$. The following conditions are equivalent:

1. For every two edges $w — x$ and $y — z$ there exists a simple circuit which contains both.
2. For every two vertices x and y there exist a simple circuit which contains both.
3. G is nonseparable.

Proof: Clearly $(1) \Rightarrow (2)$. Now, if (2) holds, then for every x and y, $N(x, y) \geqslant 2$. Thus,

$$\operatorname*{Min}_{s,t} N(s, t) \geqslant 2.$$

By Theorem 11.2, $k \geqslant 2$. Thus, G is nonseparable.

In order to prove $(3) \Rightarrow (1)$, we add a new vertex a between w and x and a new vertex b between y and z. By Lemma 11.1, the resulting graph is still nonseparable. Thus, its connectivity is at least 2. By Theorem 11.1, there are at least two vertex-disjoint paths (in fact, exactly two) between a and b. Thus, there is a simple circuit which contains $w — x$ and $y — z$ in G.

QED

The problem of finding the connectivity of a given undirected finite graph $G(V, E)$ can be solved in the following way. For every pair of vertices s, t we find $N(s, t)$ by the technique of the proof of Theorem 11.1. There are $\binom{|V|}{2}$ pairs of vertices, and each flow problem can be performed in $(|V| - 1) \cdot (2|E| + |V|)$ operations.* Thus, the bound on the number of operations is of the order of n^5, where $n = |V|$. Finally, we find k by Corollary 11.1. A more efficient approach is to use the Gomory and Hu algorithm [4, 5] for solving

---

*As in Theorem 11.1, $|\tilde{E}| = 2|E| + |V|$. The number of operations for increasing the flow by one unit is bounded by $|\tilde{E}|$, and the maximum flow is bounded by $|V| - 1$.

all the $\binom{|V|}{2}$ flow problems by actually solving only $|V| - 1$ of them. However, this only reduces the bound to the order of n^4.

One important subproblem is to check whether a given connected graph is nonseparable. The previous approaches can only improve the bound on the number of steps to the order of n^3. Tarjan [6] has shown that the DFS approach (Section 6.4) can be used to reduce the number of operations to the order of n^2 (or $|E|$). We shall now describe this algorithm.

Algorithm 11.2:

(1) $k(v) \leftarrow n + 1$ for every $v \in V$. $(n = |V|.)$
(2) $i \leftarrow 0$. Choose a vertex v.
(3) $i \leftarrow i + 1, k(v) \leftarrow i, l(v) \leftarrow i$.
(4) If there are no unused edges adjacent to v, go to step (7).
(5) Choose an unused edge $v \overset{e}{\longrightarrow} u$. Mark e as used. If $k(u) = n + 1$, then $f(u) \leftarrow v, v \leftarrow u$, and go to step (3); if not, continue.
(6) $(k(u) \leqslant n.)$ If $l(v) > k(u), l(v) \leftarrow k(u)$. Go to step (4).
(7) If $k(v) = 1$, G is nonseparable; stop.
(8) $u \leftarrow f(v)$.
(9) If $k(u) = 1$, go to step (13).
(10) If $l(v) \geqslant k(u)$, then u is a separating vertex; stop.
(11) If $l(u) > l(v)$, then $l(u) \leftarrow l(v)$.
(12) $v \leftarrow u$ and go to step (4).
(13) If there are no unused edges adjacent to u, then G is nonseparable; if there are unused edges, the u is a separating vertex. Stop.

The meaning of $k(v)$, $l(v)$, and $f(v)$ are as follows: $k(v)$ is the index of v in the sequence of first visits. Thus, in the terminology of Section 6.4, $v(k(v)) = v$. $l(v)$ is the low-point function, that is, the lowest index $k(u)$ one can reach from v by taking a directed path on the tree (through branches) and continuing with one frond. However, $l(v)$ is never higher than $k(v)$. In fact, on the first visit to v $k(v)$ and $l(v)$ get the same value. From there on $k(v)$ is never changed and $l(v)$ may only be lowered. $f(v)$ is the father of v in the implied directed tree.

The assignment of $n + 1$ to all $k(v)$'s in step (1) is just a signal that v has not been visited yet. We choose an arbitrary vertex v (step (2)) to be the root of the tree, and it has $k(v) = 1$. If $n = 1$ (no edges), then we go to step (7) and terminate immediately with the indication that the graph, which consists of one vertex only, is nonseparable. If unused edges are found, we continue with step (5). If we reach a vertex which is visited for the first time we indicate its father, move to the new vertex as the center of activity, lower its $k(v)$ to the current i, and assign the same value to $l(v)$. However, if the vertex we reach has been visited before, $l(v)$ is lowered if possible by means of the frond $v \rightarrow u$. We continue with v. If no unused edges of v are found, we backtrack to its father (step (8)). If we are back at the root ($k(u) = 1$) the conclusion (step 13)) follows. If not, we check if $l(v) \geqslant k(u)$. If the condition holds, by Lemma 6.4, there is no edge connecting the vertices of k index higher than $k(u)$ with the vertices of k index lower than $k(u)$. Thus, u is a separating vertex. If the condition fails, there is such a connection and u is not a separating vertex. In step (11) we lower $l(u)$ if possible. It is clear that we shall never reach step (7) with $k(v) = 1$ if $n > 1$.

Since this algorithm is basically a DFS, it terminates after a number of operations which is proportional to $|E|$, unless a termination (because a separating vertex has been found) occurs earlier.

11.3 Matching

In this section the graphs are assumed to be finite, have no self-loops, and no parallel edges. The set of vertices of G is partitioned into two parts, X and Y. All edges have one end point in X and one end point in Y. We shall assume that all edges of G are undirected (but one may assume that they are all directed from X to Y). Graphs like these are called *bipartite*.

A *matching* M is a subset of edges of G such that no two edges have an end point in common. A matching is called maximal if no edge of G can be added to the collection without violating the end-point condition; it is called maximum if no other matching contains more edges.

Our purpose is to find a procedure by which we can construct a maximum matching. We shall translate the matching problem into a maximum-flow problem. The flow graph is constructed from G as follows:

1. Introduce two new vertices, s (the source) and t (the sink).
2. For every $x_i \in X$, construct an edge $s \xrightarrow{e_i} x_i$ such that $c(e_i) = 1$.
3. For every $y_i \in Y$, construct an edge $y_i \xrightarrow{f_i} t$ such that $c(f_i) = 1$.
4. For every edge $x_i - y_j$ ($x_i \in X$, $y_j \in Y$) in G, construct an edge $x_i \rightarrow y_j$ with no upper bound on the flow (that is, infinite capacity).

Consider, for example, the matching graph of Fig. 11.3(a). The corresponding flow graph is shown in Fig. 11.3(b), where an initial flow is shown,

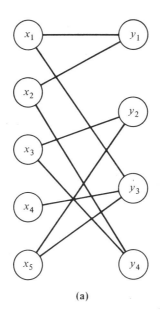

(a)

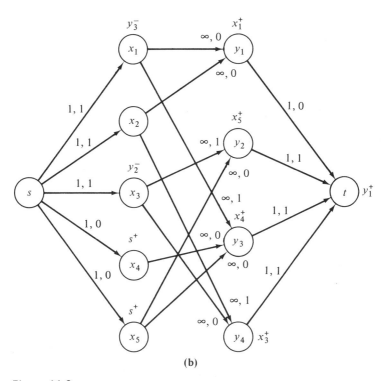

(b)

Figure 11.3

too. The total initial flow is 3. We now apply the labeling procedure. In the label the quantity Δ_v is dropped because it is always 1. The labeling is also shown in Fig. 11.3(b). The label y_1^+ has reached t. By tracing back, we increase the flow on the path $s \rightarrow x_4 \rightarrow y_3 \rightarrow x_1 \rightarrow y_1 \rightarrow t$ by one unit. The total flow is now 4, as is shown in Fig. 11.4(a). Now, we repeat the labeling, but this time it does not reach t. Thus, the flow is maximum. Now, if in G we put in M all edges which correspond to an $x \xrightarrow{e} y$ edge of the flow graph for which $\phi(e) = 1$, we get a matching. This is shown in Fig. 11.4(b).

Let us now prove that, in general, a maximum flow in the corresponding flow graph yields a matching. For every i, $\phi(e_i)$ $(s \xrightarrow{e_i} x_i)$ is either 0 or 1. If it is 0, then none of the edges which emanate from x_i carry flow. If it is 1, exactly one edge from x_i to Y carries a nonzero flow. The vertex it enters, y_j, has no other flow-carrying edge entering it, for the edge $y_j \xrightarrow{f_i} t$ has $c(f_j) = 1$.

To see that this matching must be maximum, observe that every matching can be translated to a flow whose value is equal to the number of edges in the matching. Thus, if the flow is maximum, the corresponding matching must be maximum, too.

It is easy to see that this algorithm can be applied directly to G, and there is no need to construct a flow graph first. An even more primitive labeling procedure is where vertices are just marked + when labeled without noting the place the label came from. The backtracking in this case requires a little more work. (This is known as the Hungarian method for solving maximum matching problems.) In fact, this procedure generalizes to solve matching problems in graphs which are not bipartite [7].

A matching M is called *complete* if every vertex of X is matched with some vertex of Y; that is, $|M| = |X|$. The following theorem is attributed to König and Hall [3].

Theorem 11.4:   In a bipartite graph G a complete matching of X into Y exists if and only if for every $A \subset X$ $|A| \leqslant |\Gamma(A)|$.

Proof: The necessity of the condition (that for every $A \subset X, |A| \leqslant |\Gamma(A)|$) is obvious. For if every vertex in X is to be matched, then the number of vertices in Y which are connected by an edge to vertices of A must be at least $|A|$.

To prove sufficiency, assume that the condition holds and that the corresponding flow graph has been constructed and a maximum flow has been found. Let the set of labeled vertices, in the last labeling which does not reach t, be S. Denote by A the set $S \cap X$. Thus, $X - A$ is a set of unlabeled vertices;

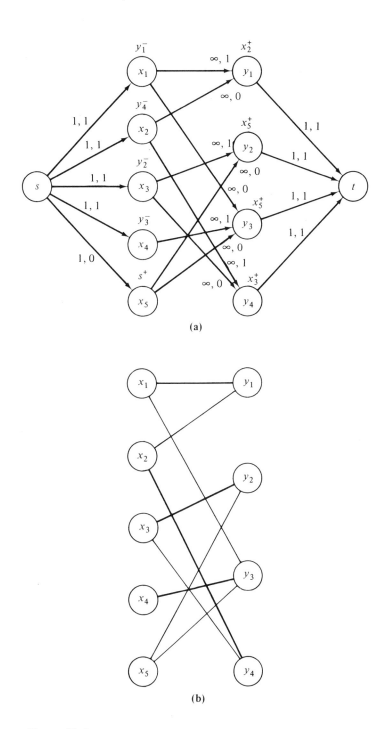

Figure 11.4

233

that is, $(X - A) \subset \bar{S}$. Also the $\Gamma(A)$ are labeled, since all edges from X to Y have infinite capacity.

Therefore,

$$S = \{s\} \cup A \cup \Gamma(A),$$

$$\bar{S} = (X - A) \cup (Y - \Gamma(A)) \cup \{t\}.$$

The value of the cut is then

$$c(S; \bar{S}) = |X - A| + |\Gamma(A)|.$$

Thus,

$$c(S; \bar{S}) = |X| - |A| + |\Gamma(A)|.$$

Now, since

$$|A| \leqslant |\Gamma(A)|$$

we have

$$c(S; \bar{S}) \geqslant |X|.$$

Since $c(S; \bar{S})$ is a minimum cut, we have

$$c(S; \bar{S}) = |X|,$$

which is also equal to the total value of the flow. Thus, $|M| = |X|$, where M is the matching implied by the flow.

$$\text{QED}$$

EXERCISES

11.1   Prove that in a PERT graph for every edge e there exists a directed path from s to t which includes e.

11.2   Find the minimum time of performing the system of processes described by the PERT graph. Find all the critical paths. Which edge lengths are worth shortening?

11.3   Find an assignment of the edges in the graph of Exercises 11.2 to a minimum number of processors, which ensures the availability of a processor whenever necessary. (Ignore the edge lengths and assume they are unknown.)

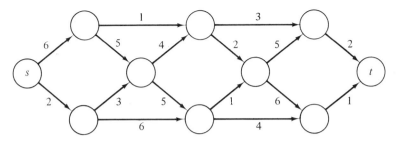

Exercise 11.2

11.4 In the graph, there are both AND-type vertices (designated by ∧) and OR-type vertices (designated by ∨). The number next to the edges are edge lengths. Find the minimum time in which the whole system of processes can be completed.

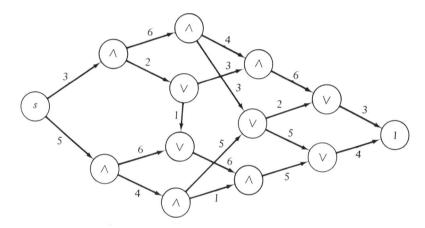

11.5 In the graph of Exercise 11.4 there are no directed circuits. Are such circuits allowed in such mixed graphs? Specify the exact conditions that a directed circuit must satisfy. How do we have to change the algorithm used in Exercise 11.4 to handle this case?

11.6 Prove that if G is k-connected, then the deletion of any one edge from it can reduce the connectivity by at most one. (You may not use Theorem 11.1 since this statement was used in its proof.)

11.7 Define an edge-separating set and k edge-connectivity analogous to these definitions for vertices. State Menger's theorem for edge-disjoint paths and prove it.

11.8 Prove that if x, y, and z are vertices of a nonseparable graph, then there exists a simple path from x to z which goes through y.

11.9   One way of describing a bipartite graph is by a matrix. The rows correspond to X, the column to Y. The i, j entry in the matrix is left blank if $x_i - y_j$, and is crossed out if $x_i \not{-} y_j$. For example:

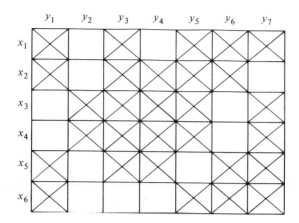

A selection of the edge $x_i - y_j$ in the matching is recorded by writing a 1 in the blank entry. Thus, a maximum matching is a maximum number of 1s written in the matrix in such a way that no more than one 1 appears in every row and every column.

Describe a labeling procedure, and demonstrate it on the given example.

11.10   In a school there are n boys and n girls. Each boy knows exactly k girls $(1 \leqslant k \leqslant n)$ and each girl knows exactly k boys. Prove that if "knowing" is a symmetric relation, then all the boys and girls can participate in one dance, where every pair of dancers (a boy and a girl) know each other.

11.11   Consider the following sets of integers:

$$\{3,5,8\}, \{4,6,7,9\}, \{1,4,5,9\}, \{2,3,6,8\}, \{1,6,7,8\}, \{2,5,6\}, \{3,4,7\}, \{1,2,9\}.$$

Can one find eight integers $i_1, i_2, \ldots, i_8$ such that if $s \neq t$, then $i_s \neq i_t$, and i_j belongs to the jth set? A selection like that is called a system of distinct representatives (SDR). Describe an algorithm for solving such problems, and demonstrate on the given example.

REFERENCES

1. Menger, K., "Zur allgemeinen Kurventheorie," *Fund. Math.*, Vol. 10, 1927, pp. 96–115.
2. Ford, L. R., Jr., and Fulkerson, D. R., *Flows in Networks*, Princeton University Press, Princeton, N.J., 1962, pp. 53–5.

3. Berge, C., *The Theory of Graphs and Its Applications*, Wiley, New York, 1962, Chap. 10.

4. Hu, T. C., *Integer Programming and Network Flows*, Addison-Wesley, Reading, Mass., 1969, Sec. 9.3.

5. Gomory, R. E., and Hu, T. C., "Multi-terminal Network Flows," *J. SIAM*, Vol. 9, No. 4, 1961, pp. 551–70.

6. Tarjan, R., "Depth-First Search and Linear Graph Algorithms," Computer Science Department, Stanford University, Stanford, Calif.

7. Berge, C., *The Theory of Graphs and Its Applications*, Wiley, New York, 1962, Chap. 18.

12

MARKED DIRECTED
GRAPHS

12.1 Live and safe markings

In this chapter we shall follow the work of Commoner, Holt, Even, and Pnueli [1]. Other related work can be found in references 2–8.

Let $G(V, E)$ be a finite directed graph. We assign a number $M(e)$ of *tokens* (a nonnegative integer) to each edge e. The function M is called a *marking* of the graph. A vertex is said to be *fireable* if the number of tokens on every edge entering it is positive. The *firing* of a fireable vertex consists of taking off one token from each incoming edge, and adding one token to each outgoing edge. Since the number of incoming and outgoing edges is not necessarily the same, the total number of tokens on the graph may increase or decrease through firing.

Lemma 12.1: The token count of a simple directed circuit does not change by vertex firing.

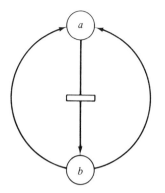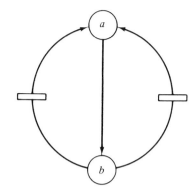

Figure 12.1

Example 12.1: A marked graph is shown in Fig. 12.1(a). There is only one token in this marking, and it is on the edge from vertex *a* to vertex *b*. Vertex *b* is fireable. After firing *b*, the two edges from *b* to *a* have one token on each, and *a* is fireable. After firing *a* we return to the original marking. Thus, the number of tokens in the graph changes from 1 to 2 and back to 1; but the token count on each of the two simple directed circuits remains 1.

Proof: The firing of a vertex of a circuit merely shifts one token from one edge of the circuit to another.

QED

A marking is called *live* if every vertex is fireable, or can be made fireable by some sequence of firings.

Theorem 12.1: A marking is live if and only if the token count of every simple directed circuit is positive.

Proof: Assume there exists a simple directed circuit of zero token count. No vertex on the simple circuit is fireable. Moreover, since the token count on this simple circuit does not change by firing any other vertices (Lemma 12.1), these vertices will always remain nonfireable.

Now assume that the token count of every directed circuit is positive. Let *v* be any vertex of the graph. Consider the token-free edges entering *v*. If there are none, the vertex is fireable. If not, consider the vertices from which these edges emanate. If each of those is immediately fireable, then, clearly, *v* will become fireable after every one of them is fired. If some are not, consider the token-free edges entering them, and so on. As we continue this backtracking, we are selecting a subgraph of G which consists of v, the token-free edges entering them, and so on. The process must terminate, since G is finite. Now, this subgraph must be circuit-free since there are no token-free directed circuits. Thus, the subgraph must have at least one vertex which has no incoming edges which belong to the subgraph. This vertex is fireable in the present marking of G. After firing it, the subgraph of the token-free backtracking from v is reduced by one vertex. By repeating this process, we can make v fireable.

QED

Corollary 12.1:   A marking that is live remains live after firing.

Proof: Since the token count of every simple directed circuit does not change by firing (Lemma 12.1), this count will stay positive after firing. By Theorem 12.1 the marking stays live.

A live marking is called *safe* if no edge is assigned more than one token, and if no sequence of firings can bring two tokens or more to one edge.

Theorem 12.2:   A live marking is safe if and only if every edge in the graph is in a simple directed circuit of token count 1.

Proof: If for every edge there exists a circuit in which this edge takes part, with exactly one token on it, by Lemma 12.1 the token count remains 1, and therefore there will never be two or more tokens placed on this edge.

Assume that there exists an edge e, $a \xrightarrow{e} b$, such that all directed circuits which go through it have a token count of 2 or more. We want to demonstrate that by a proper sequence of firings we can place two tokens on e. If there are no tokens on e, we backtrack the token-free subgraph, starting with vertex a, as in the proof of Theorem 12.1. Thus, as in that proof, we can make vertex a fireable and fire it. This places one token on e. We repeat this construction. Again, the token-free subgraph backtracked from a does not include b, since this would imply the existence of a circuit of token count 1 through e. Thus, we can fire vertex a again without firing b, and therefore place a second token on e. Therefore, the initial marking is not safe.

QED

Corollary 12.2:   If a graph has a live and safe marking, then for every edge of the graph one can find a circuit which goes through the edge.

This is an immediate consequence of Theorem 12.2. It eliminates the possibility of having sinks or sources or any separating edges in a graph which can be assigned with a live and safe marking. In fact, a much stronger statement is true:

Theorem 12.3:   If the underlying undirected graph of a directed graph $G(V, E)$ is connected, and if G can be assigned a live and safe marking, then G is strongly connected.

Proof: Assume that the underlying undirected graph of G is connected, and that G can be assigned with a live and safe marking. If G is not strongly connected, then there are two vertices a and b such that there is no directed path from a to b in G. Let A be the set of all vertices, including a, which are reachable from a. Since $A \neq V$ and since the underlying undirected graph is connected, there must exist a vertex a' in A and a vertex b' in $V - A$ which are connected by an edge e. The edge e must be oriented $b' \xrightarrow{e} a'$, or b' would belong to A. However, Corollary 12.2 implies the existence of a directed path from a' to b', which again contradicts the fact that $b' \in V - A$. Thus, G must be strongly connected.

QED

A natural question arises: Does there exist a live and safe marking for every strongly connected graph? This problem was known for some time as "Holt's toll-booth problem" and was settled by Genrich in 1969. This is the subject of our next theorem.

Theorem 12.4:   For every finite, directed, strongly connected graph there exists a live and safe marking.

Proof: Clearly we can find a live marking simply by putting one token on each edge. By Theorem 12.1 this marking is live. Now we can use the technique developed in the proofs of Theorems 12.1 and 12.2 to change the marking until it becomes safe, without changing its liveness. Assume that for a given edge the least token count for the directed circuits through it is $k > 1$. We can describe a sequence of firings that will bring k tokens to the edge. By lifting $k - 1$ of them no circuit becomes token-free, and there is now a circuit through this edge with a token count 1. This can be repeated as long as there are edges for which no circuit of token count 1 exists.

QED

12.2   Relations between markings

Let $\tilde{\sigma} = (v_{i_1}, v_{i_2}, \ldots, v_{i_l})$ be a firing sequence. We denote by σ_i the number of times that vertex v_i is fired in $\tilde{\sigma}$, that is, the number of times it appears in the sequence. Let $\bar{\sigma} = (\sigma_1, \sigma_2, \ldots, \sigma_n)$, which is the vector of the firing numbers σ_i, and where $n = |V|$ (the number of vertices). Using this notation, we get that if $\tilde{\sigma}$ is a legal firing sequence leading from a marking M to a marking M', then for each arc $v_i \xrightarrow{e} v_j$, $M'(e) = M(e) + \sigma_i - \sigma_j$. It is interesting that the converse is also true.

Theorem 12.5:   If a live marking M and a vector $\bar{\sigma}$ with nonnegative integral components σ_i for every vertex v_i, satisfy the condition $M(e) + \sigma_i - \sigma_j \geqslant 0$ for every edge $v_i \xrightarrow{e} v_j$, then there exists a firing sequence, legal for M, whose vector of firing numbers is $\bar{\sigma}$.

Proof: Let M be any marking and $\bar{\sigma}$ be a nonnegative integral vector which satisfies $M(e) + \sigma_i - \sigma_j \geqslant 0$ for every $v_i \xrightarrow{e} v_j$. We have to show that the marking M' defined by $M'(e) = M(e) + \sigma_i - \sigma_j$ is achievable through a firing sequence $\tilde{\sigma}$ such that $\bar{\sigma}$ is $\tilde{\sigma}$'s vector of firing numbers.

If $\bar{\sigma}$ is the zero vector, then the statement is trivially true by using an empty sequence of firings.

Let us show that if $\bar{\sigma}$ is not the zero vector, then there exists at least one vertex v_i, such that $\sigma_i > 0$, which is immediately fireable. Consider any v_i such that $\sigma_i > 0$. If it is immediately fireable, the claim is proved. If not, construct, as before, the token-free backward subgraph. On its boundary we find at least one fireable vertex, say v_j. There is a token-free path $v_j \rightarrow v_k \rightarrow \cdots \rightarrow v_s \rightarrow v_i$ leading from v_j to v_i, and since each arc along the path has no tokens on it, the inequality chain

$$\sigma_j \geqslant \sigma_k \geqslant \cdots \geqslant \sigma_s \geqslant \sigma_i > 0$$

holds. This proves v_j to be an immediately fireable vertex with $\sigma_j > 0$. Now we are ready to fire v_j.

Consider the resulting marking $M^{(1)}$ generated by this firing and the new firing numbers:

$$\sigma_k^{(1)} = \begin{cases} \sigma_k & \text{if } k \neq j \\ \sigma_k - 1 & \text{if } k = j. \end{cases}$$

It is obvious that

$$M^{(1)}(e) + \sigma_i^{(1)} - \sigma_j^{(1)} = M(e) + \sigma_i - \sigma_j$$

for all $v_i \overset{e}{\to} v_j$, and therefore

$$M^{(1)}(e) + \sigma_i^{(1)} - \sigma_j^{(1)} \geq 0.$$

We may now look for a v_l—such that $\sigma_l^{(1)} > 0$—which is immediately fireable, fire it, generating $M^{(2)}$ and $\sigma_k^{(2)}$, and so on, until we reach a final marking $M^{(p)}$ and $\sigma_i^{(p)} = 0$, for all $i = 1, 2, \ldots, n$. Clearly, $M'(e) = M^{(p)}(e)$ and every v_i was fired σ_i times.

QED

Theorem 12.6: If $\tilde{\sigma}$ is a firing sequence, for a graph whose underlying undirected graph is connected, and this sequence leads back to the initial marking M, then all vertices have been fired an equal number of times.

Proof: We have $M(e) = M(e) + \sigma_i - \sigma_j$ for every edge $v_i \overset{e}{\to} v_j$. Thus, every two adjacent vertices have been fired the same number of times. Since the underlying undirected graph is connected, all vertices have been fired the same number of times.

QED

Theorem 12.7: Let M be a live marking. There exists a firing sequence leading from M to itself, in which every vertex is fired exactly once.

Proof: Choose $\sigma_i = 1$ for all $i = 1, 2, \ldots, n$. Our theorem is now an immediate corollary of Theorem 12.5.

QED

The following two theorems serve as a basis for the forthcoming algorithms. Consider the system of inequalities

$$u_i - u_j + N(e) \leqslant 0 \qquad \text{for all } v_i \overset{e}{\to} v_j, \tag{12.1}$$

where the $N(e)$'s are given integers. A solution vector $\bar{u} = (u_1, u_2, \ldots, u_n)$ is a vector of integers which satisfy the system (12.1).

Theorem 12.8: Either system (12.1) has a solution $\bar{u} \geqslant 0$ or there exists a directed circuit

$$C = v_{i_1} \overset{e_{j_1}}{\to} v_{i_2} \overset{e_{j_2}}{\to} \cdots v_{i_p} \overset{e_{j_p}}{\to} v_{i_1}$$

such that

$$\sum_{k=1}^{p} N(e_{j_k}) > 0.$$

Proof: First, observe that the alternatives exclude each other, because if we have a solution $\bar{u} \geqslant 0$ to (12.1) we may sum the inequalities along any directed circuit:

$$C = v_{i_1} \overset{e_{j_1}}{\to} v_{i_2} \overset{e_{j_2}}{\to} \cdots v_{i_p} \overset{e_{j_p}}{\to} v_{i_1}.$$

Observing that

$$(u_{i_1} - u_{i_2}) + (u_{i_2} - u_{i_3}) + \cdots + (u_{i_p} - u_{i_1}) = 0,$$

we obtain

$$\sum_{k=1}^{p} N(e_{j_k}) \leqslant 0.$$

Now we attempt to find a solution $\bar{u}$ to (12.1) by a labeling procedure.

Each vertex v_i will be labeled by a pair (p_i, u_i), where p_i is a vertex number $1 \leqslant p_i \leqslant n$ to be called i's predecessor, or $p_i \leqslant 0$, in which case i has no predecessor. u_i is either an integer or the special value $-\infty$, understood to

be smaller than any other finite integer. We start by labeling all vertices
$(0, -\infty)$. The labeling procedure proceeds as follows:

Algorithm 12.1:

(1) If there is no i such that $u_i = -\infty$, stop; the present u's form a solution
    to (12.1).*
(2) Choose an i such that $u_i = -\infty$.
(3) $p_i \leftarrow -1, l \leftarrow i, u_i \leftarrow 0$ (v_l is called the *labeling vertex*).
(4) If for all edges $v_l \xrightarrow{e} v_j, u_l - u_j + N(e) \leq 0$, then go to step (8).
(5) Let $v_l \xrightarrow{e} v_k$ be an edge for which $u_l - u_k + N(e) > 0$.
(6) If $p_k \neq 0$, go to step (10).
(7) $p_k \leftarrow l, u_k \leftarrow u_l + N(e), l \leftarrow k$, and go to step (4).
(8) If $p_l = -1$ (first in chain), then $p_l \leftarrow 0$ and go to step (1).
(9) $i \leftarrow p_l, p_l \leftarrow 0, l \leftarrow i$ (set l's predecessor to be the labeling vertex) and go
    to step (4).
(10) A "positive" circuit has been found; stop.

In step (3), $p_i \leftarrow -1$ in order to mark v_i as the root of the labeling and
$u_i \leftarrow 0$. If an edge $v_l \xrightarrow{e} v_k$ on which (12.1) is violated is found, then we proceed
to relabel v_k (in step (7)) and v_k becomes the labeling vertex. (This is some-
what reminiscent of the DFS of Section 6.5 with the difference that here relabeling may occur.) Once we reach a v_l for which all edges $v_l \xrightarrow{e} v_j$ satisfy
$u_l - u_j + N(e) \leq 0$ (step (4)), we check if this is the root (step (8)). In case it is,
it ceases to be one (by $p_l \leftarrow 0$) and we search for an unattended vertex
(step (1)), and if we find one we make it the root; if not, the process is over.
In case v_l is not the root, we proceed with step (9), which is a retrace operation;
that is, v_{p_l} becomes the labeling vertex and $p_l \leftarrow 0$ to mark that it is not on the
labeling path any more.

Step (10) occurs if we attempt to relabel a vertex v_k which is an ancestor
of v_l (this is indicated by $p_k \neq 0$ of step (6); the structure here is very much
like that of DFS). Thus, we can retrace a "positive" circuit by $l, p_l, p_{p_l}, \ldots$
until we reach k.

To see that the process terminates, observe that each time a vertex is
labeled or relabeled, its value is determined by a simple directed path from
the present root (labeled $(-1, 0)$). Since there are finitely many vertices, each
of which can be assigned as the root only once, and there are finitely many

---

*Once a solution $\bar{u}$ is found, it can be made nonnegative by subtracting the least component
from every component.

simple directed paths from each root to the given vertex, it can be labeled a finite number of times only. Thus, the number of times step (5) applies is finite and the process must terminate.

Assume that the process terminates in step (1). Let $v_a \xrightarrow{e} v_b$ be any edge of the graph. Consider the last time we retraced from v_a (by step (4) when $l = a$ and going into (8), and so on). At this time $u_a - u_b + N(e) \leqslant 0$. Since this moment u_a has not been changed, and if u_b has been relabeled, relabeling, as always, is only upward. Thus, the inequality has been maintained. Therefore, if the process terminates in step (1), the u's form a solution to (12.1). As we have already seen, if it terminates in step (10), we have a directed circuit

$$C = v_{i_1} \xrightarrow{e_{j_1}} v_{i_2} \xrightarrow{e_{j_2}} \cdots v_{i_q} \xrightarrow{e_{j_q}} v_{i_1}$$

(where $i_q = l, i_{q-1} = p_1, \ldots, i_{j-1} = p_{i_j}, \ldots, i_1 = k$). We have

$$u_{i_2} = u_{i_1} + N(e_{j_1}),$$

$$u_{i_3} = u_{i_2} + N(e_{j_2}),$$

$$\vdots$$

$$u_{i_q} = u_{i_{q-1}} + N(e_{j_{q-1}}),$$

$$u_{i_1} < u_{i_q} + N(e_{j_q}).$$

By summing up these relations, we obtain

$$\sum_{k=1}^{q} N(e_{j_k}) > 0.$$

QED

Consider the system of inequalities

$$u_i - u_j + N(e) \geqslant 0 \qquad \text{for all } v_i \xrightarrow{e} v_j, \tag{12.2}$$

where the $N(e)$'s are given integers. A solution vector $\bar{u} = (u_1, u_2, \ldots, u_n)$ is a vector of integers which satisfy the system (12.2).

Theorem 12.9: Either system (12.2) has a solution $\bar{u} \geqslant 0$ or there exists a directed circuit

$$C = v_{i_1} \overset{e_{j_1}}{\rightarrow} v_{i_2} \overset{e_{j_2}}{\rightarrow} \cdots v_{i_p} \overset{e_{j_p}}{\rightarrow} v_{i_1}$$

such that

$$\sum_{k=1}^{p} N(e_{j_k}) < 0.$$

The theorem can be proved as a corollary of Theorem 12.8 (Exercise 12.3).

Let us denote by $\langle M|C \rangle$ the token count on the simple directed circuit C. We say that marking M' lies *above* marking M if for every edge e, $M'(e) \geqslant M(e)$. We say that M' has circuit count not lower than M if for every simple directed circuit C, $\langle M'|C \rangle \geqslant \langle M|C \rangle$.

Our next algorithm will test whether a given marking M' can be brought by a legal sequence of firings to lie above a given marking M, and in case such a sequence exists, will produce one such sequence. It is clear that a necessary condition for M' is that its circuit count is not lower than that of M or any simple directed circuit. The algorithm will describe the proof of the sufficiency of this condition in case M' is live.

Theorem 12.10: A live marking M' can be brought to lie above M if and only if its circuit count is not lower than that of M for every simple directed circuit.

Proof: As noted, the "only if" part is obvious. Now, for every edge e, set $N(e) = M'(e) - M(e)$. For these values assigned to $N(e)$ attempt to solve system (12.2) of inequalities. By Theorem 12.9 (through the algorithm as in the proof of Theorem 12.8) we either have a solution $\bar{u} \geqslant 0$, or there exists a circuit

$$C = v_{i_1} \overset{e_{j_1}}{\rightarrow} v_{i_2} \overset{e_{j_2}}{\rightarrow} \cdots v_{i_p} \overset{e_{j_p}}{\rightarrow} v_{i_1}$$

for which

$$\sum_{k=1}^{p} N(e_{j_k}) < 0.$$

In the latter case we have

$$\sum_{k=1}^{p} M'(e_{j_k}) < \sum_{k=1}^{p} M(e_{j_k}),$$

which means that $\langle M'|C\rangle < \langle M|C\rangle$, a contradiction. Thus, the former must hold; namely, for every edge $v_i \overset{e}{\to} v_j$,

$$u_i - u_j + M'(e) - M(e) \geqslant 0$$

or

$$u_i - u_j + M'(e) \geqslant M(e) \geqslant 0.$$

By Theorem 12.5, and through the algorithm in its proof, there exists a legal sequence of firings leading from M' to M'' defined by

$$M''(e) = u_i - u_j + M'(e),$$

and M'' lies above M.

QED

In fact, the proof of Theorem 12.10 is of more value than the theorem itself. For if we are given a live M' and any M, the proof provides a procedure for testing if M' can be brought to lie above M without checking all simple directed circuits for their count.

Theorem 12.11:   In a strongly connected graph, M can be derived by a sequence of firings from a live M' if and only if they have identical circuit counts; that is, for every simple directed circuit C,

$$\langle M'|C\rangle = \langle M|C\rangle.$$

Proof: Again the "only if" is immediate. If M' satisfies the condition, then its circuit count is not lower than that of M, and by Theorem 10, it leads to a marking M'', which lies above M. If $M'' \neq M$, then there exists an edge e such that $M''(e) > M(e)$, but this edge can be completed to a circuit in which the circuit count equality between M'' and M (and, therefore, between M' and M) is violated.

QED

Theorem 12.12: In a strongly connected graph, if a marking M can be derived by a sequence of firings from a live marking M', then M' is derivable from M.

Proof: If M' can produce M, then by Theorem 12.11 they have identical circuit counts. Thus, M is live, and again by Theorem 12.11, M' is derivable from M.

QED

This shows that the live markings of a strongly connected graph partition into equivalence classes. We have shown an algorithm for testing whether two markings belong to the same equivalence class. Let us refer to each equivalence class as a family.

12.3   The maximum marking

Simple examples show that firing may change the overall number of tokens in the graph considerably. If we interpret marked graphs as plans of continuous production which allows concurrent processing, then the number of tokens bears direct relation to the number of resources needed at a particular instance. The maximum marking belonging to a given family gives a bound on the maximum resource requirement of a particular organization of a process.

We solve this programming by making use of its dual, which is a flow problem. Let us consider a flow in the underlying strongly connected graph which is a circulation flow, that is, with no sources or sinks. We impose a lower bound of one unit on each edge, so that the flow is given by integers (the computation ensures that by starting with an integral flow and making integral changes only). We denote the flow in $v_i \overset{e}{\to} v_j$ by $\phi(e)$. The flow must satisfy the conservation rule at the vertices; that is, the total flow entering a vertex is equal to the total flow emanating from it.

The total cost $T_M(\phi)$ of the flow is computed by using any particular marking M of the family as a set of prices on the edges; that is,

$$T_M(\phi) = \sum_{e \in E} M(e) \cdot \phi(e).$$

Note that if M and M' belong to the same family, then $T_M(\phi) = T_{M'}(\phi)$. This follows from the fact that vertex firing does not change the total cost, since the reduction of the cost on the incoming edges is compensated by the increase of the cost on the outgoing edges. Thus, the minimum-flow solution is independent of the initial marking of the family which is chosen for measuring the flow. Also, if M and M' are in the same family then

$$\sum_{e \in E} M(e) \leqslant T_{M'}(\phi) \tag{12.3}$$

We solve the minimum-flow problem in two phases.

Phase 1: Establish a feasible flow. This is done by initially setting $\phi(e) = 0$ for all edges e. Now repeatedly apply the following step: If there is no edge e for which $\phi(e) = 0$, stop. If such an edge is found, locate a directed circuit which passes through e and increase the flow on all its edges by 1.

Phase 2: Define a new graph $\tilde{G}(V, \tilde{E})$ as follows: $\tilde{E}$ contains all edges $e \in E$ for which $\phi(e) > 1$; in addition, for every edge $v_i \overset{e}{\to} v_j$ in G, $\tilde{G}$ contains a counterpart $v_i \overset{e'}{\leftarrow} v_j$ (a new edge). Now define a function $N(e)$ on the edges of $\tilde{G}$ as follows:

$$N(e) = \begin{cases} M(e) & \text{if } e \in E, \\ -M(e') & \text{if } e \text{ is the counterpart of } e'(e' \in E). \end{cases}$$

Apply Algorithm 12.1 to system (12.1) defined by the $N(e)$'s for $\tilde{G}$. If we fail to find a solution to system (12.1), then we have located a circuit C' in $\tilde{G}$,

$$C' = v_{i_1} \overset{e_{j_1}}{\to} v_{i_2} \overset{e_{j_2}}{\to} \cdots v_{i_p} \overset{e_{j_p}}{\to} v_{i_1},$$

for which

$$\sum_{k=1}^{p} N(e_{j_k}) > 0.$$

The directed circuit C' (in $\tilde{G}$) corresponds to a circuit C in G. C may not be directed, since some of the edges of C' may be counterparts of edges in G and, therefore, are oppositely directed. Thus,

$$\sum_{k=1}^{p} N(e_{j_k}) = \sum_{e \in R} M(e) - \sum_{e \in W} M(e),$$

where R is the set of edges in C whose direction is as in C', and W is the set of edges in C whose direction is opposite to that in C'. Thus,

$$\sum_{e \in R} M(e) > \sum_{a \in W} M(e).$$

Now, by reducing the flow in all edges of R by one unit and increasing it in all edges of W by one unit, the conservation law is kept in all the vertices, and the total cost reduces. We redefine $\tilde{G}$ and repeat. Since the total cost is bounded from below by

$$\sum_{e \in E} M(e),$$

sooner or later a solution $\bar{u} \geqslant 0$ to the current system (12.1) will be found. Thus, we have

$$u_i - u_j + N(e) \leqslant 0 \qquad \text{for all } v_i \overset{e}{\to} v_j \text{ in } \tilde{G}.$$

For every edge $v_i \overset{e}{\to} v_j$ in G we have $v_i \overset{e'}{\leftarrow} v_j$ in $\tilde{G}$. Therefore, $u_j - u_i - M(e) \leqslant 0$ or $M(e) + u_i - u_j \geqslant 0$. By Theorem 12.5 (and through the algorithm in its proof) the marking $M'(e) = M(e) + u_i - u_j$ is in the same family. Furthermore, if $\phi(e) > 1$, then $v_i \overset{e}{\to} v_j$ belongs to $\tilde{G}$. Thus, $u_i - u_j + N(e) \leqslant 0$, which implies

$$u_i - u_j + M(e) \leqslant 0,$$

namely,

$$M'(e) = 0.$$

Thus, the flow is measured, with respect to M', only on edges e for which $\phi(e) = 1$. Thus, $T_{M'}(\phi) = \sum_{e \in E} M'(e)$, and by (12.3), the flow is now minimum and the marking M' is maximum.

The algorithm described here is a minimum-cost-circulation algorithm. Any other minimum-cost-circulation algorithm, such as that of Ford and Fulkerson [9], could serve as well. However, the present approach seems to be the natural one in this framework.

The problem of finding a minimum marking (which may be a convenient initial state for the system) can be solved in a similar way together with the dual maximum-flow problem (see Exercise 12.4).

As far as I know, the problem of finding a maximum or minimum marking, when no initial marking is given, has not been solved efficiently yet.

EXERCISES

12.1 Explain why, in the proof of Theorem 12.1, the backtracked token-free subgraph of v shrinks by one vertex when one of its fireable vertices is fired, and no new edges or vertices can be added to this subgraph by this firing. Why is this fact essential to the proof?

12.2 Prove that the set of vertices v_i for which $p_i \neq 0$, at any one moment during the performance of Algorithm 12.1, form a simple directed path whose first vertex is the vertex labeled $(-1, 0)$ and last vertex is v_l.

12.3 Show that Theorem 12.9 is a corollary of Theorem 12.8.

12.4 Show that the problem of a minimum marking, within a given family, can be solved in a way similar to the solution of the maximum-marking problem solved in Section 12.3.

12.5 Let $G(V, E)$ be a directed graph and M be a marking of its edges. Let $V' \subset V$ and $G'(V', E')$ be the vertex subgraph of G defined by V'. For every $e \in E'$ we define $M'(e) = M(e)$.

Prove the following statements in case they are true; produce counterexamples in case they are false.

(a) If M is a live marking of G, then M' is a live marking of G'.
(b) If M is safe marking of G, then M' is a safe marking of G'.

12.6 How many distinct families of live and safe markings does the graph have?

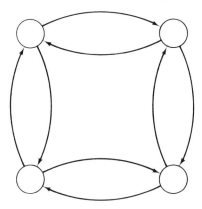

12.7 Find a maximum marking for the graph when the initial marking is as shown. Show, in detail, all the steps of the algorithm of Section 12.3.

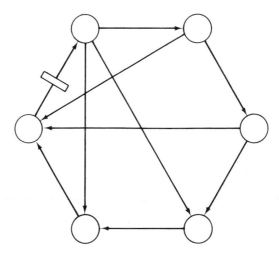

12.8 Find a live and safe marking for the graph. Show, in detail, the steps of the algorithm you use.

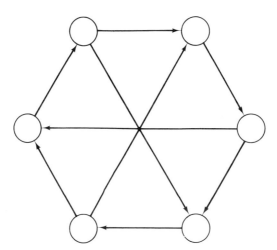

REFERENCES

1. Commoner, F., Holt, A. W., Even, S., and Pnueli, A., "Marked Directed Graphs," *J. Computer and System Sciences*, Vol. 5, No. 5, 1971, pp. 511–23.

2. Petri, C. A., "Kommunikation mit Automaten," Schriften des Rheinisch-West-falischen Institute für Instrumentelle Mathematik an der Universität Bonn, Hft. 2,

Bonn, 1962. English translation: "Communication with Automata," by C. F. Greene, Jr., for Project ISTP, a Supplement to Technical Documentary Report No. 1, prepared for Rome Air Development Center, *AF 30(602)-3344*, 1965.

3. Holt, A. W., et al., "Information System Theory Project," Technical Report for Rome Air Development Center No. RADC-TR-68-305, prepared by Applied Data Research, Inc., Princeton, N.J., 1968. Available from the Department of Commerce Clearing House, Springfield, Va., as *Report AD 676-972*.

4. Holt, A. W., and Commoner, F., "Marked Graphs and Linear Programming," unpublished notes.

5. Holt, A. W., and Commoner, F., "Events and Conditions," Research report of Applied Data Research, Lakeside Office Park, Wakefield, Mass., 1970.

6. Genrich, H. J., "Einfache Nicht-Sequentielle Prozesse," Gesellschaft für Mathematik und Datenverarbeitung, Birlinghoven, West Germany, 1970.

7. Karp, R. M., and Miller, R. E., "Properties of a Model for Parallel Computations: Determinacy, Terminations, Queueing," *SIAM J. Appl. Math.*, Vol. 14, 1966, pp. 1300–1411.

8. Reiter, R., "Scheduling Parallel Computations," *J. ACM*, Vol. 14, 1968, pp. 590–99.

9. Ford, L. R., Jr., and Fulkerson, D. R., *Flows in Networks*, Princeton University Press, Princeton, N.J., 1962, Chap. 3, Sec. 11.

INDEX